# Engineering, Quality and Experimental Design

# Engineering, Quality and Experimental Design

*Daniel M. Grove &*
*Timothy P. Davis*

LONGMAN

Addison Wesley Longman Limited
Edinburgh Gate
Harlow, Essex CM20 2JE
England.
*and Associated Companies throughout the world.*



First published 1992
Reprinted 1995, 1997 and 1998

**British Library Cataloguing in Publication Data**
A catalogue record for this title is available from the British Library

**Library of Congress Cataloging-in-Publication Data**
A catalogue record for this book is available from the Library of Congress

Set by 8 in 10/12 Garamond Simoncini Roman
Produced by Addison Wesley Longman Singapore Pte Ltd
Printed in Singapore

# Contents

*Preface* ix
*Acknowledgements* xii

1 INTRODUCTION

1.1 Engineering, experimentation and quality improvement 1
1.2 Statistically designed experiments 3
1.3 Experimentation and management 10
1.4 The reduction of variation 13
1.5 Statistical analysis 19
*Summary of Chapter 1* 22

2 EXPERIMENTS WITH FACTORS AT TWO LEVELS

2.1 Sled test example 24
2.2 Sled test example — more data 29
2.3 Prediction 36
2.4 Fractional factorial experiments 38
2.5 Some fractional plans based on $L_8(2^7)$ 42
*Summary of Chapter 2* 45

## 3 STATISTICAL METHODS

3.1 Normal plots applied to an artificial example 47
3.2 Analysis of variance 51
3.3 A real example — moulding of glove box lids 56
*Summary of Chapter 3* 62
*Appendix 3.1 Normal plots* 62
*Appendix 3.2 Normal scores* 69
*Appendix 3.3 Critical values for* F *tests* 73

## 4 PLANNING A TWO-LEVEL EXPERIMENT

4.1 A short catalogue of plans 74
4.2 Interactions and experimental strategy 80
4.3 Randomization of the run order 87
4.4 Blocks, split plots and simple trends 91
*Summary of Chapter 4* 96

## 5 EXPERIMENTS WITH FACTORS AT THREE LEVELS

5.1 Orthogonal arrays for three-level factors 98
5.2 Example — engine mapping 103
5.3 Engine mapping — more data 115
5.4 Fractional plans for three-level factors 124
*Summary of Chapter 5* 132

## 6 PLANS FOR FITTING SECOND-ORDER EQUATIONS

6.1 A plan for three factors 136
6.2 Multiple regression 145
6.3 An example with four factors — tyre testing 153
6.4 Other aspects of response surface methods 164
*Summary of Chapter 6* 169
*Appendix 6.1 Box–Behnken designs* 170

*Appendix 6.2 Critical values for* t *tests* 172

*Appendix 6.3 A direct method of standardizing contrasts* 173

7 MIXED-LEVEL FACTORIAL EXPERIMENTS

7.1 Some more orthogonal arrays 174

7.2 Assigning a two-level factor to a three-level array 177

7.3 Assigning a three-level factor to a two-level array 181

7.4 The idle column method 187

7.5 Nested factors 189

7.6 Linear graphs 190

*Summary of Chapter 7* 192

*Appendix 7.1 Mixed-level plans, and how to obtain them* 194

*Appendix 7.2 Special array based on* $L_{12}(2^{11})$ 195

8 EXPERIMENTS TO MEASURE LOCATION AND DISPERSION EFFECTS

8.1 Measuring location and disperson effects 196

8.2 Case study — tee clamps 198

8.3 A follow-up experiment 207

8.4 Response transformation and signal-to-noise ratios 212

*Summary of Chapter 8* 219

*Appendix 8.1 Data from the tee clamp experiment* 220

9 PARAMETER DESIGN AND TRANSMITTED VARIATION

9.1 Methods of parameter design 222

9.2 Seat belt example 224

9.3 Systems with transmitted variation 232

9.4 The Wheatstone bridge 237

*Summary of Chapter 9* 245

## 10 MORE CASE STUDIES

10.1 Another experiment on a welding process 247

10.2 An experiment on oil control piston ring spacers 267

10.3 A brief return to the engine mapping experiment 280

10.4 Predicting the air speed of a desk-top fan 282

*Appendix 10.1 Data from two experiments* 291

## 11 TOPICS IN QUALITY ENGINEERING I

11.1 The choice of quality characteristic 295

11.2 Ideal function and the transfer of energy 298

11.3 Signal-to-noise ratios and response transformations 299

11.4 Factor transformations and additivity 305

11.5 Compounded noise 309

11.6 Two alternative engineering strategies 313

*Summary of Chapter 11* 314

## 12 TOPICS IN QUALITY ENGINEERING II

12.1 Dynamic systems 316

12.2 Signal-to-noise ratios for dynamic systems 318

12.3 Orthogonal contrasts for dynamic systems 321

12.4 Experimentation with dynamic systems 323

12.5 Transformations in the dynamic setting 327

12.6 An experiment to achieve a robust engine starting system 329

*Summary of Chapter 12* 353

*References 356*

*Index 358*

# Preface

This is a book about planning and running experiments in an engineering environment. It has been strongly influenced by the work of Genichi Taguchi. Taguchi is a Japanese engineer and statistician who became widely known in the West in the early 1980s when the Ford Supplier Institute began promoting his ideas. This organisation later became the independent American Supplier Institute (ASI), of which Taguchi is now the Executive Director.

As a result of the ASI's efforts the term 'Taguchi methods' is now in common use in industry, and is often applied very loosely to any industrial experiment with a statistical basis. In fact, statistically designed industrial experiments have a history stretching back at least to L H C Tippett's work in the 1930s, but in general this methodology had little influence on the sectors of manufacturing industry which are based primarily on mechanical engineering. We suspect that the explanation lies partly in poor communication between statisticians and engineers, and partly in the available teaching material which was, with a very few notable exceptions, developed from agricultural applications and did not recognize some of the special features operating in other industries. However, the arrival of the 'quality movement' of the 1980s gave renewed impetus to industrial applications of a range of well-established statistical methods, including the design and analysis of experiments as well as the techniques which have come to be known as Statistical Process Control (SPC).

Like SPC, Taguchi methods could legitimately be presented as part of the explanation for the extraordinary progress in quality improvement made by the Japanese. Although Taguchi's work is often obscure, at least in translation, it was clear from the beginning that the mathematical and statistical detail was there to support a general philosophy of quality improvement based on the need to reduce variation. Accepting the relevance of Taguchi's general approach to quality – and to engineering in particular –

large numbers of engineers have managed to struggle through the complicated arithmetic and, undaunted, actually run experiments.

In common with many people who work in industrial statistics and quality improvement, we have strong reservations about some of the methods which Taguchi advocates. On the other hand, this book could not have existed without Taguchi, because encountering his work has changed the way each of us thinks about the role of experimentation in engineering. In fact the promotion of Taguchi's ideas set off a new round of research, initiated by George Box and his co-workers at the University of Wisconsin, into the best ways of using experimentation in industry. In a sense, Taguchi has asked the right questions without always supplying the right – or at any rate the best – answers. However, one area where Taguchi has supplied a good answer is that of deciding what to measure in engineering experiments. Books on the design of experiments tend to take the response variable for granted, but, to summarize Taguchi's view, engineers should measure what the engineering hardware is meant to do, and not yield to the temptation of measuring what it is *not* meant to do.

We think we are in a good position to present an accurate account of Taguchi's ideas because we have had the opportunity to meet him on his regular visits to the Ford Motor Company, and we are grateful to the management of the company for having the foresight to invite Taguchi in this way. One of us (TPD) has worked with Taguchi and teams of engineers in developing experiments. There has been an enthusiastic exchange of ideas on these occasions, and this is, we hope, reflected in the book.

Our overall objective is identical to Taguchi's, namely the provision of methods which the engineer can understand without extensive prior training in statistics, and can use to advance engineering knowledge about products and processes. A key point is that statistical methods are *not* a substitute for engineering knowledge. The results of our efforts may sometimes be frustrating for the more statistical reader, but we hope that the interesting case studies will provide adequate compensation.

Each chapter begins with a short introduction and ends with a summary. Taken together these provide a quick overview of the book. The only exception to that format is Chapter 10, which has no summary because it contains details of several case studies but only a small amount of new technical material.

All of the case studies have originated through our work with engineers in Ford and its suppliers. We are tremendously grateful to all the engineers who ran experiments and let us publish them in this book. They are credited at appropriate places in the text. We have learnt as much about engineering from them as – we hope – they have learnt about statistics from us.

We would like to thank Ed Henshall, Bob Moesta and Ian Puzey for helping to shape our understanding of industrial experimentation, and John Charles for reading the book in draft and offering helpful comments. Any errors and omissions are of course our own responsibility. Ian Puzey also deserves thanks for commissioning the first version of some of this material.

Finally, we would like to thank our wives, Janet and Jackie, and our families for the encouragement they have given us and the patience they have shown while this project came slowly to fruition.

Dan Grove
Fareham, Hants

Tim Davis
Dunton, Essex

*March 1992*

# Acknowledgements

We are grateful to the following for permission to reproduce copyright material:

Asian Productivity Organization for Figs 7.1, 10.3 from Taguchi G 1986 *Introduction to Quality Engineering*; BBBF Books for Fig. 9.8 from Box G E P, Bisgaard S, Fung C 1990 *Designing Industrial Experiments*, p. 175; Cambridge University Press and the author for Fig. 1.1 from Deming W E 1986 *Out of the Crisis*.

Whilst every effort has been made to trace the owners of copyright material, in a few cases this may have proved impossible and we take this opportunity to offer our apologies to any copyright holders whose rights we may have unwittingly infringed.

# CHAPTER 1

# Introduction

## 1.1 ENGINEERING, EXPERIMENTATION AND QUALITY IMPROVEMENT

This book is concerned with running experiments in product and process engineering. The engineering process can be viewed as a combination of *designing* and *testing*, which often manifest themselves within a cycle of design, test, re-design, re-test, and so on. Whichever way designing and testing are combined, experiments of one sort or another need to be carried out. By an *experiment* we mean any test, evaluation or trial designed to evaluate a change, which requires the collection of measurements (data) so that a judgement (prediction) on the performance of the system can be formed, and a decision can be made as to whether further re-design (with further experimentation and prediction) is necessary.

The sequence of activities involved in planning, running, analysing and reacting to the results of an experiment can be described by the PDCA (Plan, Do, Check, Act) cycle, otherwise known as the Deming cycle or Shewhart cycle (see Fig. 1.1). The 'Plan' includes a protocol for carrying out the experiment and gathering data, some preliminary ideas for how the data should be analysed, and a tentative list of the actions that might follow (no such list can ever be comprehensive). The collection and analysis of results take us through the 'Do' and 'Check' steps of the cycle. The 'Act' may be a decision to start the PDCA cycle again by planning another experiment, and we will suggest later that this should be the norm rather than the exception. In his book *Out of the Crisis*, Deming (1986) advocates that the next 'Plan' stage is conducted *with knowledge* **accumulated** *from the previous cycle*. Here, knowledge means common knowledge as well as individual knowledge. The word 'accumulated' is deliberately emphasized. The accumulation of a

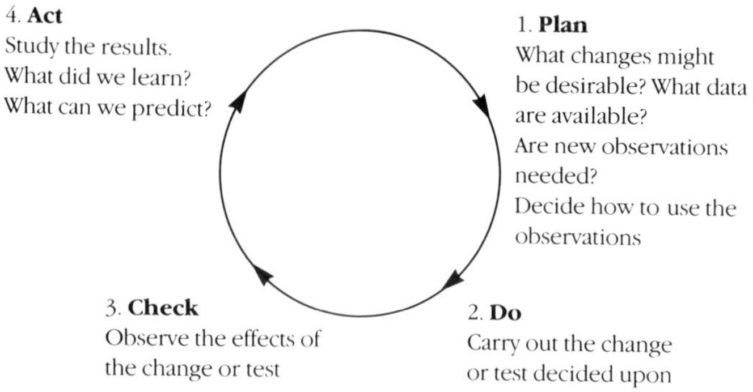


*Fig. 1.1* The Plan, Do, Check, Act (PDCA) cycle (after W E Deming; Deming now calls it the PDSA cycle, with 'check' replaced by 'study')

common knowledge requires co-operation and co-education between groups of co-workers. Experiments are a primary generator of knowledge in engineering, and therefore the importance of effective experimentation cannot be over-emphasized.

Another way of describing an experiment is as a framework for *making things happen* in a systematic way and in the presence of an observer (engineer or more generally *experimenter*) who is trained to recognize the significance of the results, so that action can be taken accordingly.

If the performance of an engineering system is judged in terms of its *function*, then experimentation leads naturally into the area of quality improvement — here we take the definition of quality in the engineering sense to be the ability of the product or process to perform its intended function. One important lesson that Western industries have learnt over the past 10 years or so is that quality can be improved without increasing costs. However, there is no miraculous recipe for cost-effective quality improvement, but, as our previous remarks suggest, a vital prerequisite is knowledge. We shall show that the technique of *(statistical) design of experiments* can be used to make discoveries — to add to knowledge — in an efficient manner. Efficiency here is with regard to the ability to make predictions about engineering systems, as well as to the amount of experimentation that has to be done, so that time, cost and energy are kept to a minimum. With efficient experimentation, knowledge can be gained more quickly and motivation for *continuous improvement* is naturally increased.

It is usually possible with a properly planned experiment to interpret the data using only simple statistical methods and without calling on the help of an expert statistician or a complicated computer program. Nevertheless, the ability to obtain knowledge from data is a skill that must be developed, and one component of this skill is *statistical thinking*. We will emphasize aspects of statistical thinking throughout this book (rather than give a contrived definition here). The use of simple statistical methods to support this thinking will be a constant theme.

## 1.2 STATISTICALLY DESIGNED EXPERIMENTS

It is often true that experimentation as currently practised in engineering is *ad hoc* — that is to say, changes are made to the design as the engineering process develops, based on the most recent test information available. Sometimes, these changes are made without any thought as to how they affect the product or process overall, and usually with little thought as to what to do *if* the proposed changes do not give the desired result. In its worst manifestation, this *ad hoc* experimentation means changing one thing at a time, while keeping everything else fixed.

This 'change-one-thing-at-a-time' approach comes about primarily for two reasons. First, it is often thought that the only way to measure precisely the effect of a design change is to keep everything else fixed while the latest change is evaluated. Only after this has been done can we move on to evaluate the next change. The second reason for this type of experimentation is related to the framework within which management allows experimentation to take place. A management approach that requires commitment from engineers to provide signed-off designs based on the latest results will force engineers to make *ad hoc* design changes, followed by (possibly premature) judgements on what should be done next, until they get a system that works. Some design changes may have a particular effect on the system that depends on how the system was configured when the test was made; but subsequent changes to other parts of the system may nullify or even reverse the effects of the original system changes. The knowledge gained from this approach will, therefore, usually be incomplete, and, as we have pointed out, knowledge is what is required for continuous improvement of quality.

Is there a better way? The alternative to the change-one-thing-at-a-time approach is to use statistically designed experiments to plan the programme of testing. Statistical design of experiments means making many design changes at once and conducting several tests and evaluations before decisions are taken as to what the next steps in the development process should be. First impressions of this idea may be that changing several things at once will make the situation worse, in the sense that it will be impossible to tell which changes made the difference to the performance of the design. However, with statistically designed experiments, these design changes are not just *any* design changes.

We will call the things that we want to change *factors*. To run a statistically designed experiment, otherwise known as a *factorial* or *multi-factor* experiment, we have to identify several factors *prior* to experimentation. We will suppose that we are interested in just two possibilities or values for each of these factors. We call these possibilities *levels*. For a first experiment, two levels for each factor are usually adequate: the opposite extreme from a one-factor-at-a-time experiment (which answers one question at a time) is an attempt to answer *all* possible questions at once. This is a mistake, because further experimentation can always be conducted to investigate any unresolved issues. Results from a preliminary experiment often suggest new lines of approach, which require more experimentation.

It is convenient to have a simple *code* for the factor levels, and we will begin by calling them simply level 1 and level 2. In Chapter 2 we will introduce a different code, using (−) and (+) to represent the levels, and explain why we prefer it. We will often refer to the factors by single letter labels (*A*, *B*, etc.). It is then sometimes convenient to use the notation $A_1$, $A_2$ to represent the two levels of factor *A*. There are basically two types of factor, *qualitative* and *quantitative*.

Qualitative factors are those where there is no numerical hierarchy to separate the two levels, for example two types of material, or the presence and absence of some feature.

Quantitative factors, on the other hand, are measurable on a scale (preferably continuous), for example the diameter of a spindle, which may be chosen at any value between 50 mm and 60 mm say.

The performance of the engineering system is characterized by a measurement of some aspect of function (or lack of it). We will call the quantity that we measure in an experiment the *response*. When the response relates to some measure of quality, it can be called a *quality characteristic*.

## An example

By way of an introductory example, we consider an experiment concerned with the cleanliness of carburettors after assembly. This experiment is therefore concerned with *process design* rather than *product design*, but the ideas of experimentation apply equally well to both, as we shall see throughout this book. We would like to thank Morrell Murphy of Ford Motor Co. Ltd for providing us with this example.

Process engineers had for some time wanted to improve the cleanliness of the carburettors, and experimentation had already taken place on a small scale. A team of seven production, engineering and laboratory staff held a meeting to discuss which factors were most likely to affect cleanliness. From an initial list of 13 factors, obtained by brainstorming, they selected seven, as shown on the following page.

The response that the team decided to measure was a count of the number of dirt particles in a sample of 10 carburettors assembled under a particular set of process conditions. In this example, the response can be called a quality characteristic. Of course, it is desirable for this measure to be as small as possible.

Figure 1.2 is a run chart of the (total) numbers of dirt particles in a sequence of samples of five carburettors assembled in the period before the experiment. Taking the chart as a whole, the variation is not in *statistical control* (for concepts of statistical process control, see Section 1.4), but in the period immediately before the experiment the variation is fairly stable, with an average of about 15 particles per carburettor.

| | Level | |
|---|---|---|
| Factor | 1 | 2 |
| (*A*) Time of flushing | Normal | Normal × 4 |
| (*B*) Prior washing of internal components | Washed | Not washed |
| (*C*) Lubricate emulsion tubes and jets during assembly? | No | Yes |
| (*D*) Pre-clean wells in body? | No | Yes |
| (*E*) Environmental cleanliness of benches, fixtures, trays, etc. | Normal | Extra-clean |
| (*F*) Assembly sequence of emulsion tubes and jets | Normal | Double assembly with intermediate flush |
| (*G*) Speed of screwing-in the emulsion tubes and jets | Normal | Slower |

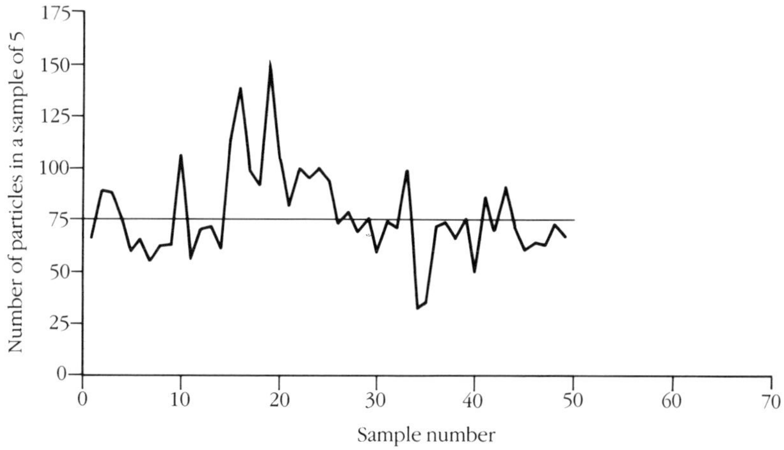


*Fig. 1.2* Carburettor assembly experiment. Run chart of particle count before the experiment

In an attempt to achieve cleaner assemblies, the team experimented with the seven chosen factors in a particular way, which is laid out in Table 1.1. We will refer to each process configuration as a *run*, so that in the first configuration (run 1 in the table) all the factors are set at level 1. The quality characteristic for this run is measured and recorded as 145 particles of dirt in the 10 carburettors. This run in fact corresponds to the usual process settings, and 145 particles per 10 units is close to the recent average of 15 particles per carburettor.

The next configuration (run 2) involves factors *A*, *B* and *C* at level 1 and *D*, *E*, *F* and *G* at level 2, so that in going from run 1 to run 2 we have

*Table 1.1* The carburettor assembly experiment

| Run | Factor *A* | *B* | *C* | *D* | *E* | *F* | *G* | Number of particles in a sample of 10 carburettors |
|---|---|---|---|---|---|---|---|---|
| 1 | 1 | 1 | 1 | 1 | 1 | 1 | 1 | 145 |
| 2 | 1 | 1 | 1 | 2 | 2 | 2 | 2 | 83 |
| 3 | 1 | 2 | 2 | 1 | 1 | 2 | 2 | 63 |
| 4 | 1 | 2 | 2 | 2 | 2 | 1 | 1 | 131 |
| 5 | 2 | 1 | 2 | 1 | 2 | 1 | 2 | 111 |
| 6 | 2 | 1 | 2 | 2 | 1 | 2 | 1 | 113 |
| 7 | 2 | 2 | 1 | 1 | 2 | 2 | 1 | 145 |
| 8 | 2 | 2 | 1 | 2 | 1 | 1 | 2 | 73 |

changed the levels of four of the seven factors — we have made four (process) design changes at once rather than just one as in the one-factor-at-a-time approach. The experiment proceeds through to run 8, with the levels of four factors being changed between each pair of runs. We call all eight runs together *the experiment*, and the particular eight combinations of factor levels defined by the array of 1s and 2s in the table the *experimental design*, *experimental plan* or *experimental layout*.

Looking at the results, we see that there is a lot of variation in the numbers, but variation would be expected even if the process had been left alone. The purpose of statistical analysis in the experimental context is to try to relate the variation in the response directly to the changes in the factor levels.

At first sight this type of experimentation seems confusing and even counter-productive. Some runs produced a decrease in dirt particles (as required) but other runs increased them again. Why did the engineers not go back to the configuration of run 3 after run 4 had made things worse? And what is the point of relating the variation in response to variation in factors — why not pick the best run (again, as it happens, run 3) as the process design for the future?

Suppose that the engineers *had* stopped after run 3, or selected configuration 3 after looking at all the results. They would almost certainly have improved the process, but they would not know why. They would have no idea which factors have an important effect on cleanliness and which do not. All the factors would have to be treated as equally significant and *managed* accordingly, including four at levels different from their current settings.

Apart from the implications for process management, there are other advantages of being able to focus in on a few important factors. It may be possible to experiment further with just these factors, using other levels to learn more about their effects. It may be worth using three or even five levels of each factor in such a follow-up experiment (see Chapters 5 and 6). Just as important, if a factor has very little effect on quality, we have the freedom to choose the level that is cheapest or most convenient.

## Measuring the effects of the factors

To evaluate the impact of each factor we can simply look at the average value of the quality characteristic when that factor was at level 1, and compare it with the average value of the quality characteristic when the factor was at level 2. In other words we *contrast* the results according to the levels of each factor. So, for example, take factor $G$ (the speed of screwing-in the emulsion tubes and jets). The average value of the particle count when $G$ is at level 1 is 133.5 and is 82.5 when $G$ is at level 2. The difference between these two numbers ($-51$) measures the *effect* of $G$ on particle count, and in this case is quite large, so that there is a strong indication that the speed of screwing-in the tubes and jets has some bearing on the particle count. The negative answer means that changing from level 1 to level 2 had a beneficial effect. When the levels are designated 1 and 2, it is usual to calculate the effect by subtracting the average for level 1 from the average for level 2.

This simple calculation to determine the effect of a factor is possible because of the *balance* in the experiment. If we look at the experimental plan as a whole we see that the process changes are not at all *ad hoc* but follow a systematic pattern. Each factor is tested exactly four times at level 1 and four times at level 2. Further, for the runs where a particular factor is at one level, all other factors are tested twice at level 1 and twice at level 2. For example, take factors $D$ and $E$. Factor $D$ is at level 1 for runs 1, 3, 5 and 7. Within these four runs factor $E$ is at level 1 twice (runs 1 and 3) and at level 2 twice (runs 5 and 7). The same is true for *any pair of factors*, so the experiment is *balanced* in the way in which factor levels are varied, i.e. balanced with regard to the design changes. This property of balance is crucially important in statistically designed experiments, and we will discuss how to generate such experimental plans in later chapters.

Because of the balance in the experiment, if one factor has a large effect on the quality characteristic then this will cancel out when the effects of other factors are determined. To illustrate this conclusively, if we add say 50 particles to the response on the first four runs (corresponding to factor A at level 1) we get 107.5 as the new average for factor $G$ at level 2 and 158.5 as the new average at level 1. Although these two averages are not the same as those obtained with the original data, their *difference* is still $-51$! So we have the same effect of factor $G$ as before.

The effects of each factor in turn can be established by similar calculations, and it is convenient to display them in simple tabular form in a *response table* — see Table 1.2. The response table can be used to pick out which factor levels are (apparently) best for the quality characteristic, simply by choosing the levels that give the lower average particle count. Whether this is the best *action* to take on the basis of the results is a point we will discuss below.

*Table 1.2* Response table for the carburettor assembly experiment

| Factor | *A* | *B* | *C* | *D* | *E* | *F* | *G* |
|---|---|---|---|---|---|---|---|
| Average 1 | 105.5 | 113 | 111.5 | 116 | 98.5 | 115 | 133.5 |
| Average 2 | 110.5 | 103 | 104.5 | 100 | 117.5 | 101 | 82.5 |
| Effect | +5 | −10 | −7 | −16 | +19 | −14 | −51 |

It is always useful to present numbers graphically, and the graphical version of a response table is called an *effects plot* (Fig. 1.3). This picture indicates the average response for each factor at each level, so that the (vertical) distance between points is equal to the size of the effect. Factor $G$ stands out clearly on this plot. The other six factors have only relatively small effects. The second largest effect is that of factor $E$ (cleanliness of environment). From the response table and effects plot it appears that having an extra-clean environment *increases* the particle count! If the engineers were to act on the information in the numbers alone, then they would conclude that making the environment as dirty as possible would help to remove dirt particles from carburettors. This of course makes no sense intuitively, and this example serves as an early reminder not to forget engineering knowledge and common sense when interpreting data from factorial experiments. In order to make engineering progress we need to *combine* engineering knowledge and numerical information to select those factor levels which the data suggest improve the situation *and make sense.*

One way of making sense of this result is to recognize that there is variation inherent in the process irrespective of the changes made during the experiment. All the effects we have calculated are influenced to some extent by this variation, and it seems *possible* that the counter-intuitive effect of factor $E$ is just a fluke — an extra-clean environment may not really have any effect at all. One important function of statistical methods is to sort out which

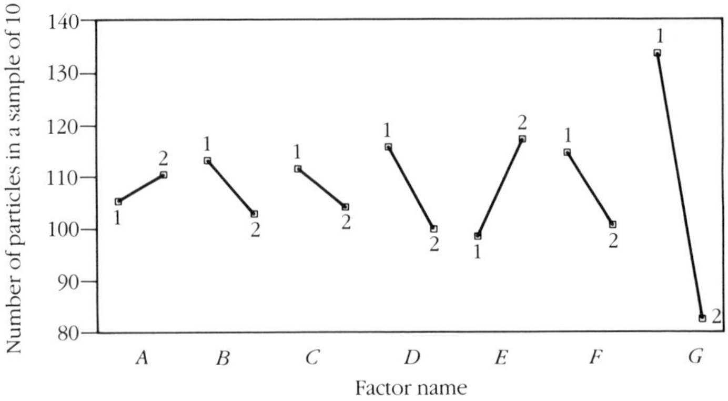


*Fig. 1.3* Carburettor assembly experiment. Effects plot

effects are too large to be accounted for by the inherent variability of the process. We have deferred our introduction to statistical methods until Section 1.5, so we will not attempt to decide whether statistics points in the same direction as engineering common sense with regard to factor *E*.

For the moment we just recall our earlier point, that to find a factor with no effect or only a small effect can be as important as finding a large effect. When managing a process there are usually good reasons for leaving factors alone unless there is a clear advantage to be gained from changing them. In the carburettor example the engineers decided to change only factors *B* and *G*. The results of the experiment established a clear case for trying a slower screwing-in speed, and level 2 of factor *B* (no pre-washing of the components) is obviously more convenient. The configuration selected was therefore $A_1$, $B_2$, $C_1$, $D_1$, $E_1$, $F_1$, $G_2$, which has not actually been evaluated in the experiment. So this configuration needs to be tested to *confirm* the analysis of the experiment, and to verify that the proposed process settings do give an improvement. If we assume that only factor *G* has any real effect on the particle count, the response table tells us to expect a drop in the particle count of about 50 in a sample of 10, or five per assembly. Since the average had been running at about 15, this gives a prediction of about 10 particles per carburettor.

Looking at the example in terms of the PDCA cycle, we have now completed stage 4; planning a *confirmation run* starts us off on a second cycle. It turned out that the confirmation run gave an average of 10.9 particles (from a sample of 20), close to the prediction, and a much needed improvement over the previous situation. The improvement was maintained when the conditions of the confirmation run were introduced into normal production — see the 'before and after' run chart in Fig. 1.4. The average particle count in the period after the experiment is 10.4.

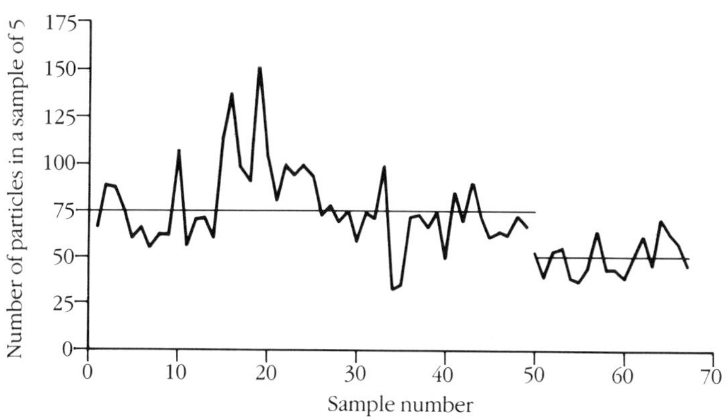


*Fig. 1.4* Carburettor assembly experiment. Run chart of particle count before and after the experiment

In fact after two months the average particle count started to increase again and reached nearly 30. With the *knowledge* that the speed of screwing the assembly together influenced the particle count, the process engineers looked to the assembly speed as the first cause. They found a worn component in the clutch governing the screwing-in speed, which had the effect of increasing the speed and thus increasing the particle count. *Diagnosis* is therefore easier with knowledge.

We should add at this point that, in making a prediction based on the change in factor *G*, we assumed that the factors have independent effects — in other words that when factor *G* is changed from 1 to 2, it always decreases the particle count *by the same amount* regardless of the levels at which other factors are set. Since the prediction was approximately confirmed, the assumption is probably true in this case. When it is not true, when for example the effect of factor *G* depends on the level of factor *B*, we say that factors *G* and *B* exhibit *interaction*.

Interactions are a nuisance, and severely reduce the usefulness of experimental conclusions. It is possible to take counter-measures against interactions (see Chapter 11), but the counter-measures are by no means guaranteed to work. In the experimental framework we can measure interaction numerically, but at the cost of either reducing the number of factors in the experiment or increasing the number of runs. Many industrial experiments follow the pattern of the carburettor example, with an initial analysis and prediction made on the assumption of no interaction. If this prediction is not successful they are *followed up* by further runs that are intended to yield information about interactions. This topic is pursued in Chapter 4.

## 1.3 EXPERIMENTATION AND MANAGEMENT

It should be obvious that, in the type of experiment we have been discussing, factors have to be identified and resources allocated before the experiment can be conducted. This requirement is contrary to an environment that promotes the use of one-factor-at-a-time experiments. This is an important management issue, and workers in management have to understand that the emphasis of experimental design is to obtain knowledge by making things happen in a systematic way.

### Teamwork

Planning an experiment is a very important part of the process of running successful designed experiments. It is essential that everybody concerned with the engineering design is involved (remember we are accumulating knowledge), so that the important factors, with relevant levels, can be identified before the experimentation begins. People have to work as a cross-functional team. A lack of teamwork is another reason why one-factor-at-a-time experiments are often conducted — one engineer makes a change to the design based on his or her current knowledge and tests it. Quite independently, another engineer makes a design change relevant to his or her area of knowledge, and tests it, but without the knowledge of other changes. Some time spent together before these changes were made, pooling all currently accumulated knowledge, could easily have resulted in making the same changes, but in a systematic way via a designed experiment. In this way, *all* current knowledge can be put to maximum use to obtain *more* knowledge in total — because any critical events that occur during the experiment are jointly observed — which is then accumulated among *all* the people involved.

Ensuring that the right people come together prior to the experiment is therefore essential for the accumulation of knowledge. This is another important management issue. A team can also provide a mechanism for scrutinizing the conclusions drawn from an experiment. A cross-functional team will usually find it easier to call in outside expertise, if it is needed, than individuals working in isolation.

## Conduct of the experiment

The aim is to carry out the experiment in a disciplined manner, observing scientific 'best practice'. The notion of scientific discipline should extend from the planning stage through to the analysis of results, and includes the following:

- providing checklists to help those carrying out the experiment to make the planned changes in factor levels without error;
- providing a convenient medium for recording the results and matching individual results to factor configurations;
- making provision for recording the nature and time of any unplanned events;
- interpreting the results according to recognized theory and previous knowledge, where appropriate;
- drawing conclusions in an unbiased and logical manner;
- recognizing the limitations of an experimental procedure and the data obtained from it; and
- subjecting the results and the conclusions drawn from them to as wide a range of scrutiny as possible.

Many of these points may seem too obvious to be worth saying, but they are easily overlooked in the heat of the moment.

## Resources

Although it is important to identify factors prior to any experimentation, it is a mistake to run 'big-bang' experiments, trying to answer all conceivable questions at once. One rule of thumb, suggested on p. 304 of the book by Box *et al.* (1978), is that no more than 25% of the total experimental effort should be invested in an initial experiment for any investigation, because designed experiments should be seen as a method for use in a dynamic environment, one where engineers can change their line of approach based on an unexpected discovery that might be made early in the development of a product. However, this argument for flexibility should not be carried too far, because in its extreme form it becomes a justification for the one-factor-at-a-time approach.

Another reason for holding back resources is inherent in the nature of multi-factor experiments. A large number of factors can be evaluated very efficiently, particularly if we make what one might call a *working assumption* that the factors do not interact with one another. In the carburettor example this assumption led to a successful prediction of the effect of changing one of the factors, but it is often necessary to find out more about interactions, for example by investigating a smaller number of factors in more detail, the reduced list of factors being selected on the basis of the initial experiment.

Box *et al.*'s rule of thumb may be too extreme to be realistic in the real world of the engineer, but resources should never be committed to an initial experiment without a clear understanding that further experimentation will usually be required.

We will touch on issues of experimental management throughout this book, using case studies drawn from our own experiences, but our main emphasis will be on using simple statistical methods to harvest the experimental data for knowledge. Simple statistical methods are all that is needed to draw conclusions from well planned experiments, while, conversely, even the most complicated methods of analysis cannot rescue a poorly planned investigation. This point is well made in Box *et al.*'s book. It is also important to use statistical methods as a *catalyst* for engineering, not as a substitute for it. (The same might be said of other tools such as computers.)

We end this section with some guidelines for running an experiment, presented as a sequence of 10 steps:

(i) Decide on the objective (or objectives) of the programme of experimentation.
(ii) Bring the right team of people together to plan, run and learn from the experiment.
(iii) Choose the response (or responses) to measure — for commentary on this step, see Section 11.1.
(iv) Verify the capability of the process of measurement.
(v) Choose the factors that it is believed have an effect.
(vi) Choose the number of levels for the factors, and the values of the levels.

(vii) Choose the experimental plan, which may involve cutting out some of the factors originally listed, and decide the run order (see Chapter 4).
(viii) Conduct the experiment.
(ix) Analyse the results.
(x) Take action on the findings.

If step (x) includes planning another experiment, it may be necessary to go through the sequence again from as far back as step (iii), step (ii) or even step (i).

## 1.4 THE REDUCTION OF VARIATION

The reader may well be familiar with the name of the Japanese engineer Genichi Taguchi. If not, turn to the Preface for a brief account of his impact on industrial experimentation. This book contains many examples of Taguchi's crucial insights into the relationship between experimentation and quality improvement. Underlying all of Taguchi's work is an idea that is also fundamental to the teaching of W E Deming, that the *reduction of variation* is essential for quality improvement.

The motivation for thinking in terms of variation is as follows. Consider some traditional engineering specification limits, where there is a nominal value for a particular characteristic and a tolerance, probably symmetrical about the intended nominal, as shown in Fig. 1.5. Such specification limits are often used to decide what is good product and what is bad, particularly when achieving quality is dependent on mass inspection. A component just inside specification is considered good (the system of which it forms part will function adequately), and a component outside is considered bad (the system will not function adequately).

In reality, of course, there is not much difference between a component that is 'nearly good' and one that is 'nearly bad', and this motivates us to think of quality in a different way. In particular, Taguchi has suggested that the *deviation* from the nominal measures the quality (or perhaps the *lack* of quality), rather than whether the product is within specification or not. Taguchi's emphasis is on whether the system functions *as intended* rather than functions adequately. He calls the lack of quality *loss*, and has invented what he calls the *quality loss function*, illustrated in Fig. 1.6.

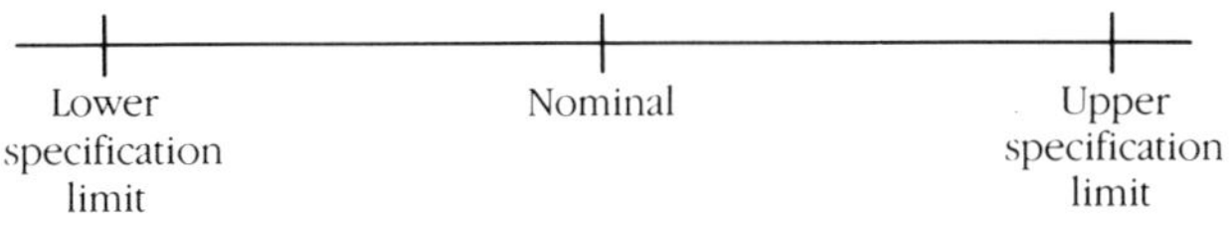


*Fig. 1.5* Traditional specification limits

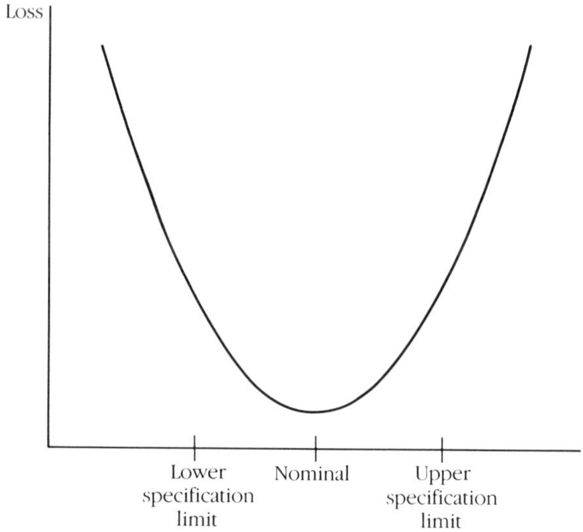


*Fig. 1.6* Taguchi's quality loss function

The loss function indicates that the best quality component is one exactly on nominal — it causes the least loss because when all components are at nominal the system functions as intended. As components deviate from the nominal in either direction they contribute more loss, and the further from nominal they are the greater the loss that is accumulated. Usually the shape of the loss function is taken to be quadratic, because this is the simplest curve that satisfies these requirements. What do we mean by loss? Taguchi and his followers are very specific about this and say that what we should measure is loss *to society* (beyond the manufacturer's gates) *from the time the product is shipped* (Taguchi and Wu 1979). They believe that all such losses should and can be quantified in monetary terms.

Our main use of the loss function will be to motivate the idea of reducing variation. Suppose that the piece-to-piece variation of a product characteristic is described well by a normal distribution, in the sense that a histogram based on a long production run would have approximately this shape. The normal distribution is a convenient one to use for statistical analysis generally, but the appeal here is that this distribution is symmetrical. This distribution can be superimposed on the loss function as illustrated in Fig. 1.7.

Mathematically, the average loss per product unit can be calculated as the area under the *product of the two curves*. If we make some improvement in quality such that the spread of the distribution is narrower, the average loss per unit decreases, as is intuitively obvious from Fig. 1.8. Taguchi uses this idea of reducing the average loss to introduce an economic angle to quality improvement. This approach better reflects customer perceptions of quality, since loss is derived from a customer viewpoint.

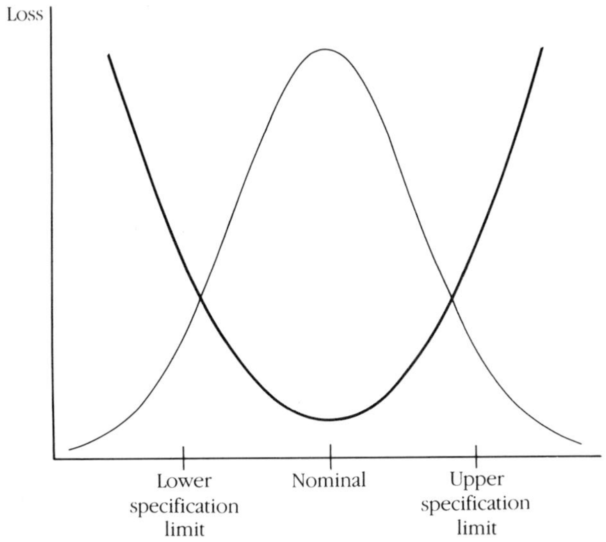


*Fig. 1.7* Quality loss function with a distribution to describe piece-to-piece variation

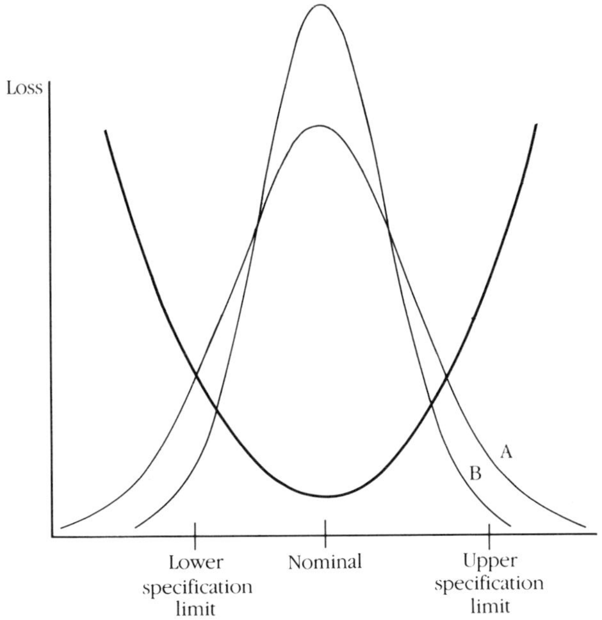


*Fig. 1.8* Reducing the spread of the distribution will also reduce the average loss per piece

Now it must cost some money to go from distribution A to distribution B, but is the reduction in variation worth it? The answer to this question depends on the reduced loss per product. It is not an easy question to answer, though Taguchi and his followers certainly try. We will not attempt to discuss the use of the loss function for economic analysis. It should be borne in mind that to establish the loss function for use in this economic way requires that we know *all* the costs involved. As Lloyd Nelson has said, and W E Deming has often repeated: 'The most important costs are unknown and unknowable.' Taguchi's use of a simple quadratic curve could be seen as a way of making at least *some* progress in the economic analysis of quality improvement while recognizing the impossibility of designing an accounting system to measure the loss with a high degree of predictive ability.

## The use of a distribution to represent piece-to-piece variation

We have represented piece-to-piece variation by a distribution, but it is important to note that this type of statistical model is only useful to describe *stable* variation, as seen for example in Fig. 1.9.

In this type of situation, data gathered over a relatively short period of time will generate effective predictions of the long-term variability in the quality characteristic. A process that displays stable variation is said to be in a state of *statistical control*. In the terminology introduced by W E Deming, such a process is said to be subject to *common* (universal) causes of variation; and a *special* cause is anything that disrupts (either temporarily or permanently) the stable pattern of variation. Stable variation can usually be treated as if it arose from *random* causes — we will return to the word 'random' in Section 1.5.

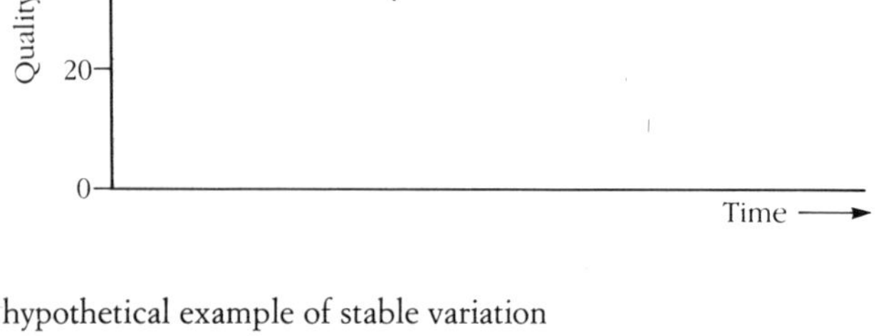


*Fig. 1.9* A hypothetical example of stable variation

## Location and dispersion effects

If $y$ is a product characteristic and $A$ is an experimental factor, the idea that the characteristic has a distribution gives us a way of expressing the fact that *$A$ affects $y$* over and above the common causes of variation. One possibility is represented in Fig. 1.10. Changing from $A_1$ to $A_2$ shifts the whole distribution to the right. Some units with $A$ set at level 1 will have a higher $y$ value than some units with $A$ at level 2 (just as some women are taller than some men), but on average $A_2$ gives higher $y$ values. Factor $A$ is said to have a *location effect*.

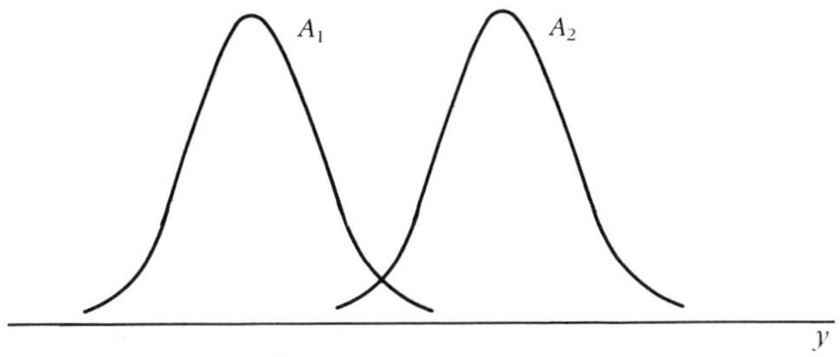


*Fig. 1.10* Factor $A$ has a location effect on $y$

Figure 1.11 shows another possibility. In this case changing the level of $A$ does not shift the distribution but does produce a much smaller spread, and this is known as a *dispersion effect.*

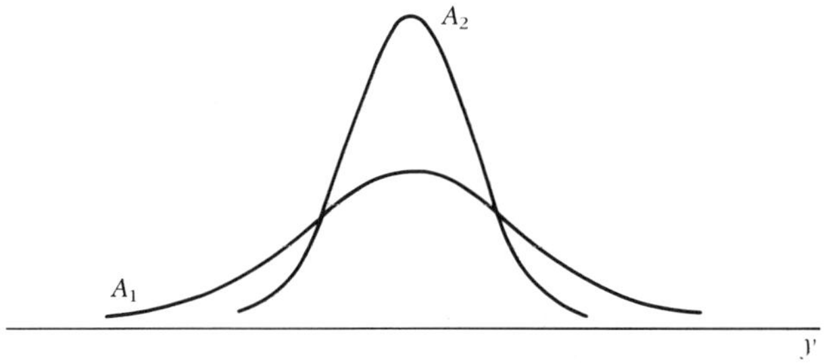


*Fig. 1.11* Factor $A$ has a dispersion effect on $y$

To improve quality through decreasing loss requires that the distribution should be located close to the nominal with as small a dispersion as possible. The simple type of experiment introduced in Section 1.2 is intended to discover location effects. The study of dispersion effects usually requires more data — see Chapter 8 for a case study in which one of the objectives is to find a configuration of design factors such that the dispersion is minimized and the quality characteristic is located on the intended target.

We have defined location and dispersion effects in terms of long-run distributions, but experiments are necessarily concerned with the short run. The best we can do in practice is to use the experimental data to *estimate* the long-run effects. Effects that are defined in terms of distributions are often called *true* or *real* effects, and effects calculated from data are called *estimated*, *empirical*, *observed*, or *apparent* effects. This is a very important distinction, although the words *true* and *real* are somewhat misleading, because distributions are partly hypothetical — they are a model of what would happen *if* the process continued to display stable variation. Another perspective on the idea of a 'real' effect will be introduced in Section 1.5.

## Strategies for the reduction of variation

There are two strategies for the reduction of variation in product function, which have come to be known as 'removing the cause of the effect' and 'removing the effect of the cause'. The ideas of Shewhart and Deming have encouraged the use of the first strategy, employing *control charts* to help identify and remove special causes of variation, and 'continuous improvement of the system', which really means the removal or at least the attenuation of common causes. Taguchi emphasizes a different approach. He argues that there is bound to be a cost in removing or partially removing a cause of variation, and therefore one should try to find design variables that can easily be manipulated and set them to achieve a design for which the dispersion in function is small *despite* variability in upstream variables such as the quality of raw materials, and the inherent variability of any manufacturing process.

Taguchi's approach extends downstream to cover variation in the environment in which a product is used, for example the varying temperatures under which starter motors have to be able to crank the engine of a car. Taguchi uses the word *noise* to refer to any cause of variation in product function in the hands of the user, whether it originates in the manufacturing process, the customer's method of use or the environment. A product or process that can function well against a background of noise is said to be *robust*.

Taguchi uses the idea of statistically planned experimentation to discover robust designs. A measure of robustness is established for each potential design, and this measure of robustness becomes the quality characteristic with which to experiment and predict. In some experiments, the chief concern is with piece-to-piece variation arising from common causes, as illustrated in Fig. 1.8. Any measure of the dispersion of the distribution (the standard deviation, for example) is also a measure of robustness, and any factor that is found to have a dispersion effect can be set to reduce loss by minimizing dispersion, i.e. maximizing robustness. In other types of experiment noise is *deliberately* included, and this is clearly a special cause of variation. Taguchi has suggested that one particular type of robustness criterion, known as a signal-to-noise ratio, is equally appropriate to both types of experiment. This discussion is continued in Chapters 8 and 9.

## 1.5 STATISTICAL ANALYSIS

Statistical analysis is a combination of statistical methods and statistical thinking. The statistical methods included in this book are on the whole very simple to carry out and we rely heavily on graphical methods to stimulate thinking and achieve an analysis. The motivation throughout is the acquisition of knowledge, and the function of a statistical analysis in this context is to harvest the experimental data for this knowledge.

The use of simple statistical methods in experimentation will be illustrated throughout the book with reference to case studies. The intention is also to use these case studies to highlight why statistical thinking is important to quality improvement in the engineering field.

Statistical computer packages are available that will analyse data from experiments. Although such packages have some very useful features, for example they are designed to avoid the build-up of rounding errors in complicated calculations, special software is not required in the majority of experiments. Most of the statistical methods advocated in this book are easily accomplished using software no more complicated than a spreadsheet. In fact spreadsheets promote statistical thinking, because of the flexibility that they possess in handling data, particularly with regard to drawing graphs. They are also a very convenient medium for trying out *data transformations* (for example, working with the data on a logarithmic scale), which may simplify the analysis — see Chapters 8, 10 and 11. From time to time throughout the book we give indications of how to use spreadsheets to achieve particular results and graphs. These instructions are designed for readers who already have some knowledge of spreadsheets.

The 'seven tools of Ishikawa' (Ishikawa 1982), which include run charts, histograms and scatter plots, are a good starting point for graphical analysis of data and provide a link with other areas of quality improvement activity such as statistical process control (SPC). For the initial analysis of data we use dot plots (e.g. Fig. 8.4) in preference to histograms.

Another type of statistical method is designed to tackle the problem of distinguishing between 'significant' and 'insignificant' effects in an experiment. Although simple to carry out, these methods have their origins in quite sophisticated mathematical arguments. Most experimenters do not need to be concerned with mathematical details, but they do need to have some understanding of the concepts that link the mathematics to the real world. Without this understanding, they are likely either to use statistical methods indiscriminately or to believe that they are only applicable in very special circumstances.

The basic reason for using statistical methods to judge the size of effects is the presence of variation that the experimenters did not deliberately introduce. In the carburettor experiment we speculated that such variation might be the explanation for the paradoxical finding that an extra-clean environment makes for dirtier carburettors. To see the detailed implications

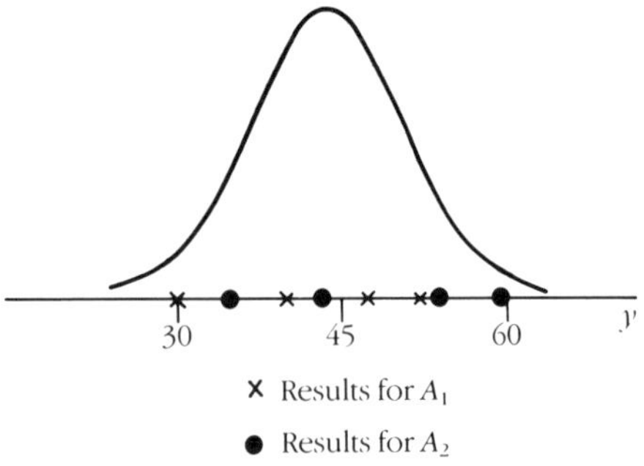


*Fig. 1.12* An apparent effect may be the result of random variation

of this type of variation, consider a one-factor experiment in which four pieces are made with $A$ at level 1, with results 53, 47, 30 and 40, and four at level 2, with results 53, 60, 35 and 44. We suppose that piece-to-piece variation is stable, and that $A$ is irrelevant to the response $y$, so that a single distribution curve represents the variation in $y$, whatever the level of $A$. This curve is displayed in Fig. 1.12, together with the hypothetical results. In the experiment, the location effect of $A$ would be measured by the difference between the averages of the two sets of points, amounting to about 5 in this example.

In this hypothetical case the apparent location effect of $A$ is entirely the result of random piece-to-piece variation, which in Taguchi's terminology is a form of noise. In practice we cannot know for certain which short-run effects would be maintained in the long run, and which are entirely due to noise. No set of results should ever be taken entirely at face value, and an important aim of a statistical analysis in this context (see Chapter 3) is to separate the apparent effects into two sets:

- those which will be treated as if they were real (at least provisionally); and
- those which will be treated as arising from random noise.

We will sometimes use the phrase 'active effects' — with the implication that such factors *do* something — as an alternative to 'real effects'.

Conventional statistical practice takes a sceptical view of apparent effects: only those which clearly stand out from the noise (in a sense that is made more precise in Chapter 3) are treated as real. It is sometimes argued that statisticians are *too* sceptical in this regard. If this is true, it may be because many of the statistical methods used in analysing experimental data were developed in the agricultural industry where it was generally necessary to wait a year for the agricultural cycle to repeat before experimental results could be confirmed. Therefore agricultural experimenters needed to be as sure as possible about effects before resources were committed on the basis of experimental conclusions. In engineering, however, confirmation can usually be conducted very quickly, and so we can afford to relax some of the statistical rules about the significance of factors — the only 'significance test' that counts in the end is a demonstration that a result is or is not repeatable.

We think this a legitimate subject for debate; what we are clear about is that there are losses associated with both kinds of potential mistake. Ignoring a factor that has a real effect can obviously lead to loss; but, on the other side of the coin, treating an unimportant factor as if it was important distracts attention from the real opportunities for progress, removes our freedom to pick the cheapest level, and may lead to the waste of experimental resources in a follow-up experiment that is larger than it needs to be.

Note that a decision to treat an effect as real is a *prediction* about future results. For example, if the average result for level 2 of $A$ is higher than the average for level 1, and this effect is treated as real, we are predicting that, if one more run was made at $A_1$ and another at $A_2$, the result for $A_2$ would be higher. Prediction will be a recurrent theme of this book, starting from Chapter 2.

The discussion in this section has concentrated on location effects, but it can be extended to cover dispersion effects and other measures of robustness.

## Experimental error

Piece-to-piece variation affects both the experimental data and the 'real-life' production process. Other types of variation derive from the experimental process itself, such as variation in measuring equipment and variation in setting up the experimental runs. This type of variation is often called *experimental error* but this is an unfortunate expression because it suggests that there was an ideal experimental procedure to which the experimenter failed to conform. In reality, even the best experimental protocols produce variable results. This type of variation does not fall within Taguchi's definition of noise, but for brevity's sake we will sometimes use the word 'noise' without worrying about this distinction.

In judging whether it is appropriate to carry out a formal statistical analysis, the most fundamental concept is that of statistical control or stable variation. This means that the variation — whether arising from piece-to-piece differences or from the experimental process — can be treated (modelled) as if it were random. It is important to note that we do not assume that the variation is *really random*, whatever that may mean. The concept of randomness is of great philosophical interest, but for our present purpose the important point is that this concept, when expressed in mathematical terms, leads via probability theory to the development of *effective* methods for the interpretation of data. Good experimental technique helps to ensure that statistical analysis is effective by removing the sources of variation that cannot be treated as random. These are the special or assignable causes. But even the most careful experimenter cannot rule out the possibility that an unforeseen source of variation will lead to misleading results. We return to this point in Chapter 4.

## SUMMARY OF CHAPTER 1

The sequence of activities that go to make up an experiment can be described by the Plan, Do, Check, Act (PDCA) cycle. The 'Act' is often a decision to run another experiment, with knowledge accumulated from the first cycle. Experiments are a primary generator of knowledge for cost-effective quality improvement.

Statistically designed (factorial or multi-factor) experiments are a more efficient way of gaining knowledge than *ad hoc* one-factor-at-a-time experimentation. We use an example to illustrate some aspects of a multi-factor experiment: selecting the factors that will be changed, and the levels that will be used; making several design changes before each run, in such a way that the experimental plan as a whole has a systematic and balanced pattern; exploiting the balance in the experiment to obtain a measure of the effect of each factor on the response (quality characteristic); summarizing the results in a response table and effects plot; using engineering knowledge and common sense in interpreting the results; making a prediction based on the results and checking the prediction with a confirmation run on the process.

Among the management issues related to experimentation are the following: the necessity to support a systematic rather than *ad hoc* approach; the essential role played by cross-functional teams (experiments need teams to plan them, and provide a mechanism by which a team can accumulate a common stock of knowledge); the necessity for holding back resources for follow-up experiments. We describe the process of running an experiment in the form of a 10-step sequence of guidelines.

Taguchi, like Deming, regards the reduction of variation as fundamental to quality improvement. Taguchi's approach to quality in engineering puts the emphasis on whether a system functions as intended, implying that the lack of quality of a component should be measured by its deviation from nominal rather than by reference to specification limits. The purpose of Taguchi's quality loss function is to measure the loss to society that results when products do not function as intended.

There are two strategies for the reduction of variation, known as 'removing the cause of the effect' and 'removing the effect of the cause'. Statistical process control concentrates on the first but Taguchi puts more emphasis on the second. Any cause of variation in product function is called noise, and a robust product or process is one for which functional variation is low despite the presence of noise. Robust designs can be discovered by experimentation, using a measure of robustness as the quality characteristic. In some of these experiments, noise is deliberately introduced.

When a process is in statistical control its output can be represented by a distribution. Factors may have location or dispersion effects (or both) on a distribution. 'True' or 'real' effects are defined in terms of distributions — experiments provide estimated (apparent) effects.

The case studies in the book will highlight the importance of statistical thinking supported by simple statistical methods, with a particular emphasis on graphical methods. Most of the methods in the book can easily be accomplished in a spreadsheet.

One important function of statistical methods is to separate the apparent effects into those which will be treated as real (provisionally at least) and those which will be treated as arising from random noise. A decision to treat an effect as real is a prediction about future results.

The need for statistical methods in this context arises from the presence of variation from sources other than the changes made by the experimenters. The methods will only be fully effective if this other variation comes from processes that are in statistical control.

# CHAPTER 2

# Experiments with factors at two levels

*In the carburettor example in Section 1.2 we interpreted the data on the assumption that the effect of any one factor on the response was independent of the other factors, in other words that there were no* interactions *between the factors. This interpretation led to a successful prediction about the effect of changing one of the factors. If the prediction had failed, one possible explanation would have been the existence of interactions between the factors. In this chapter we explore the concept of interaction in some detail for two-level experiments, and look at the consequences of running only a subset of the possible factor combinations. We introduce the idea of an* orthogonal array *and show how such arrays can be used both to define the experimental plan and to summarize the data in a set of orthogonal contrasts. We also give a formula for predicting the results of further runs, in the light of the original experimental results.*

## 2.1 SLED TEST EXAMPLE

As part of the effort to develop an effective passenger air bag to supplement the conventional car seat belt, tests are carried out with dummies riding on sleds. John Charles of the Ford Motor Co. Ltd and Jack Higgins of TRW Repa Ltd co-ordinated this experiment with Dino DePaolis and Tim Slack of TRW Safety Systems Inc. in the US, where the experiment was actually conducted. In this particular experiment three responses were measured, each reflecting a different aspect of the dummy's experience in the crash. In this chapter we will use the results for *chest g*, the maximum deceleration experienced by the chest. There were three experimental factors:

| Factor | Label | Level (−) | Level (+) |
|---|---|---|---|
| Speed of inflation of bag | *S* | Slow | Fast |
| Size of vent | *V* | Small | Large |
| Size of bag | *B* | Small | Large |

We have now adopted (−) and (+) rather than 1 and 2 as codes for the two levels of each factor. See Section 2.2 for some remarks about these alternative codings. This is an example of *product* rather than *process* design, and was carried out at a fairly early stage in the design process. Another difference from the carburettor experiment is that neither of the factor levels corresponds to a *current* setting. The purpose is still of course to study the effect of *changes* in the factor levels.

The vent (hole) in the bag allows air to escape after the passenger makes contact with the bag. This escape of air absorbs some of the passenger's kinetic energy, and thus helps to reduce injury. Chapter 11 includes a discussion of the air bag as an energy transfer system. In this chapter we will simply use the data to illustrate some basic ideas, paying very little attention to practical interpretation.

In getting to grips with interactions it is helpful to start by considering only two factors, then move on to three, and so on. We will therefore begin by presenting only half the results of the experiment. With the vent size at the (−) level, the four combinations of inflation speed and bag size gave the results summarized in Table 2.1. One way to display these results graphically is shown in Fig. 2.1. The line labelled $B+$ joins the two results obtained with a large bag size. The vertical distance between the left and right ends of this line represents the effect of changing the inflation speed from slow to fast when the bag size is large, a decrease of 9.4 in chest *g*. The other line relates to the runs made with a small bag, and shows a much smaller decrease (0.6). The effect of inflation speed is markedly different for the two bag sizes, so we have observed an interaction between these two factors. A situation of no interaction would be represented by a pair of parallel lines.

*Table 2.1* Plan and results for part of the sled test example

| Run | *S* | *B* | Chest *g* |
|---|---|---|---|
| 1 | − | − | 56.2 |
| 2 | + | − | 55.6 |
| 3 | − | + | 61.6 |
| 4 | + | + | 52.2 |

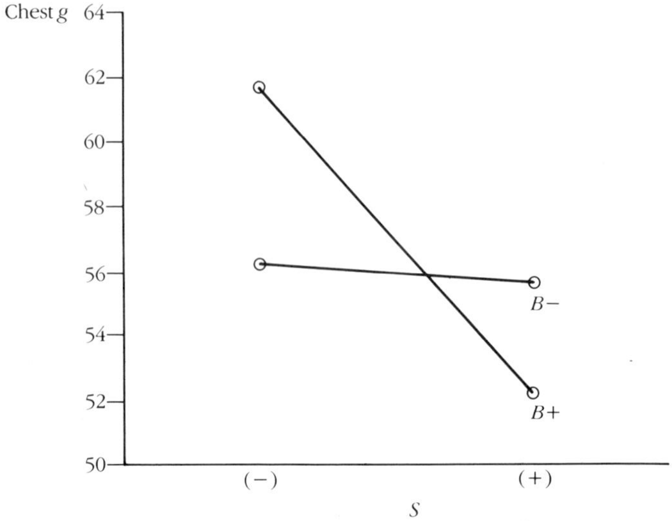


*Fig. 2.1* One way of plotting the sled test results in Table 2.1

## Main effects

In Chapter 1 we measured the effect of a factor by dividing the runs into two halves, corresponding to the two levels of that factor, and calculating the average result in each half. In this section we will look at this calculation in more detail. When the (−) and (+) codes are used, the average for the (−) level is subtracted from the average for the (+) level. For factor $S$ this gives

$$\text{effect of } S = \frac{55.6 + 52.2}{2} - \frac{56.2 + 61.6}{2} \qquad [2.1]$$

$$= \frac{(55.6 - 56.2) + (52.2 - 61.6)}{2} \qquad [2.2]$$

In equation [2.2], (55.6 − 56.2) is the effect of $S$ when $B$ is at the (−) level, and (52.2 − 61.6) is the effect of $S$ when $B$ is at (+). We are therefore averaging the two effects shown by the lines in Fig. 2.1. The technical name for formula [2.1] is the *main effect* of factor $S$. Another way of writing [2.1] is

$$\text{main effect of } S = \frac{-56.2 + 55.6 - 61.6 + 52.2}{2} \qquad [2.3]$$

a version that will be seen to be very useful later on.

In our data the main effect of $S$ is −5.0 (a fall of 5.0 in chest $g$). The usefulness of a calculated main effect for practical interpretation depends on the amount of interaction. A main effect of −5 sounds quite substantial, but

Fig. 2.1 suggests that over the range considered in the experiment the inflation speed may not be very important for a small bag. As another example, we can plot the data in a different way to get Fig. 2.2. $B$ has a positive effect for $S-$ and a negative effect for $S+$. Averaging these two effects would produce a very misleading measure of the importance of factor $B$.

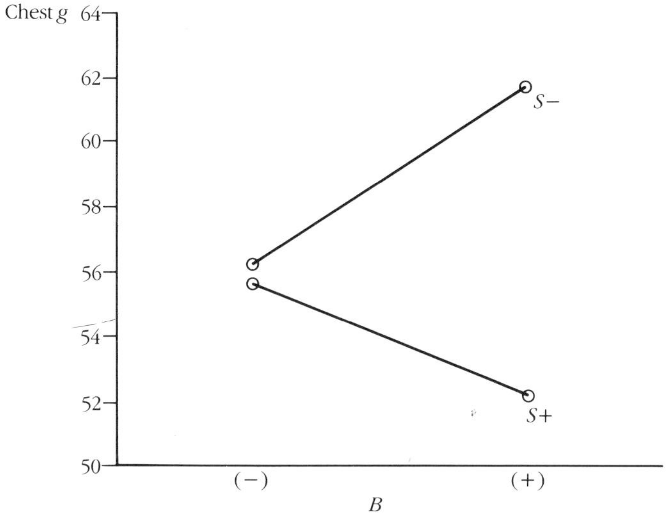


*Fig. 2.2* An alternative display of the sled test results in Table 2.1

Practical interpretation apart, calculated main effects (and the measures of interaction developed below) can serve as convenient numerical summaries of a set of data. They facilitate the process of *prediction*, as we shall show in Section 2.3.

For factor $B$ the formula corresponding to [2.2] is

$$\text{main effect of } B = \frac{(52.2 - 55.6) + (61.6 - 56.2)}{2}$$

which can also be written as

$$\text{main effect of } B = \frac{-56.2 - 55.6 + 61.6 + 52.2}{2} \qquad [2.4]$$

to fit the pattern of [2.3].

## Formulae for interaction

We will refer to the interaction between factors $S$ and $B$ as $S \times B$ interaction. $S \times B$ interaction is measured by *half the difference* between the effect of $S$ for

$B+$ and the effect of $S$ for $B-$. The corresponding formula is

$$\frac{(52.2 - 61.6) - (55.6 - 56.2)}{2}$$

which can also be written as

$$\frac{(52.2 - 55.6) - (61.6 - 56.2)}{2}$$

which is half the difference between the effect of $B$ for $S+$ and the effect of $B$ for $S-$. The fact that both versions give the same answer shows that when thinking about $S \times B$ interaction we can choose whichever version is most meaningful to us at the time: we can either think about the way the effect of $B$ varies with the level of $S$, or vice versa. For the data in Table 2.1, the numerical measure of interaction is $-4.4$.

The interaction formula can also be re-written to fit the pattern of [2.3] and [2.4]. We get

$$\frac{56.2 - 55.6 - 61.6 + 52.2}{2} \qquad [2.5]$$

Note that the divisor is half the number of runs, for the interaction as well as the main effects. This is convenient from a statistical point of view, as we will show in Chapter 3. Because the formulae for main effects and interactions are so similar, we will often use the word *effect* to mean either a main effect or an interaction.

## Contrasts

The formulae [2.3], [2.4] and [2.5] are so similar that it is easy to devise a scheme for writing them down together in a concise way. Table 2.2 shows one way of doing it, based on the layouts in the book by Box *et al.* (1978). For example, to reconstruct [2.3] we find the *inner product* of the first column in the matrix and the column of responses, i.e. multiply the column entries row by row and add the results, and finally divide by 2. Formulae [2.3], [2.4] and [2.5] are all contrasts in the response values. In general, any set of coefficients that sums to zero generates a contrast, and we will present much more complicated examples of contrasts in subsequent chapters. Note that:

- The columns in the matrix part of Table 2.2 are *orthogonal*, meaning that the inner product of each pair of columns is zero.
- The first two columns in the matrix are re-coded versions of the columns of the experimental plan in Table 2.1, with $(-)$ replaced by $-1$ and $(+)$ replaced by $+1$. The same thing happens in all two-level experiments.
- The coefficients in the $S \times B$ interaction contrast can be found by multiplying the other two columns row by row.

*Table 2.2* Three contrasts for the results in Table 2.1

| | Formula | | | |
|---|---|---|---|---|
| | [2.3] | [2.4] | [2.5] | Chest $g$ |
| | −1 | −1 | +1 | 56.2 |
| | +1 | −1 | −1 | 55.6 |
| | −1 | +1 | −1 | 61.6 |
| | +1 | +1 | +1 | 52.2 |
| Divisor | 2 | 2 | 2 | |

If we use a set of orthogonal columns to define a set of contrasts, the contrasts themselves are called orthogonal. From a statistical point of view it is very convenient to work with orthogonal contrasts, as we show in Chapter 3. In general, a set of $n$ results can be used to generate $(n - 1)$ orthogonal contrasts.

**Generating contrasts**

If main effect contrasts are typed into columns of the worksheet, interaction contrasts can be generated by multiplying these main effect contrasts cell by cell using the routine spreadsheet formula of cell-by-cell multiplication. This makes a spreadsheet an ideal computer environment for analysing experimental data using orthogonal contrasts.

Checking the orthogonality of two contrasts is achieved by multiplying the contrasts cell by cell and summing the resulting set of numbers. Orthogonal contrasts will return an answer of zero.

If the experimental (response) data are typed into another column of the worksheet, contrast values can be calculated by multiplying the data column by each contrast in turn, thus creating a new set of columns in the worksheet. These new columns can be summed, and the results divided by the appropriate divisors, giving the contrast values.

## 2.2 SLED TEST EXAMPLE — MORE DATA

The data given previously in Table 2.1 were obtained with factor $V$, the vent size, at the (−) level. Four more runs were made at $V+$, and the complete set of results is laid out in Table 2.3.

Given the results of eight runs, at most seven orthogonal contrasts can be generated. There are many different sets of orthogonal contrasts that might be useful in special circumstances, but we will concentrate on one set that has

*Table 2.3* Plan and results for the sled test example

| Run | $S$ | $B$ | $V$ | Chest $g$ |
|---|---|---|---|---|
| 1 | − | − | − | 56.2 |
| 2 | + | − | − | 55.6 |
| 3 | − | + | − | 61.6 |
| 4 | + | + | − | 52.2 |
| 5 | − | − | + | 54.0 |
| 6 | + | − | + | 50.0 |
| 7 | − | + | + | 60.3 |
| 8 | + | + | + | 51.1 |

very general utility. They are an obvious generalization of the contrasts in Table 2.2, and are given by applying the coefficients and divisors in Table 2.4 to the column of results. It will be shown below that among this set of contrasts are three which measure the main effects of $S$, $B$ and $V$, three more which measure the interaction between each pair of variables ($S \times B$, $S \times V$ and $B \times V$), and one which measures $S \times B \times V$ interaction, which we have not defined yet but is discussed below. The labels on the columns indicate what each one measures. The numerical values of the contrasts are shown in the last row. The matrix part of Table 2.4 is called the *contrast matrix*. One way to generate the coefficients is to use the *multiplication rule* which we noted in the two-factor case: the coefficients for an interaction contrast can be found by multiplying the appropriate main effect columns row by row. The reader should check that the rule applies to the $S \times B \times V$ contrast as well as to all the two-factor interactions.

*Table 2.4* Seven orthogonal contrasts for the data in Table 2.3

| | $S$ | $B$ | $S \times B$ | $V$ | $S \times V$ | $B \times V$ | $S \times B \times V$ | Chest $g$ |
|---|---|---|---|---|---|---|---|---|
| | −1 | −1 | +1 | −1 | +1 | +1 | −1 | 56.2 |
| | +1 | −1 | −1 | −1 | −1 | +1 | +1 | 55.6 |
| | −1 | +1 | −1 | −1 | +1 | −1 | +1 | 61.6 |
| | +1 | +1 | +1 | −1 | −1 | −1 | −1 | 52.2 |
| | −1 | −1 | +1 | +1 | −1 | −1 | +1 | 54.0 |
| | +1 | −1 | −1 | +1 | +1 | −1 | −1 | 50.0 |
| | −1 | +1 | −1 | +1 | −1 | +1 | −1 | 60.3 |
| | +1 | +1 | +1 | +1 | +1 | +1 | +1 | 51.1 |
| Divisor | 4 | 4 | 4 | 4 | 4 | 4 | 4 | |
| Contrast value | −5.80 | 2.35 | −3.50 | −2.55 | −0.80 | 1.35 | 0.90 | |

## The $L_8(2^7)$ orthogonal array

The $L_8(2^7)$ orthogonal array is shown in Table 2.5. The subscript 8 refers to the number of runs. The $2^7$ part will be explained later. Although the name $L_8(2^7)$ comes from Taguchi, his version of the array looks very different from ours. In particular, he uses 1 and 2 to represent the factor levels. We can see advantages in both codings. For example, when both the actual levels of a factor are positive numbers, coding one of them as (−) may be confusing. On the other hand, there can be no doubt that having the array in −/+ form makes it far easier to 'see' the relationships between the columns, and we have found that this helps people to understand and use orthogonal arrays. There are other differences between Taguchi's version and ours, but they are not fundamentally important. We will compare the two versions of the array in Chapter 4. $c_1$, $c_2$ etc. are just labels for the columns.

*Table 2.5* The $L_8(2^7)$ array

| Row | $c_1$ | $c_2$ | $c_3$ | $c_4$ | $c_5$ | $c_6$ | $c_7$ |
|---|---|---|---|---|---|---|---|
| 1 | − | − | + | − | + | + | − |
| 2 | + | − | − | − | − | + | + |
| 3 | − | + | − | − | + | − | + |
| 4 | + | + | + | − | − | − | − |
| 5 | − | − | + | + | − | − | + |
| 6 | + | − | − | + | + | − | − |
| 7 | − | + | − | + | − | + | − |
| 8 | + | + | + | + | + | + | + |

When applied to an array of symbols such as (−) and (+), 'orthogonal' means *balanced*: in any pair of columns, each combination of (−) and (+) signs occurs equally often. The contrast matrix in Table 2.4 is just a re-coding of $L_8(2^7)$, with (−) and (+) replaced by −1 and +1. When the array is re-coded the columns are orthogonal in the inner product sense that we used above.

The experimental plan in Table 2.3 consists of the first, second and fourth columns of $L_8(2^7)$, and a concise way of defining the plan is to say that factor $S$ is *allocated* to $c_1$ of $L_8(2^7)$, $B$ is allocated to $c_2$ and $V$ to $c_4$.

## Main effects and interactions

We will use the $S$ column in Table 2.4 as an example of a main effect contrast. It can be written out as

$$\frac{(55.6 - 56.2) + (52.2 - 61.6) + (50.0 - 54.0) + (51.1 - 60.3)}{4} \qquad [2.6]$$

This is an average of four effects, one for each of the four combinations of $B$ and $V$. The individual effects are $-0.6$, $-9.4$, $-4.0$, and $-9.2$. The main effect of $S$ is $-5.8$, similar to the value obtained above from only half the data.

As an example of a two-way interaction, the column labelled $B \times V$ generates a contrast that can be rearranged as

$$\frac{1}{2}\left(\frac{55.6 - 52.2 - 50.0 + 51.1}{2} + \frac{56.2 - 61.6 - 54.0 + 60.3}{2}\right) \qquad [2.7]$$

Inside the parentheses formula [2.5] has been applied twice, first to the runs that have $S$ at the (+) level, then to the remainder. This contrast therefore measures the interaction between $B$ and $V$, averaged over the levels of $S$. The $B \times V$ interactions in the two halves of the data are 2.25 and 0.45, with an average of 1.35.

An equivalent method of measuring the $B \times V$ interaction begins by averaging the data over the levels of $S$. Figure 2.3 shows the average value of chest $g$ for each combination of $V$ and $B$. This is sometimes called an *interaction graph*. The $B \times V$ interaction is then measured, for example, by

$$\begin{aligned} &\tfrac{1}{2}(\text{effect of } B \text{ for } V+ \quad - \quad \text{effect of } B \text{ for } V-) \\ &= \tfrac{1}{2}\{(55.7 - 52.0) - (56.9 - 55.9)\} \\ &= 1.35 \end{aligned}$$

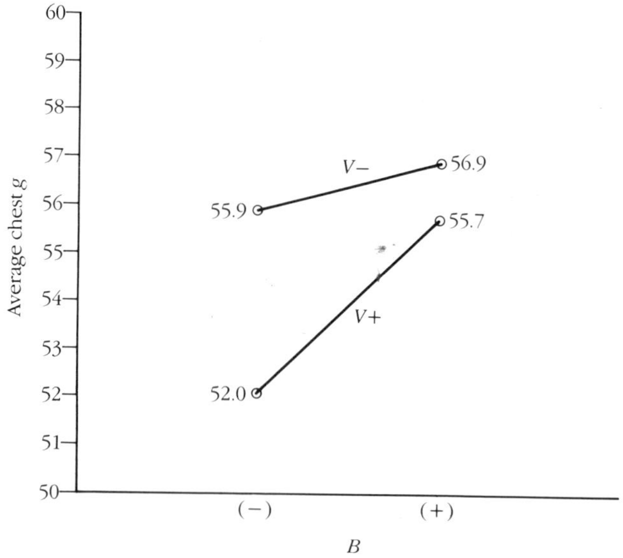


*Fig. 2.3* Sled test data. Interaction graph for $B \times V$

The column labelled $S \times B \times V$ can be written out as

$$\frac{1}{2}\left(\frac{55.6 - 52.2 - 50.0 + 51.1}{2} - \frac{56.2 - 61.6 - 54.0 + 60.3}{2}\right)$$

which is half the difference between the $B \times V$ interaction for $S+$ and the $B \times V$ interaction for $S-$. In the example we get

$$\tfrac{1}{2}(2.25 - 0.45) = 0.9$$

$S \times B \times V$ interaction arises when the $B \times V$ interaction varies with the level of $S$, but it turns out that the formula is *symmetric* in the factors: it can equally well be interpreted as measuring the variation in $S \times B$ interaction over the levels of $V$, or in $S \times V$ interaction over the levels of $B$. If there is substantial three-way interaction, the 'lower order' measures — main effects and two-factor interactions — are virtually useless for interpretive purposes.

## Geometrical interpretation of the contrast calculations

In Fig. 2.4 the eight runs in Table 2.3 are represented as the corners of a cube in three dimensions, with each factor corresponding to one dimension. The main effect of $S$ is the difference between the average result on the left face of the cube and the average on the right face. The $B \times V$ contrast [2.7] can be

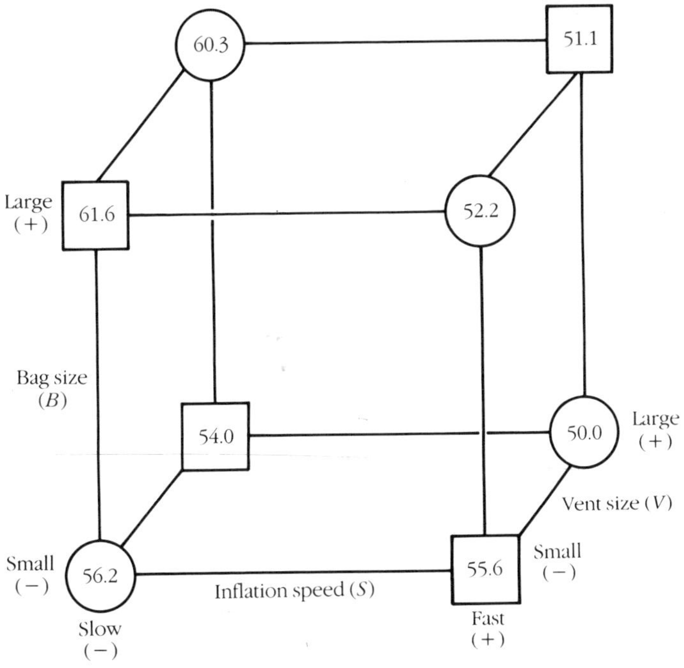


*Fig. 2.4* The sled test data displayed in three dimensions

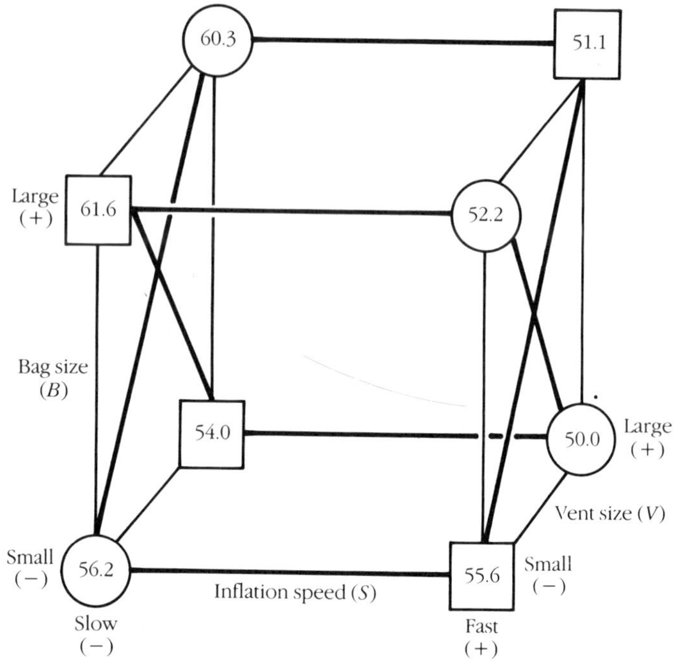


*Fig. 2.5* Sled test data. The $B \times V$ contrast interpreted as two intersecting planes

rearranged so that it too represents the difference between two averages. In this case the two groups of points lie on intersecting diagonal planes, as shown in Fig. 2.5.

In fact, all seven contrasts in Table 2.4 can be calculated by separating the corners of the cube into two sets and finding the difference between the averages.

## Interpretation of the contrast values

The next step in our analysis of the sled test data ought to be the application of a statistical method to decide which of the effects are large enough (in absolute value) to be treated as real, the remainder being regarded as the products of random variation. We have deferred the introduction of statistical methods until Chapter 3, so for the moment we will simply note that in Table 2.4 the three-way interaction and two of the two-way interactions are small in relation to the main effects, but that the $S \times B$ interaction may need to be taken into account. We will continue the discussion of this experiment in Chapter 11.

## Efficiency of balanced experiments

In a balanced multi-factor experiment, each calculated main effect is the difference between two averages. With a total of eight runs, each average involves four results, and this averaging process helps to reduce the effect of noise and makes it more likely that any conclusions we draw from the data will be sound (by 'sound', we mean for example that if the experiment were repeated we would come to essentially the same conclusions). To obtain the same benefits of averaging in a one-factor-at-a-time setting would require at least 16 runs. For example, the experimenters might proceed along the following lines:

- Four runs with all factors at $(-)$.
- Four runs with the configuration $S+$, $B-$, $V-$; contrasting these with the first set gives a measure of the $S$ effect.
- Four runs with the configuration $S-$, $B+$, $V-$; contrasting these with the first set gives a measure of the $B$ effect.
- Four runs with the configuration $S-$, $B-$, $V+$; contrasting these with the first set gives a measure of the $V$ effect.

This procedure has been summarized in Table 2.6. Despite using twice as many runs as the balanced array, this experiment *can provide no information about interactions* because the effect of each factor is measured for only one setting of the other factors and we cannot draw graphs like Fig. 2.1.

*Table 2.6* A one-factor-at-a-time experiment

| Run | $S$ | $B$ | $V$ |
|---|---|---|---|
| 1 | − | − | − |
| 2 | − | − | − |
| 3 | − | − | − |
| 4 | − | − | − |
| 5 | + | − | − |
| 6 | + | − | − |
| 7 | + | − | − |
| 8 | + | − | − |
| 9 | − | + | − |
| 10 | − | + | − |
| 11 | − | + | − |
| 12 | − | + | − |
| 13 | − | − | + |
| 14 | − | − | + |
| 15 | − | − | + |
| 16 | − | − | + |

## 2.3 PREDICTION

Although we have not yet covered statistical methods, this is a convenient place to explore one of the practical implications of treating an effect as indistinguishable from random noise, which is that *it should not be taken into account in making predictions.*

Suppose that the sled test experiment was run again, using the same experimental plan as in Table 2.3. What results would we expect to see? What predictions can we make on the basis of the results we have already seen? It might appear that if we are required to nominate a single numerical prediction (not a range) for each configuration, our only possible strategy is to predict that each will give the same result as before, even though we realize that exact repetition of the previous results is most unlikely. But there is, in most cases, a better way.

The method we are about to outline is based on the theory of least squares. We are not going to give a mathematical derivation and we hope that a few simple examples will be sufficient to demonstrate that the method is sensible. In the sled test example, suppose we want a prediction for the configuration $S-$, $B-$, $V-$, treating only the $S$, $B$, $V$ and $S \times B$ effects as real. A row of $\pm 1$s is written down for these effects, which resembles a row from a contrast matrix. For the main effects the signs are given by the configuration we are predicting. For interactions the usual product rule applies. Underneath, write down the calculated values of the effects (from Table 2.4):

| $S$ | $B$ | $V$ | $S \times B$ |
|---|---|---|---|
| [ −1 | −1 | −1 | +1 ] |
| −5.80 | 2.35 | −2.55 | −3.50 |

The prediction is given by equation [2.8]:

$$\text{prediction} = \bar{y} + \frac{1}{2}\begin{pmatrix}\text{inner product of row of } \pm 1\text{s} \\ \text{with row of effects}\end{pmatrix} \qquad [2.8]$$

where $\bar{y}$ is the average response in the experiment. In our example this gives

$$\begin{aligned}\text{prediction} &= 55.13 + \frac{1}{2}\left\{\begin{matrix}(-1)(-5.80) + (-1)(2.35) \\ + (-1)(-2.55) + (+1)(-3.50)\end{matrix}\right\} \\ &= 58.73\end{aligned}$$

Although this prediction is quite close to the value of 56.2 that was actually observed for $S$, $B$ and $V$ at the $(-)$ level, it takes all the data into account. As well as its interpretation as our best guess of what we would get if the configuration $S-$, $B-$, $V-$ was run again just once, the prediction also

**Prediction equations**

Predictions are easily accomplished in a spreadsheet. Prediction equations in the form of [2.8] involve $\bar{y}$ and an inner product of contrast values (effects) and factor levels ($\pm 1$s). Most spreadsheets have a built-in formula to calculate an average for a set of data. The inner product between a row of effects and a row of $\pm 1$s is accomplished by multiplying each pair of cell elements in the two rows and adding. These two operations combined into one formula enable predictions to be calculated and displayed in cells of the worksheet.

represents the average chest $g$ we would expect to see if we repeated the test over and over again with $S$, $B$ and $V$ at the $(-)$ level, provided that no special causes of variation intervene.

Another way to write [2.8] is

$$\text{prediction} = \bar{y} + (\bar{y}_{S-} - \bar{y}) + (\bar{y}_{B-} - \bar{y}) + (\bar{y}_{V-} - \bar{y}) + (\bar{y}_{[S\times B]-} - \bar{y}) \qquad [2.9]$$

where $\bar{y}_{S-}$ is the average chest $g$ for $S$ at the $(-)$ level, $\bar{y}_{B-}$ the average chest $g$ for $B$ at the $(-)$ level, likewise for $V$, and $\bar{y}_{[S\times B]-}$ is the average chest $g$ corresponding to runs where the $S\times B$ interaction has a $-1$ in its contrast column. We will leave it to the reader to verify that the two prediction equations amount to the same thing. Our chief reason for including [2.9] is that it corresponds to the method of prediction favoured by Taguchi in his writing (though Taguchi rarely includes interactions in his predictions).

## Predictions for a $2^2$ example

To help give the reader a better understanding of equation [2.8], we apply it to the simplest possible case, with two factors each at two levels. This is known as a $2^2$ experiment. We call the factors $A$ and $B$. To begin with, only the $A$ and $B$ main effects will be treated as real. If predictions are required for every configuration, we get a matrix of coefficients as shown in Table 2.7. We also show the prediction formulae that equation [2.8] generates in this case.

*Table 2.7* Prediction for a $2^2$ example, main effects only

| $A$ | $B$ | Original response | Prediction formula |
|---|---|---|---|
| $-1$ | $-1$ | $y_1$ | $\bar{y} - \frac{1}{2}$(main effect of $A$) $- \frac{1}{2}$(main effect of $B$) |
| $+1$ | $-1$ | $y_2$ | $\bar{y} + \frac{1}{2}$(main effect of $A$) $- \frac{1}{2}$(main effect of $B$) |
| $-1$ | $+1$ | $y_3$ | $\bar{y} - \frac{1}{2}$(main effect of $A$) $+ \frac{1}{2}$(main effect of $B$) |
| $+1$ | $+1$ | $y_4$ | $\bar{y} + \frac{1}{2}$(main effect of $A$) $+ \frac{1}{2}$(main effect of $B$) |

Note the following points:

- Subtracting the first prediction from the second, and the third from the fourth, shows that for both levels of $B$ the *predicted effect* of $A$ is equal to the calculated main effect of $A$. Omitting the $A \times B$ interaction imposes a structure on the predictions that was not present in the original data.
- Each individual prediction is the sum of a term that involves neither $A$ nor $B$, a term in $A$ alone and a term in $B$ alone. The predictions are said to have an *additive* structure. In general, when all interactions are negligible the factors are said to have additive effects.
- $\bar{y}$ can itself be thought of as a prediction. If both factors are quantitative and have separate linear effects on the response, $\bar{y}$ would be our prediction for a configuration in which both $A$ and $B$ are at a level midway between $(-)$ and $(+)$; anticipating developments in Chapter 5, we could code this point as $A = 0$, $B = 0$ and refer to it as the centre point of the $2^2$ plan. If the factors are qualitative the idea of a centre point has no meaning, but $\bar{y}$ can still be interpreted as the predicted average of the four individual results. In general $\bar{y}$ can be thought of as a *baseline* from which the individual predictions deviate by an amount that varies according to the factor levels.

The individual predictions can be expressed as simple functions of the original data, which we refer to as $y_1$, $y_2$, $y_3$ and $y_4$. For example, the prediction for the configuration $A-$, $B-$ is $\frac{3}{4}y_1 + \frac{1}{4}y_2 + \frac{1}{4}y_3 - \frac{1}{4}y_4$, which shows that the greatest weight is attached to $y_1$, the observed result for $A-$, $B-$, with all the other results having equal importance.

If we allow for the $A \times B$ interaction, Table 2.7 is replaced by Table 2.8. As we have indicated in the last column, although the prediction formulae look complicated, the answers are very simple in this case. In effect, equation [2.8] is telling us that if we do not feel justified in imposing a structure on the predictions by constraining them to show zero interaction, the best we can do is predict 'same again'.

## 2.4 FRACTIONAL FACTORIAL EXPERIMENTS

In the sled test example there were three factors, each with two levels, and all eight possible combinations were run. This is known as a *full* or *complete* $2^3$ factorial experiment. Although it is more efficient than a one-factor-at-a-time plan, with a larger number of factors this strategy requires an unrealistically large commitment of resources, and we need a method for obtaining useful information from a smaller number of runs. The carburettor example in Section 1.2 points the way: using a carefully balanced plan it was possible to assess the effects of seven factors in only eight runs, based on a working assumption that the effects of the factors were additive. In general, $n$

*Table 2.8* Prediction for a $2^2$ example with interaction

| $A$ | $B$ | $A\times B$ | Prediction formula | Prediction |
|---|---|---|---|---|
| −1 | −1 | +1 | $\bar{y} - \frac{1}{2}$(main effect of $A$) − $\frac{1}{2}$(main effect of $B$) + $\frac{1}{2}$($A\times B$ interaction) | $y_1$ |
| +1 | −1 | −1 | $\bar{y} + \frac{1}{2}$(main effect of $A$) − $\frac{1}{2}$(main effect of $B$) − $\frac{1}{2}$($A\times B$ interaction) | $y_2$ |
| −1 | +1 | −1 | $\bar{y} - \frac{1}{2}$(main effect of $A$) + $\frac{1}{2}$(main effect of $B$) − $\frac{1}{2}$($A\times B$ interaction) | $y_3$ |
| +1 | +1 | +1 | $\bar{y} + \frac{1}{2}$(main effect of $A$) + $\frac{1}{2}$(main effect of $B$) + $\frac{1}{2}$($A\times B$ interaction) | $y_4$ |

experimental runs are sufficient to give some information about any number of factors up to $(n - 1)$, but, as the number of factors increases, our interpretation of the data necessarily becomes more tentative.

Any experiment that involves running only a subset of the possible factor combinations is called a *fractional* factorial experiment. As a simple example we return to the sled test experiment and invite the reader to imagine that only four of the eight actual runs were made, as listed in Table 2.9. Because only half the full factorial is run, this is often known as a *half replicate* of the full factorial. Figure 2.6 is a copy of Fig. 2.4 with four of the results deleted. The corners that remain correspond to the rows in Table 2.9. This subset is special, because for any pair of factors we have a complete $2^2$ array. The reader might like to think about *projecting* the cube onto one of its faces. Whichever face is chosen, there will be a result at each corner.

The columns in Table 2.9 form an orthogonal array, a smaller relative of $L_8(2^7)$ that is known — not surprisingly — as $L_4(2^3)$.

Now consider the calculation of contrasts from the results in Table 2.9. At most three orthogonal contrasts can be defined, and the most convenient set is laid out in Table 2.10. Note that we have not put letter labels on the columns, because we have not yet established what each of them measures,

*Table 2.9* A new (fictitious) plan for the sled test example

| Run | $S$ | $B$ | $V$ | Chest $g$ |
|---|---|---|---|---|
| 1 | − | − | + | 54.0 |
| 2 | + | − | − | 55.6 |
| 3 | − | + | − | 61.6 |
| 4 | + | + | + | 51.1 |

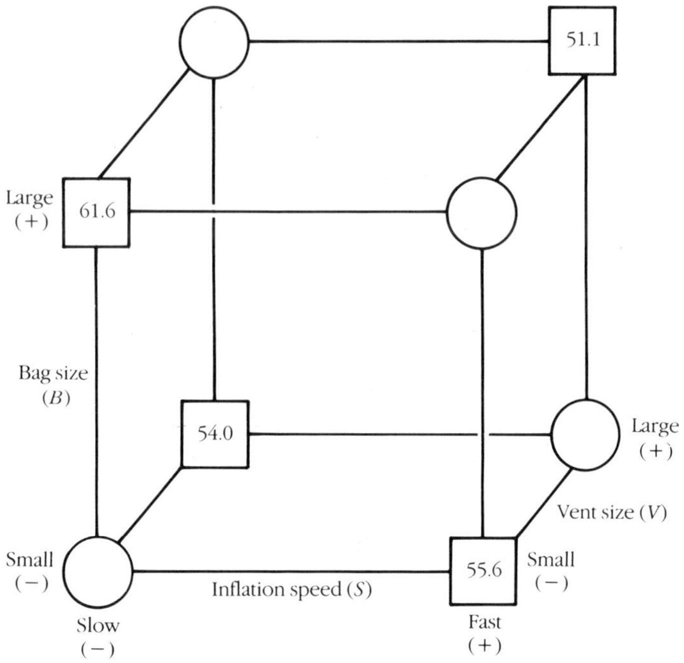


*Fig. 2.6* The sled test results in Table 2.9

and that the columns themselves are just a re-coding of the $L_4(2^3)$ array. In fact we used exactly the same contrast matrix in Table 2.2. On that occasion the three contrasts could be unambiguously interpreted as measuring the $S$ main effect, $B$ main effect and $S \times B$ interaction. Now that we have one more factor to take account of, interpretation is bound to be more complicated. To put the point another way, three contrasts cannot provide independent estimates of three main effects, three two-way interactions and a three-way interaction.

We will consider in detail the interpretation of the $c_1$ contrast in Table 2.10. Since it is calculated from a subset of the corners of the cube, we will refer to it for brevity as the subset contrast. It can be written out as

*Table 2.10* Three contrasts for the data in Table 2.9

| | $c_1$ | $c_2$ | $c_3$ | Chest $g$ |
|---|---|---|---|---|
| | −1 | −1 | +1 | 54.0 |
| | +1 | −1 | −1 | 55.6 |
| | −1 | +1 | −1 | 61.6 |
| | +1 | +1 | +1 | 51.1 |
| Divisor | 2 | 2 | 2 | |
| Contrast value | −4.45 | 1.55 | −6.05 | |

$$\frac{55.6 + 51.1}{2} - \frac{61.6 + 54.0}{2} \qquad (= -4.45)$$

which is the difference between an average for runs with $S$ at the (+) level and a similar average for $S-$. It looks, at least at first glance, like a main effect contrast. On the other hand, its column of coefficients is the (re-coded) product of the $B$ and $V$ columns in the experimental plan (Table 2.9), suggesting that it measures $B \times V$ interaction! In a sense, both of these interpretations are correct. The facts are as follows:

- If we can ignore the possibility of $B \times V$ interaction, the subset contrast is a valid estimate of the main effect of $S$.
- If $S$ has no effect on the response, the subset contrast is a valid estimate of the $B \times V$ interaction.
- In general this contrast measures the sum of the $S$ and $B \times V$ effects, and we should label it as '$S + B \times V$'.

With respect to the last statement, note that for the data in Table 2.4

$$S \text{ contrast} + B \times V \text{ contrast} = -5.80 + 1.35 = -4.45$$

Starting from formulae [2.6] and [2.7], it can be shown algebraically that the subset contrast can always be interpreted as the sum of the $S$ and $B \times V$ contrasts that we *would* have obtained if we had run all the corners of the cube in Fig. 2.4.

The $S$ and $B \times V$ effects are said to be *confounded* or *aliased*. Note the possibility that the true $S$ and $B \times V$ effects may have opposite signs and so may wholly or partially cancel each other out in the subset contrast, so that we may end up with a totally false picture of the situation based on data from a fractional experiment. Similar considerations apply to the $c_2$ and $c_3$ contrasts in Table 2.10. Table 2.11 is a repetition of Table 2.10 but now with the columns appropriately labelled. These contrast values should be compared with those in Table 2.4. It is clear that if these results were interpreted on the assumption that there are no interactions, each contrast being taken as the measure of a main effect, the relative importance of factor $V$ would be greatly exaggerated.

*Table 2.11* Three contrasts for the data in Table 2.9 (with labels)

| | $S + V \times B$ | $B + S \times V$ | $V + S \times B$ | Chest $g$ |
|---|---|---|---|---|
| | −1 | −1 | +1 | 54.0 |
| | +1 | −1 | −1 | 55.6 |
| | −1 | +1 | −1 | 61.6 |
| | +1 | +1 | +1 | 51.1 |
| Divisor | 2 | 2 | 2 | |
| Contrast value | −4.45 | 1.55 | −6.05 | |

## 2.5 SOME FRACTIONAL PLANS BASED ON $L_8(2^7)$

The purpose of this final section of the chapter is to give some fairly simple examples of the different patterns of confounding that can occur, using examples based on the $L_8(2^7)$ array. The factors *A*, *B*, *C*, etc., are now entirely abstract, and no attempt will be made to give realistic illustrations.

Suppose that we want to study four factors, and that we allocate them to the $L_8(2^7)$ array as follows: *A* to $c_1$, *B* to $c_2$, *C* to $c_4$ and *D* to $c_7$. The resulting plan is shown in Table 2.12. Since we have eight runs, at most seven orthogonal contrasts can be calculated, and we can once again generate them by re-coding the seven columns of $L_8(2^7)$. We end up with the same set of contrasts as in Table 2.4, but the labels will be different. Table 2.13 shows the contrasts with their new labels. Note that all the main effects are confounded with three-way interactions; in most industrial experimentation it is necessary to assume that such interactions are small or negligible.

*Table 2.12* Experimental plan for four factors, based on $L_8(2^7)$

| *A* | *B* | *C* | *D* |
|---|---|---|---|
| − | − | − | − |
| + | − | − | + |
| − | + | − | + |
| + | + | − | − |
| − | − | + | + |
| + | − | + | − |
| − | + | + | − |
| + | + | + | + |

*Table 2.13* Seven orthogonal contrasts for the plan in Table 2.12

| *A* +*B*×*C*×*D* | *B* +*A*×*C*×*D* | *A*×*B* +*C*×*D* | *C* +*A*×*B*×*D* | *A*×*C* +*B*×*D* | *B*×*C* +*A*×*D* | *D* +*A*×*B*×*C* | Result |
|---|---|---|---|---|---|---|---|
| −1 | −1 | +1 | −1 | +1 | +1 | −1 | $y_1$ |
| +1 | −1 | −1 | −1 | −1 | +1 | +1 | $y_2$ |
| −1 | +1 | −1 | −1 | +1 | −1 | +1 | $y_3$ |
| +1 | +1 | +1 | −1 | −1 | −1 | −1 | $y_4$ |
| −1 | −1 | +1 | +1 | −1 | −1 | +1 | $y_5$ |
| +1 | −1 | −1 | +1 | +1 | −1 | −1 | $y_6$ |
| −1 | +1 | −1 | +1 | −1 | +1 | −1 | $y_7$ |
| +1 | +1 | +1 | +1 | +1 | +1 | +1 | $y_8$ |
| Divisor 4 | 4 | 4 | 4 | 4 | 4 | 4 | |

The confounding pattern shown in Table 2.13 is a consequence of the fact that for $L_8(2^7)$ *the product of any two columns is another column of the array*. By 'product', we mean multiplying the two columns row by row. If the array is in its original $-/+$ coding, take $(-) \times (-) = (+)$, $(-) \times (+) = (-)$, etc. If the array has been re-coded with $-1/+1$, use straightforward multiplication. The 'multiplication table' is shown in Table 2.14. For example, $c_1 \times c_2 = c_3$, but also $c_4 \times c_7 = c_3$, which is why the $A \times B$ and $C \times D$ interactions are confounded. Furthermore,

$$c_2 \times c_4 \times c_7 = (c_2 \times c_4) \times c_7 = c_6 \times c_7 = c_1$$

which explains why the $B \times C \times D$ interaction is confounded with the main effect of $A$.

*Table 2.14* Multiplication table for the $L_8(2^7)$ array

| Column number | Column number 2 | 3 | 4 | 5 | 6 | 7 |
|---|---|---|---|---|---|---|
| 1 | 3 | 2 | 5 | 4 | 7 | 6 |
| 2 | | 1 | 6 | 7 | 4 | 5 |
| 3 | | | 7 | 6 | 5 | 4 |
| 4 | | | | 1 | 2 | 3 |
| 5 | | | | | 3 | 2 |
| 6 | | | | | | 1 |

Patient inspection of the multiplication table will reveal that there is no better way of selecting four columns from $L_8(2^7)$. For example, if we move $D$ to $c_6$ then three main effects will be confounded with two-way interactions: $D$ with $B \times C$, $B$ with $C \times D$ and $C$ with $B \times D$. Given a choice, it is better to confound the main effects with interactions that involve as many factors as possible, the so-called *higher-order* interactions.

In larger examples, studying the multiplication table is a cumbersome method of discovering the pattern of confounding. Fortunately there is a quicker method, known as *alias algebra* or by some similar name. In practice, however, there is a relatively small collection of experimental plans that are likely to be useful. What the experimenter needs is not a general method of working out confounding patterns but a list of the useful plans with a guide to their interpretation. We have included some tables of fractional plans in Chapter 4.

## Five or more factors

When five factors are to be allocated to $L_8(2^7)$ there is no advantage to any one choice of columns: we arbitrarily choose the first five. The reader should by now be fairly familiar with the $L_8(2^7)$ array so on this occasion we will not write out the experimental plan. We simply list (in Table 2.15) the combination of effects that is estimated by each of the seven contrasts. All effects are now confounded with three others. As the number of factors grows, each effect will be confounded with many others, and from now on we will omit all three-way and higher-order interactions.

*Table 2.15* Pattern of confounding for five factors allocated to the first five columns of $L_8(2^7)$

| Contrast | Effects estimated |
|---|---|
| $c_1$ | $A + B\times C + D\times E + A\times B\times C\times D\times E$ |
| $c_2$ | $B + A\times C + C\times D\times E + A\times B\times D\times E$ |
| $c_3$ | $C + A\times B + B\times D\times E + A\times C\times D\times E$ |
| $c_4$ | $D + A\times E + B\times C\times E + A\times B\times C\times D$ |
| $c_5$ | $E + A\times D + B\times C\times D + A\times B\times C\times E$ |
| $c_6$ | $B\times D + C\times E + A\times C\times D + A\times B\times E$ |
| $c_7$ | $B\times E + C\times D + A\times C\times E + A\times B\times D$ |

For the $L_8(2^7)$ array the limit is of course seven two-level factors, which helps to explain its name. The experimental plan for the carburettor example in Section 1.2 was constructed by allocating seven factors to Taguchi's version of $L_8(2^7)$. Even if the higher-order interactions are ignored, the confounding pattern of this plan is very complicated: details will be found in Table 4.2.

Larger fractional factorial plans can be constructed by allocating the factors to orthogonal arrays known as $L_{12}(2^{11})$, $L_{16}(2^{15})$, and so on. We have deferred this material until Chapter 4, but we hope that our examples in this chapter have established the following principles of fractional factorial experiments:

- A fractional plan can be generated by allocating the factors to a set of columns from an orthogonal array. It is sometimes important that this set of columns be chosen carefully.
- A set of orthogonal contrasts can be generated by re-coding the complete orthogonal array using $-1/+1$.
- The confounding pattern of the experiment tells us which effects are measured by which contrasts. In $L_8(2^7)$ (and in some, but not all, of the larger arrays), the confounding pattern can be worked out by studying the multiplication table of the array.

### Prediction in fractional experiments

In Section 2.3 we introduced a method of prediction in the context of a full factorial experiment. In that setting, the aim is to use the data in the best possible way to predict what would happen if a particular configuration were *repeated*. Of even more importance is the ability to use the results of a fractional experiment to predict the outcome of a configuration that was *not* included in the original experiment. In principle, the method given in Section 2.3 applies here as well, but the situation is more complicated because of the confounding of effects. This discussion is continued in Section 4.2.

## SUMMARY OF CHAPTER 2

Interaction exists when the effect of one factor is different at different levels of the other factors. When there is substantial interaction, average effects (known as main effects) are of little use on their own. Interaction can be illustrated geometrically, but it is also useful to have a numerical measure. $A \times B$ interaction is measured by half the difference between the $A$ effect for $B+$ and the $A$ effect for $B-$.

When there are three factors the $A \times B$ interaction measure is given by averaging the $A \times B$ interactions at $C-$ and $C+$. Any difference between these two-way interactions represents three-way interaction $A \times B \times C$. These ideas can be generalized to any number of factors, but in most industrial experiments it is necessary to assume that three-way and higher-order interactions are negligible.

Main effects and interactions all represent contrasts in the response values and can be written concisely using a contrast matrix. The columns of this matrix are orthogonal. It can be constructed using a multiplication rule or by re-coding an orthogonal array, replacing $(-)$ and $(+)$ with $-1$ and $+1$. For three factors (with all combinations run) the appropriate array is $L_8(2^7)$. This type of experiment can be represented geometrically as a cube in three-dimensional space; each contrast can then be calculated by separating the corners of the cube into two sets and comparing the average result for each set. The divisor of each contrast is half the number of runs.

A fairly simple formula is available for predicting the response in the light of the experimental results. In using this formula, interactions can be included or ignored. If all interactions are ignored, an additive structure is imposed on the predictions.

In a fractional factorial experiment only a subset of the possible factor combinations are run. A total of $n$ runs is enough to provide some information about $(n - 1)$ factors, but, as the number of factors increases, our interpretation becomes more tentative, because of confounding between different effects. Fractional plans can be constructed by allocating factors to some or all of the columns of an orthogonal array. Usually, some allocations are better than others. The contrast matrix is generated by re-coding the complete array. In some arrays the pattern of confounding can be worked out by studying the multiplication table of the array.

# CHAPTER 3

# Statistical methods

*In Chapter 1 we suggested that no set of experimental results should ever be taken entirely at face value, and that statistical methods should be used to help decide which effects might be treated as real, for example when making predictions. This chapter describes and illustrates two methods that can be used for this purpose: normal plots (including half normal plots, which we call Daniel plots) and* F *tests.*

## 3.1 NORMAL PLOTS APPLIED TO AN ARTIFICIAL EXAMPLE

The experimental plan for this example is based on the $L_{16}(2^{15})$ orthogonal array. $L_{16}(2^{15})$ is a larger version of $L_8(2^7)$ which we introduced in Chapter 2; full details will be found in Table 4.5. Five factors were allocated to columns $c_1$, $c_2$, $c_4$, $c_8$ and $c_{15}$, to produce the plan shown in Table 3.1. The artificial response data appear in the last column. It was constructed in such a way that the only real effects were: main effect of $A$, 4 units; main effect of $B$, 2 units; $A \times B$ interaction, 1 unit. Random variation was superimposed on these effects by sampling numbers from a normal distribution with a standard deviation equal to 1 unit.

Fifteen contrasts were calculated, as shown in Table 3.2. As in Chapter 2, the contrast matrix can be generated either by multiplying the main effect columns or by re-coding the 15 columns of $L_{16}(2^{15})$. The column labels in Table 3.2 show that none of the main effects and two-way interactions are confounded with each other. We have ignored three-way and higher-order interactions. In fact, each main effect is confounded with one four-way interaction, and each two-way interaction is confounded with one three-way interaction.

*Table 3.1* Plan and results of an artificial example

| Run | *A* | *B* | *C* | *D* | *E* | Response |
|---|---|---|---|---|---|---|
| 1 | − | − | − | − | + | 6.77 |
| 2 | + | − | − | − | − | 11.62 |
| 3 | − | + | − | − | − | 9.02 |
| 4 | + | + | − | − | + | 13.08 |
| 5 | − | − | + | − | − | 8.85 |
| 6 | + | − | + | − | + | 11.88 |
| 7 | − | + | + | − | + | 8.19 |
| 8 | + | + | + | − | − | 13.50 |
| 9 | − | − | − | + | − | 5.86 |
| 10 | + | − | − | + | + | 10.25 |
| 11 | − | + | − | + | + | 8.86 |
| 12 | + | + | − | + | − | 14.10 |
| 13 | − | − | + | + | + | 8.31 |
| 14 | + | − | + | + | − | 10.14 |
| 15 | − | + | + | + | − | 8.58 |
| 16 | + | + | + | + | + | 13.30 |

The contrast values in Table 3.2 will be used to form normal plots. There are two basic types of normal plot, known as half normal and full normal. Details will be found in Appendix 3.1. For the purpose of this chapter — partitioning the measured effects into 'real' and 'random' — we have generally found the half normal plot to be easier to interpret. On the other hand, a full normal plot may reveal problems with a data set that are hidden in a half normal plot, and when graphs are so easy to produce on a computer there is no reason why both types of plot should not be produced as a matter of routine.

Figure 3.1 is the half normal plot for the contrast values in Table 3.2. We will often refer to half normal plots as Daniel plots, after the author Cuthbert Daniel, who first suggested using them to analyse experimental data. In a Daniel plot the absolute values of the contrasts are plotted, so that all the large contrasts appear on the right-hand side of the graph.

For the larger contrasts we have labelled the points to indicate which effects they measure. For the remainder we have written their column number in italics, so that for example *12* represents the contrast based on the $c_{12}$ column in $L_{16}(2^{15})$.

Most of the points in Fig. 3.1 cluster fairly closely around a straight line through the origin of the plot, but two points lie well clear of the line. These two effects (*A* and *B*) would be treated as real and — in the absence of other evidence — the rest as the products of random variation. The bad news is that the $A \times B$ effect is not detected by the plot: it ought to be the third largest, but it happens that two of the 'random' contrasts are larger in absolute value than $A \times B$, and $A \times B$ is completely obscured. Effects that are real but small in relation to the amount of random variation in the data are liable to be obscured in this way.

*Table 3.2* Fifteen contrasts for the data in Table 3.1

| | $A$ | $B$ | $A\times B$ | $C$ | $A\times C$ | $B\times C$ | $D\times E$ | $D$ | $A\times D$ | $B\times D$ | $C\times E$ | $C\times D$ | $B\times E$ | $A\times E$ | $E$ | Response |
|---|---|---|---|---|---|---|---|---|---|---|---|---|---|---|---|---|
| | −1 | −1 | +1 | −1 | +1 | +1 | −1 | −1 | +1 | +1 | −1 | +1 | −1 | −1 | +1 | 6.77 |
| | +1 | −1 | −1 | −1 | −1 | +1 | +1 | −1 | −1 | +1 | +1 | +1 | +1 | −1 | −1 | 11.62 |
| | −1 | +1 | −1 | −1 | +1 | −1 | +1 | −1 | +1 | −1 | +1 | +1 | −1 | +1 | −1 | 9.02 |
| | +1 | +1 | +1 | −1 | −1 | −1 | −1 | −1 | −1 | −1 | −1 | +1 | +1 | +1 | +1 | 13.08 |
| | −1 | −1 | +1 | +1 | −1 | −1 | +1 | −1 | +1 | +1 | −1 | −1 | +1 | +1 | −1 | 8.85 |
| | +1 | −1 | −1 | +1 | +1 | −1 | −1 | −1 | −1 | +1 | +1 | −1 | −1 | +1 | +1 | 11.88 |
| | −1 | +1 | −1 | +1 | −1 | +1 | −1 | −1 | +1 | −1 | +1 | −1 | +1 | −1 | +1 | 8.19 |
| | +1 | +1 | +1 | +1 | +1 | +1 | +1 | −1 | −1 | −1 | −1 | −1 | −1 | −1 | −1 | 13.50 |
| | −1 | −1 | +1 | −1 | +1 | +1 | −1 | +1 | −1 | −1 | +1 | −1 | +1 | +1 | −1 | 5.86 |
| | +1 | −1 | −1 | −1 | −1 | +1 | +1 | +1 | +1 | −1 | −1 | −1 | −1 | +1 | +1 | 10.25 |
| | −1 | +1 | −1 | −1 | +1 | −1 | +1 | +1 | −1 | +1 | −1 | −1 | +1 | −1 | +1 | 8.86 |
| | +1 | +1 | +1 | −1 | −1 | −1 | −1 | +1 | +1 | +1 | +1 | −1 | −1 | −1 | −1 | 14.10 |
| | −1 | −1 | +1 | +1 | −1 | −1 | +1 | +1 | −1 | −1 | +1 | +1 | −1 | −1 | +1 | 8.31 |
| | +1 | −1 | −1 | +1 | +1 | −1 | −1 | +1 | +1 | −1 | −1 | +1 | +1 | −1 | −1 | 10.14 |
| | −1 | +1 | −1 | +1 | −1 | +1 | −1 | +1 | −1 | +1 | −1 | +1 | −1 | +1 | −1 | 8.58 |
| | +1 | +1 | +1 | +1 | +1 | +1 | +1 | +1 | +1 | +1 | +1 | +1 | +1 | +1 | +1 | 13.30 |
| Divisor | 8 | 8 | 8 | 8 | 8 | 8 | 8 | 8 | 8 | 8 | 8 | 8 | 8 | 8 | 8 | |
| Contrast value | 4.18 | 1.87 | 0.65 | 0.40 | −0.46 | −0.77 | 0.64 | −0.44 | −0.13 | 0.70 | 0.28 | −0.08 | −0.31 | −0.08 | −0.13 | |

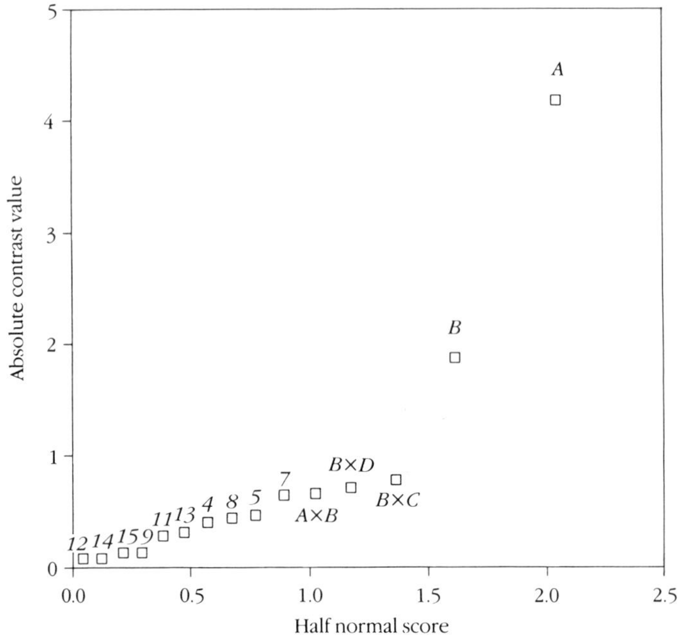


*Fig. 3.1* Daniel plot for the artificial data in Table 3.1. The italic numbers refer to the columns of $L_{16}(2^{15})$, as listed in Table 3.2

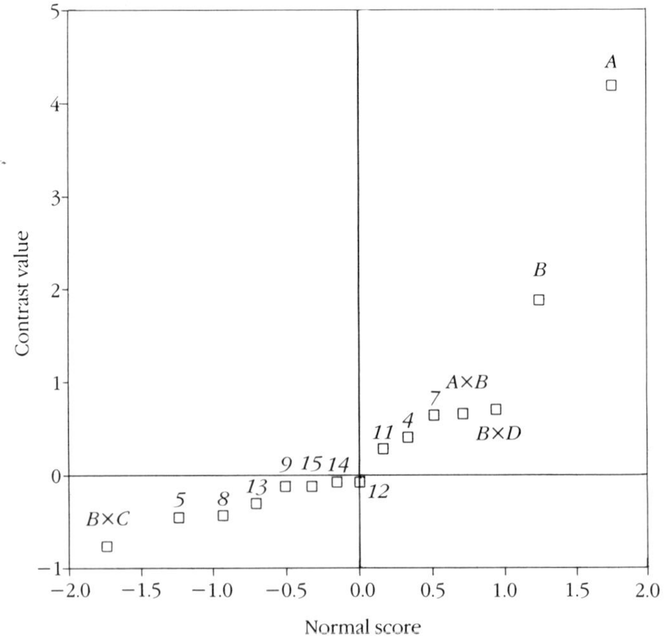


*Fig. 3.2* Full normal plot for the artificial data, to compare with Fig. 3.1

The good news about Fig. 3.1 is that there are no false positives: none of the genuinely random contrasts would be treated as real.

The full normal plot for the artificial data is in Fig. 3.2. There is little to choose between the two types of plot in this example.

## 3.2 ANALYSIS OF VARIANCE

Analysis-of-variance (anova) tables turn up in different forms in many types of statistical analysis. Using $y_i$ to represent a typical response value, $\bar{y}$ to represent the mean response and $SS_T$ to represent the 'total sum of squares around $\bar{y}$', we define $SS_T$ as follows:

$$SS_T = \sum_{i=1}^{n} (y_i - \bar{y})^2 \qquad [3.1]$$

Given a set of $(n - 1)$ orthogonal contrasts calculated from $n$ data values, $SS_T$ can also be obtained by adding up a contribution from each contrast. In two-level experiments each contrast makes a contribution given by

$$\text{contribution to } SS_T = \frac{n}{4} \times (\text{value of contrast})^2 \qquad [3.2]$$

Table 3.3 shows the contributions to $SS_T$ from each contrast in the artificial example from Section 3.1. The value given for $SS_T$ was obtained

*Table 3.3* Analysis of variance for the artificial example

| Contrast | Effect measured | Contribution to $SS_T$ |
|---|---|---|
| $c_1$ | $A$ | 69.87 |
| $c_2$ | $B$ | 13.96 |
| $c_3$ | $A \times B$ | 1.72* |
| $c_4$ | $C$ | 0.63* |
| $c_5$ | $A \times C$ | 0.83* |
| $c_6$ | $B \times C$ | 2.39* |
| $c_7$ | $D \times E$ | 1.64* |
| $c_8$ | $D$ | 0.77* |
| $c_9$ | $A \times D$ | 0.07* |
| $c_{10}$ | $B \times D$ | 1.98* |
| $c_{11}$ | $C \times E$ | 0.32* |
| $c_{12}$ | $C \times D$ | 0.03* |
| $c_{13}$ | $B \times E$ | 0.39* |
| $c_{14}$ | $A \times E$ | 0.03* |
| $c_{15}$ | $E$ | 0.06* |
| | | $SS_T = 94.67$ |

*These contrasts form the 'straight line' in Fig. 3.1; their total contribution is 10.86

**Sums of squares**

After calculating contrast values, equation [3.2] can be constructed for each contrast in a separate range of cells, yielding a complete set of single-degree-of-freedom sums of squares. The sum of these single-degree-of-freedom sums of squares yields the total sum of squares given by equation [3.1]. As a check, the result of equation [3.1] can be obtained directly if the spreadsheet has a formula for calculating a variance, since a variance is $(1/n) \times$ (total sum of squares around $\bar{y}$). Sometimes, $1/(n - 1)$ is used in place of $1/n$.

from [3.1]; the individual contributions do not sum exactly to this value because of rounding error.

In general, the term 'analysis of variance' refers to the process of partitioning $SS_T$ into a number of components, each of which is either a contribution like [3.2] or a sum of such contributions. The purpose is to measure and compare different sources of variation in the data. In an experimental context one of the prime purposes is to estimate the standard deviation $\sigma$, which is used to quantify the amount of random variation in the data.

As we explained in Chapter 1, one premise of a statistical analysis is that the results are affected by variation that is not associated with the changes in the experimental factors. Statistical analysis works by treating this variation as random. Models of random variation can be extremely complex, but many of the methods in this book have their origins in the simplest possible model, which states that, for any given configuration of the factor levels, variation in the response $y$ can be described by a roughly symmetric distribution, *and that the spread of the distribution does not vary with the configuration.* Figure 3.3 represents this simple model in an idealized form.

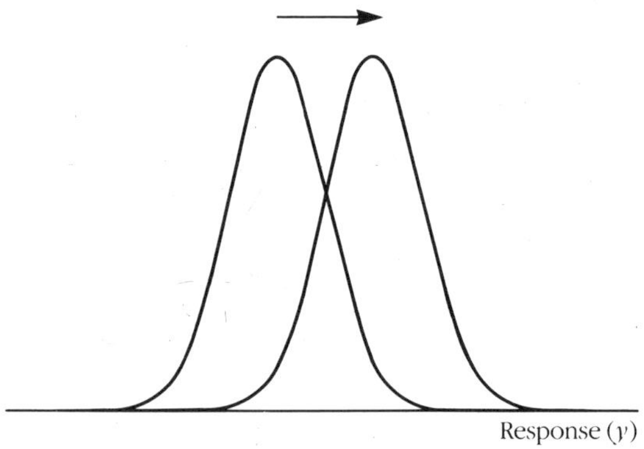


*Fig. 3.3* The 'constant σ' model: mean response depends on the factor configuration, but the dispersion does not (the factors have location but not dispersion effects)

It is customary to measure the spread of the distribution by its standard deviation, represented by the Greek letter $\sigma$. For a general distribution curve $\sigma$ is defined by the equation

$$\sigma^2 = \int (x - \mu)^2 \, \phi(x) \, dx$$

where $\mu$ represents the mean and $\phi(x)$ the height of the curve, but this equation is less important than various rather more down-to-earth facts about $\sigma$, such as the following: most of the area under the curve is contained in the range $\mu \pm 3\sigma$. The importance of this kind of fact in practice is that, although experiments rarely produce enough data to indicate the shape of a curve with any precision, it is possible to get a useful estimate of $\sigma$ from quite small amounts of data. But it should always be borne in mind that when data are scarce very little can be done to check whether the 'constant $\sigma$' model is appropriate, or even whether the variation is stable enough for a distribution to be a useful model. Hence, although an *estimate* of $\sigma$ is just a number calculated from a formula, its interpretation is always at least partly hypothetical. For similar remarks about the idea of a real effect, see Section 1.4.

An estimate of $\sigma$ can be used to:

- set confidence limits on estimated effects (for details see Box *et al.* (1978); and
- check for improvement (or deterioration) in experimental technique, which should be reflected by a change in $\sigma$.

## Estimation of $\sigma$ from an anova table

Given a set of contrasts that measure only random variation, an estimate of $\sigma$ is given by averaging their contributions to $SS_T$ and then taking the positive square root. The overall contribution that these contrasts make to $SS_T$ is called the sum of squares for estimating $\sigma$, and the number of contrasts that contribute to the estimate is called the number of *degrees of freedom* for estimating $\sigma$. Using $\hat{\sigma}$ to denote our estimate of $\sigma$, we have

$$\hat{\sigma} = \sqrt{\left(\frac{\text{sum of squares for estimating } \sigma}{\text{degrees of freedom for estimating } \sigma}\right)}$$

For brevity we write

$$\hat{\sigma} = \sqrt{\left(\frac{SS_\sigma}{f_\sigma}\right)} \qquad [3.3]$$

In practice there is no way of knowing for certain which contrasts should contribute to $SS_\sigma$, but we can use a full or half normal plot to guide us. There are 13 points 'on the line' in Fig. 3.1, and Table 3.3 shows that they make an overall contribution of 10.86, so we have

$$\hat{\sigma} = \sqrt{\left(\frac{10.86}{13}\right)} = 0.91$$

Since the data were generated using $\sigma = 1$, our estimate is quite good.

In the artificial example, 10 of the 15 contrasts do not measure main effects. Faced with such an experiment in practice (and in ignorance of the small systematic $A \times B$ interaction that was in fact built into the data) we might assume that all interactions are negligible. So as an alternative approach we could by-pass the normal plot and use these 10 contrasts to calculate $SS_\sigma$. Table 3.4 is a rearrangement of Table 3.3, with $SS_T$ partitioned into six components, each given a label in the 'Source' column. The column headed 'Degrees of freedom' shows how many contrast contributions have been combined into each component of $SS_T$. The column of $F$ ratios will be explained below.

*Table 3.4* Anova for the artificial example, assuming negligible interactions

| Source | Degrees of freedom | Contribution to $SS_T$ | $F$ ratio |
|---|---|---|---|
| $A$ | 1 | 69.87 | 74.3 |
| $B$ | 1 | 13.96 | 14.9 |
| $C$ | 1 | 0.63 | 0.7 |
| $D$ | 1 | 0.77 | 0.8 |
| $E$ | 1 | 0.06 | 0.1 |
| Columns that measure interactions | 10 | 9.40 | |

Our estimate of $\sigma$ based on Table 3.4 is

$$\hat{\sigma} = \sqrt{\left(\frac{9.4}{10}\right)} = 0.97$$

## $F$ tests

$F$ tests have been used for many years as a purely numerical (i.e. non-graphical) method of deciding which effects are to be treated as real. However, they can also be used in conjunction with a normal plot or other graphical tool, as we shall point out below.

In their traditional form, $F$ tests are carried out as follows. Certain contrasts are identified before the experiment as likely to reflect only random variation. A sum of squares $SS_\sigma$ is formed from these contrasts. For each contrast that did not contribute to $SS_\sigma$ an $F$ ratio is calculated from the formula

$$F \text{ ratio} = \frac{\text{contrast contribution}}{SS_\sigma / f_\sigma}$$

A contrast is said to be *statistically significant* if its $F$ ratio exceeds a specified threshold, usually called a *critical value*. In the experimental context, finding that an effect is statistically significant usually leads to a decision to treat it as real. A certain amount of arbitrariness is inevitable in the choice of a critical value; the most commonly used value is the upper 5% point of an $F$ distribution, specifically, the $F$ distribution with 1 and $f_\sigma$ degrees of freedom, abbreviated as $F(1,f_\sigma)$. Other percentage points (percentiles) of the $F$ distribution are sometimes used in place of the 5% point. A table of 10%, 5% and 1% critical values is given in Appendix 3.3. The 1% point clearly represents a more stringent criterion than the 5% and 10% points. Its use will result in fewer false positives, but also in more false negatives.

If the 5% point is used, the figure 5% is called the significance level of the test. It can be given a precise but hypothetical interpretation along the following lines. Suppose that factor $A$ has no real effect on the response. Then the probability that the $A$ contrast will be found to be significant purely by chance is 5%, provided:

(i) the data were actually generated by a model with constant $\sigma$ (the distribution can deviate quite a lot from the 'normal' shape without a serious effect on the significance level); and
(ii) the contrasts chosen to form $SS_\sigma$ really do measure only random variation.

Statistical textbooks often recommend that this interpretation of the significance level be used as the basis for choosing the threshold value in the test, after taking account of the losses that arise from false positive and false negative decisions. As with all loss calculations, this suggestion is easier to describe than to implement, and in practice — as we suggested above — the 5% criterion is often used.

In the artificial example the (false) assumption that all interactions are negligible leads to the $F$ ratios shown in the last column of Table 3.4. The 5% critical value for the $F$ tests is obtained from Appendix 3.3. The table is entered with $f_\sigma$ equal to 10, giving a critical value of 4.96. The $F$ ratios for the $A$ and $B$ main effects easily exceed this threshold, and in fact they exceed the 1% critical value, which is 10.04.

An alternative approach to $F$ tests, somewhat less 'pure' from a statistical point of view, is to combine them with the use of a normal plot. Points that plot 'on the line' make a contribution to $SS_\sigma$. $F$ tests are carried out on the remainder. In the artificial example this leads to the analysis of variance and $F$ ratios shown in Table 3.5. The 5% critical value for 13 degrees of freedom is 4.67, and both $F$ ratios easily exceed it.

A third, and definitely less acceptable, approach to $F$ tests is to order the contrasts on the basis of the size of their contributions to $SS_T$ and form $SS_\sigma$ from the contributions that fall below some threshold value. The threshold might be, for example, 10% of $SS_T$. This kind of arbitrary rule takes no

*Table 3.5* Anova for the artificial example, with $SS_\sigma$ based on the normal plot in Fig. 3.1

| Source | Degrees of freedom | Contribution to $SS_T$ | $F$ ratio |
|---|---|---|---|
| $A$ | 1 | 69.87 | 83.6 |
| $B$ | 1 | 13.96 | 16.7 |
| Contrasts 'on the line' | 13 | 10.86 | |

account of the statistical behaviour of contrasts and their contributions to $SS_T$, and we do not recommend using $F$ tests in this way. In fact, we believe that $F$ tests are of limited value in industrial experimentation. We certainly advise making a preliminary normal plot in preference to the blanket assumption that all interactions are negligible. But once the plot has been made we see little value in applying a further screening process, based on the $F$ ratios, to the contrasts that are selected by the plot.

Donald J. Wheeler (1988) has suggested an interesting alternative method, a hybrid technique consisting of a modified form of $F$ test followed by a graph known as a *scree plot.*

## 3.3 A REAL EXAMPLE — MOULDING OF GLOVE BOX LIDS

To bring some of these issues to life we will look at an experiment on a manufacturing process. The process involved was the liquid injection moulding of plastic lids for car glove boxes. This experiment was co-ordinated by Willi Beckers of Ford Werke AG.

On some of the items the finished surface of the plastic was disfigured by flow marks. Figure 3.4 gives an idea of the problem. The extent of the problem was quantified by drawing the lines L (left side) and R (right side) shown in the picture, counting the number of marks crossing each line and averaging these two numbers. Eight factors were investigated at two levels. The factors and levels were as follows:

| Factor | Label | Level (−) | Level (+) |
|---|---|---|---|
| Injection stroke (mm) | *I* | 40 | 70 |
| Melt temperature (°C) | *Me* | 200 | 250 |
| Mould temperature (°C) | *Mo* | 40 | 80 |
| Change-over point (mm) | *Ch* | 13 | 23 |
| Nozzle aperture (mm) | *N* | 4 | 6 |
| Mould clamping force (tonnes) | *Cl* | 480 | 630 |
| First-stage injection speed ($mm\,s^{-1}$) | *S1* | 15 | 25 |
| Second-stage injection speed ($mm\,s^{-1}$) | *S2* | 20 | 30 |

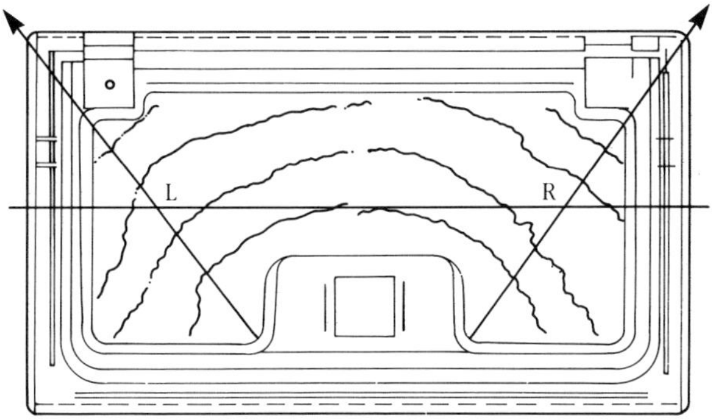


*Fig. 3.4* Flow marks on a glove box lid

The change-over point marks the position in the injection stroke at which the first stage ends and the second stage begins. The experimental plan was based on the $L_{16}(2^{15})$ array. Most of these factors can be changed fairly easily, but in order to vary the nozzle aperture it is necessary to change nozzles, so it is sensible to allocate this factor to column 8, for which only one change is required if the array is run in standard order.

In Chapter 2, and in the artificial example above, we made a point of keeping the experimental plan and the contrast matrix separate, even though they are closely related and both can be derived from the same orthogonal array. We believe that it is helpful to have both concepts available for describing the design and analysis of an experiment based on an orthogonal array, but we recognize that there are more concise ways of doing this. Table 3.6 is an example. In this version, the column labels have a dual role: they specify the allocation of the factors to a subset of the columns of the array (these eight columns are in bold type), and they indicate the confounding pattern. A formal contrast matrix can be generated, when required, by re-coding with $\pm 1$s. We will make some use of this more concise version in subsequent chapters, but we will also write down separate plan and contrast matrices when we think it will assist the explanation.

Fifty lids were produced in each run, and the final column of Table 3.6 shows the average (mean) number of flow marks for each set of 50 lids. The values of 15 contrasts calculated from these averages are in the last line. These were obtained as in Table 3.2, by applying + and − signs to the column of data, adding the results and finally dividing by 8. As we have previously demonstrated, this method is equivalent to constructing a response table and then subtracting the average for level (−) from the average for (+). For completeness we have included the response table as Table 3.7.

The Daniel plot of the 15 contrasts is in Fig. 3.5. The italic numbers refer to the column order in Table 3.6. There appear to be five points 'off the line', and this impression is reinforced by Fig. 3.6, which was obtained by omitting the two largest contrasts and re-plotting the remainder.

*Table 3.6* The glove box lid experiment

| Run | ***I*** | ***Me*** | $I \times Me$<br>$Mo \times Ch$<br>$N \times Cl$<br>$S1 \times S2$ | ***Mo*** | $I \times Mo$<br>$Me \times Ch$<br>$N \times S1$<br>$Cl \times S2$ | $I \times Ch$<br>$Me \times Mo$<br>$Cl \times S1$<br>$N \times S2$ | ***Ch*** |
|---|---|---|---|---|---|---|---|
| 1 | − | − | + | − | + | + | − |
| 2 | + | − | − | − | − | + | + |
| 3 | − | + | − | − | + | − | + |
| 4 | + | + | + | − | − | − | − |
| 5 | − | − | + | + | − | − | + |
| 6 | + | − | − | + | + | − | − |
| 7 | − | + | − | + | − | + | − |
| 8 | + | + | + | + | + | + | + |
| 9 | − | − | + | − | + | + | − |
| 10 | + | − | − | − | − | + | + |
| 11 | − | + | − | − | + | − | + |
| 12 | + | + | + | − | − | − | − |
| 13 | − | − | + | + | − | − | + |
| 14 | + | − | − | + | + | − | − |
| 15 | − | + | − | + | − | + | − |
| 16 | + | + | + | + | + | + | + |
| Contrast value | −0.34 | −2.96 | −0.26 | −2.44 | 1.11 | −1.16 | 0.44 |

The five contrasts prominent in Fig. 3.5 measure three main effects (melt temperature, mould temperature and clamping force) and two sets of interactions. It is interesting that $c_6$ measures, among other things, the *Me*×*Mo* interaction. For both these factors (and for clamping force) the (+) level gave the better (lower) response; if we assume that the value of the $c_6$ contrast reflects only *Me*×*Mo* interaction and ignore the more ambiguous $c_5$ contrast we get the following prediction for the configuration *Me*+, *Mo*+, *Cl*+:

| | *Me* | *Mo* | *Cl* | *Me*×*Mo* |
|---|---|---|---|---|
| | [ +1 | +1 | +1 | +1 ] |
| Estimated effects | −2.96 | −2.44 | −0.99 | −1.16 |

$$\text{Prediction} = 3.76 - \tfrac{1}{2}(2.96 + 2.44 + 0.99 + 1.16)$$
$$= 0.0 \text{ (to 1 dp)}$$

Note that because the estimated *Me*×*Mo* interaction is negative our prediction is lower than it would be from the main effects alone.

The configuration *Me*+, *Mo*+, *Cl*+ was in fact run twice during the experiment, and no flow marks were recorded on either occasion. After the

| *N* | *I*×*N* *Me*×*Cl* *Mo*×*S1* *Ch*×*S2* | *I*×*Cl* *Me*×*N* *Ch*×*S1* *Mo*×*S2* | ***Cl*** | *Mo*×*N* *Ch*×*Cl* *I*×*S1* *Me*×*S2* | ***S1*** | ***S2*** | *Mo*×*Cl* *Ch*×*N* *Me*×*S1* *I*×*S2* | Average no. of flow marks |
|---|---|---|---|---|---|---|---|---|
| − | + | + | − | + | − | − | + | 6.2 |
| − | − | + | + | + | + | − | − | 5.2 |
| − | + | − | + | + | − | + | − | 4.3 |
| − | − | − | − | + | + | + | + | 3.0 |
| − | + | + | − | − | + | + | − | 5.3 |
| − | − | + | + | − | − | + | + | 4.0 |
| − | + | − | + | − | + | − | + | 0.0 |
| − | − | − | − | − | − | − | − | 1.9 |
| + | − | − | + | − | + | + | − | 6.3 |
| + | + | − | − | − | − | + | + | 5.8 |
| + | − | + | − | − | + | − | + | 6.0 |
| + | + | + | + | − | − | − | − | 3.0 |
| + | − | − | + | + | − | − | + | 3.3 |
| + | + | − | − | + | + | − | − | 5.8 |
| + | − | + | − | + | − | + | − | 0.0 |
| + | + | + | + | + | + | + | + | 0.0 |
| 0.04 | 0.09 | −0.09 | −0.99 | −0.56 | 0.39 | −0.34 | −0.44 | |

*Table 3.7* Response table for the glove box lid experiment

| Column in $L_{16}$ | 1 | 2 | 3 | 4 | 5 | 6 | 7 | 8 |
|---|---|---|---|---|---|---|---|---|
| Average (−) | 3.93 | 5.24 | 3.89 | 4.98 | 3.20 | 4.34 | 3.54 | 3.74 |
| Average (+) | 3.59 | 2.28 | 3.63 | 2.54 | 4.31 | 3.17 | 3.98 | 3.77 |
| Column in $L_{16}$ | 9 | 10 | 11 | 12 | 13 | 14 | 15 | |
| Average (−) | 3.71 | 3.80 | 4.25 | 4.04 | 3.56 | 3.93 | 3.98 | |
| Average (+) | 3.80 | 3.71 | 3.26 | 3.47 | 3.95 | 3.59 | 3.54 | |

experiment a further run was made under these conditions, with the same result. These process settings were adopted for routine use at the plant, and the problem was cured.

The experiment was therefore a success in practical terms. It was also fairly successful as a process for increasing engineering knowledge, three factors having been identified which probably affect this aspect of quality, and five which are probably unimportant. Some questions about interactions remain to be resolved. The experiment could be *augmented* to provide more information about interactions (see Chapter 4), and it would be worth putting some effort into thinking of alternative response variables that might not generate interactions (see Chapter 11).

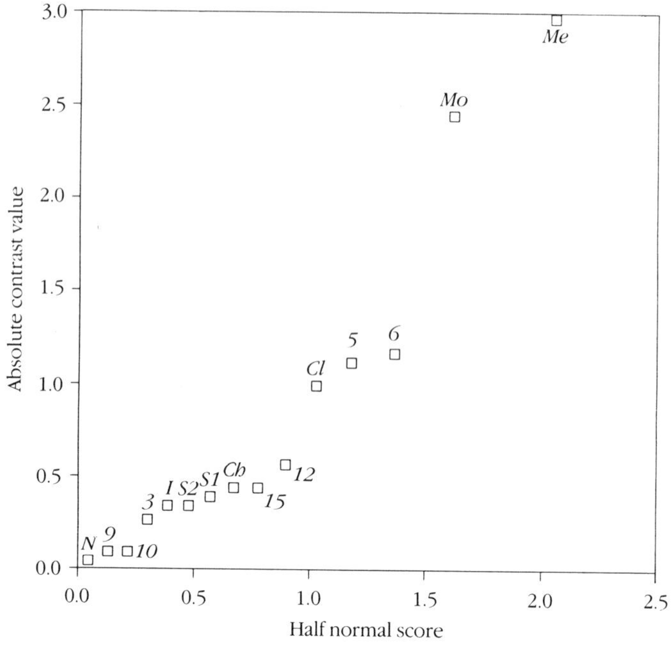


*Fig. 3.5* Glove box lid experiment. Daniel plot. The italic numbers refer to the columns in Table 3.6

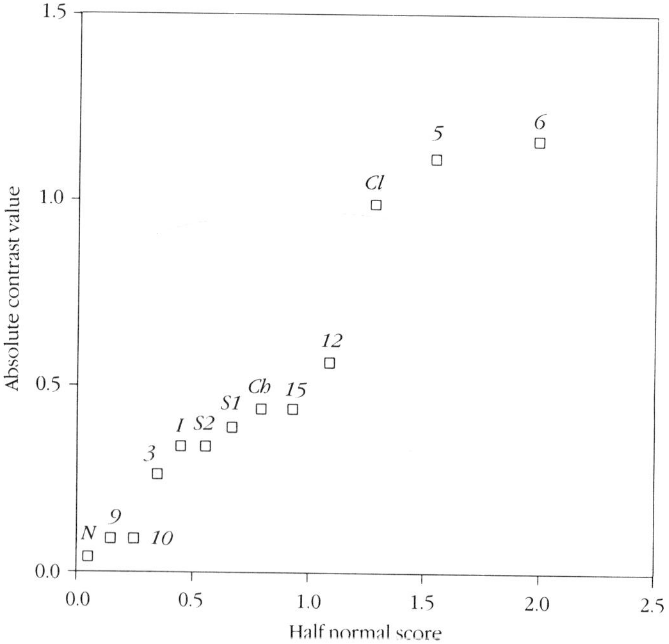


*Fig. 3.6* Glove box lid experiment. Re-plot of Fig. 3.5 with two contrasts removed

The data also provoke some statistical questions. The three flawless runs, looked at in the light of the rest of the data, are simply *too* consistent. They suggest that the 'constant spread' model is inadequate, because it appears that there is less *variability* in the number of flow marks when the *average* is low. This topic is pursued in later chapters, but it is worth pointing out that there is a simple alternative model — the Poisson distribution — which is often effective when defects occur 'at random' in space or time. For the Poisson distribution the standard deviation is equal to the square root of the mean. For details see Box *et al.* (1978), p. 137.

## Analysis of variance and *F* tests

Table 3.8 is an anova table for the glove box example, with all the 'random' contrasts grouped together. Our estimate of σ based on Table 3.8 would be

$$\hat{\sigma} = \sqrt{\left(\frac{4.67}{10}\right)} = 0.68$$

This is an estimate of the standard deviation *for the mean of 50 observations*, and must be multiplied by $\sqrt{50}$ to obtain an estimated standard deviation for an individual result:

$$\sqrt{50} \times 0.68 = 4.8 \text{ flow marks}$$

*Table 3.8* Analysis of variance for the glove box lid experiment

| Contrast | Effect measured | Contribution to $SS_T$ |
|---|---|---|
| $c_2$ | *Me* | 35.11 |
| $c_4$ | *Mo* | 23.77 |
| $c_5$ | Interactions | 4.95 |
| $c_6$ | Interactions | 5.41 |
| $c_{11}$ | *Cl* | 3.90 |
| $c_1$ | *I* | 0.46* |
| $c_3$ | Interactions | 0.28* |
| $c_7$ | *Ch* | 0.77* |
| $c_8$ | *N* | 0.01* |
| $c_9$ | Interactions | 0.03* |
| $c_{10}$ | Interactions | 0.03* |
| $c_{12}$ | Interactions | 1.27* |
| $c_{13}$ | *S1* | 0.60* |
| $c_{14}$ | *S2* | 0.46* |
| $c_{15}$ | Interactions | 0.77* |
| | | $SS_T = 77.78$ |

*These contrasts form the 'straight line' in Fig. 3.5; their total contribution is 4.67

This figure is totally at odds with the evidence from the runs which produced 50 lids without a single flow mark, and the discrepancy reinforces the point we made above, that the 'constant σ' model is inappropriate for this example.

If we nevertheless carry out $F$ tests (using a 5% critical value), they lead to the same conclusions as the normal plot. The smallest of the 'off the line' contrasts has an $F$ ratio of

$$\frac{3.90}{4.67/10} = 8.35$$

which is larger than the critical value of 4.96.

## SUMMARY OF CHAPTER 3

Normal plots can be used to help decide which effects should be treated as real and which should be treated as arising from random variation. Two types of normal plot are available. In a full normal plot the contrasts are arranged in ascending order and plotted against a set of full normal scores. The half normal, or Daniel, plot is similar, but uses the ordered absolute values of the contrasts and a set of half normal scores. We have found the half normal plot to be, on the whole, easier to interpret, but we recommend that both are produced on a routine basis.

Analysis of variance can be used to estimate σ, the standard deviation of the random component of the data. The method requires the calculation of a sum of squares $SS_\sigma$ by adding together contributions from a number of contrasts. These contrasts can be identified either from a normal plot (they are the points that plot 'on the line') or by *a priori* assumption (for example, that all interactions are negligible).

$F$ tests provide an alternative non-graphical method of deciding which effects are to be treated as real.

Although it is helpful to think about the experimental plan and the contrast matrix as distinct entities, they are closely related and it may be worth blurring this distinction to save space in writing down experimental results.

## APPENDIX 3.1 NORMAL PLOTS

For the benefit of readers who are familiar with probability plotting techniques we should point out that the methods we are about to describe are in practical terms equivalent to various ways of using normal probability graph paper. The alternative methods have the advantage that the graphs they produce can be plotted on ordinary linear scales, which is especially helpful if we want to use a computer.

## Expected ordered values

The figures in the first column of Table A3.1 were sampled (using a pseudo-random number generator) from the normal distribution with mean 10 and standard deviation 1, and then arranged in ascending order. Focusing on the *fourth* figure in the list, we see that it is less than 10. This is as it should be, because on average the *eighth* (middle) figure should equal 10. What value should we expect the fourth value to take, on average? This question can be given a precise numerical answer, but the calculation is complicated. Fortunately, there is an approximate way of obtaining an answer, which can be explained quite simply.

Assuming that every figure is unique, the fourth figure has a fraction $\frac{3}{15}$ of the data below it, and $\frac{11}{15}$ above it. These fractions do not add to 1, because there is a 'missing' $\frac{1}{15}$ that corresponds to the fourth value itself. It may look odd at first, but it does make sense to say that the fourth figure in the order divides up the data in the ratio $3\frac{1}{2}:11\frac{1}{2}$. We now turn to the normal distribution with mean 10 and standard deviation 1 (Fig. A3.1) and look for

*Table A3.1* Fifteen random values from a normal distribution with a mean of 10, and a standard deviation of 1

| Actual ordered values | Expected* ordered values | Expected spacings |
|---|---|---|
| 7.79 | 8.17 | |
| | | 0.55 |
| 8.38 | 8.72 | |
| | | 0.31 |
| 8.75 | 9.03 | |
| | | 0.24 |
| 8.98 | 9.27 | |
| | | 0.21 |
| 9.34 | 9.48 | |
| | | 0.18 |
| 9.37 | 9.66 | |
| | | 0.17 |
| 9.44 | 9.83 | |
| | | 0.17 |
| 9.46 | 10.00 | |
| | | 0.17 |
| 9.84 | 10.17 | |
| | | 0.17 |
| 9.90 | 10.34 | |
| | | 0.18 |
| 10.19 | 10.52 | |
| | | 0.21 |
| 10.79 | 10.73 | |
| | | 0.24 |
| 10.92 | 10.97 | |
| | | 0.31 |
| 11.24 | 11.28 | |
| | | 0.55 |
| 12.13 | 11.83 | |

* These are, strictly speaking, *approximate* expected values.

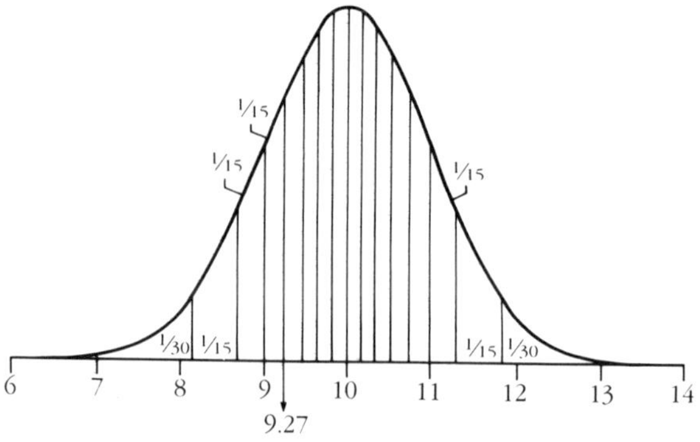


*Fig. A3.1* A normal distribution with a mean of 10 and a standard deviation of 1, divided into 15 equal areas

the value that divides the area under the curve in the ratio $3\frac{1}{2}:11\frac{1}{2}$. In the diagram, the areas between the vertical lines are each equal to $\frac{1}{15}$ of the total, and the first and last areas are each equal to $\frac{1}{30}$. The value we are looking for is therefore located at the fourth vertical, which occurs at 9.27. The other verticals indicate the positions of the theoretical or expected values for the first, second, etc., ordered figures. They are listed in the second column of Table A3.1. The third column shows the spacings between these expected ordered values. They are roughly equal in the middle two-thirds of the column, but much larger at the extremes.

The expected values depend on the sample size, but in quite a complicated way. The most obvious consequence of increasing the sample size is that the lowest and highest expected values move further out from the mean.

If we change the mean and variance of the sampled distribution the effect on the expected values is very simple. For example, if the new distribution has mean 20 and standard deviation 2, the new expected values are given by the relationship

$$\text{new} = (2 \times \text{old}) + 10$$

This is a convenient property of the *family* of normal distributions.

## Full normal plot

If the ordered figures in column 1 of Table A3.1 are plotted against the expected values in column 2, the result is Fig. A3.2. This is called a full normal plot. The points cluster fairly closely around a straight line. Of course, random variation will occasionally produce all kinds of odd pattern, but obvious systematic departures from linearity are rare. The presence of clear curvature, or a well defined line with a few outlying points at the extremes,

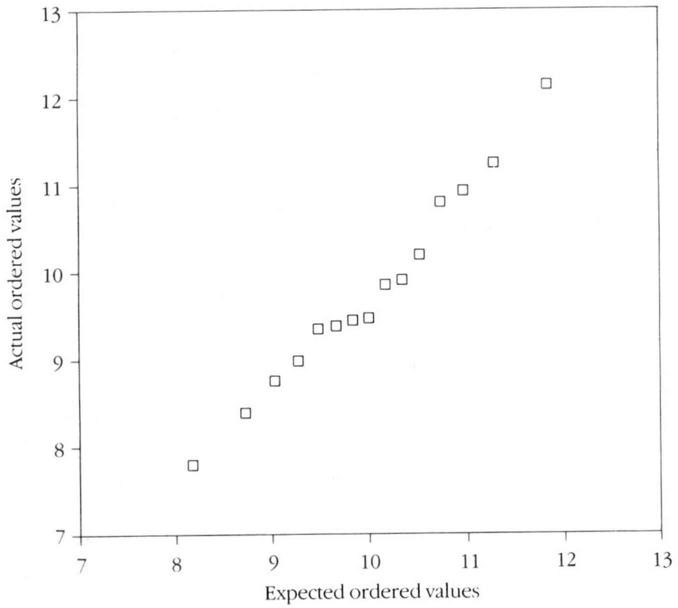


*Fig. A3.2* Full normal plot based on columns 1 and 2 of Table A3.1

would be taken as evidence that the data (or parts of the data) were not generated by random selection from a normal distribution.

Because of the simple relationship between the expected values for different normal distributions, if we had used the wrong mean and standard deviation in constructing Fig. A3.2 the plot would have shifted and tilted but the 'amount of linearity' would have been the same. Full normal plots are usually based on the expected values for the *standard* normal distribution, which has mean 0 and standard deviation 1. This not only saves computation; it makes it possible to 'test the normality' of a set of data without having to specify a mean and standard deviation.

The expected ordered values for the standard normal distribution are known as *normal scores*. Their unit of measurement is, in effect, *number of standard deviations from the mean*. Appendix 3.2 is a table of normal scores for a selection of sample sizes. The MINITAB statistical package was used to generate this table.

## Application to experimental data

Suppose that none of the factors has an effect, and that the whole set of contrasts is the product of random variation. Even if this random variation does not, strictly speaking, have a normal distribution, the averaging processes that go into the calculation of the contrast values will make them more 'normal' than the original observations. This effect is known technically as the central limit theorem. Provided that the contrast values are based on *orthogonal* columns of coefficients, they behave roughly like a set of values chosen independently from a normal distribution, and should produce a roughly linear normal plot.

On the other hand, suppose that a few of the effects are real, and that the size of these effects is substantial compared with the random variation. Most of the contrasts should still plot as a rough straight line, but there will be a few outliers: above the line if the effect is positive, below it if the effect is negative.

Full normal plots also have the potential to draw attention to problems in a set of results. Inspection of the $L_{16}(2^{15})$ array (for example) shows that a single 'wild' value occurring in any of the first 15 rows will make eight contrasts extreme in the negative direction and seven extreme in the opposite direction. Suppose, for example, that the result for run 11 of the glove box experiment had been mis-recorded as 16.0. The full normal plot (Fig. A3.3) shows two distinct 'lines'.

Full normal plots can also be used in the analysis of *residuals*, as we will demonstrate in Chapter 6.

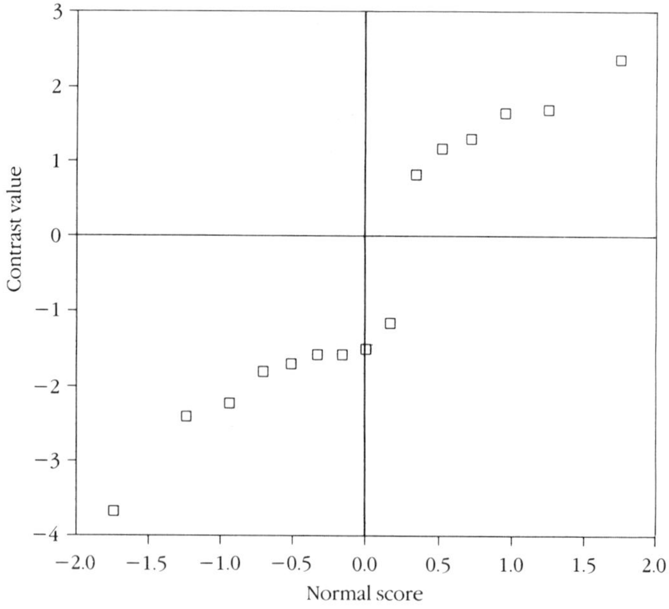


*Fig. A3.3* Glove box lid experiment. The effect of a mis-recorded value on the full normal plot

## Half normal plots

A half normal plot is similar to a full normal plot, but uses the *absolute values* of the contrasts and a set of *half normal scores*. For a normal distribution with mean 0, the expected ordered values for a sample of size $2n$ would consist of two sets of $n$ values that are mirror images of each other: for every negative score there is an equal and opposite positive score. If only $n$ values are sampled, but they are converted into absolute values before being ordered, they are indistinguishable (in terms of average behaviour) from the top half of a sample of size $2n$. Hence the half normal scores for a sample of size $n$ are just the positive half of a set of $2n$ full normal scores.

As in the case of full normal plots, a change of standard deviation affects only the slope of the plot. However, the symmetry of the distribution about zero is crucial to the argument in the last paragraph. If the data are sampled from a distribution with non-zero mean we should not expect their absolute values to be linearly related to the half normal scores. This is the reason why a half normal plot cannot be used for a general-purpose test of normality. But for experimental data, in the absence of any real effects each contrast will have a distribution that is approximately symmetrical about zero, so a half normal plot is appropriate. The 'line' should point at the origin. Instead of being split between the two ends of the plot, all the large contrasts appear on

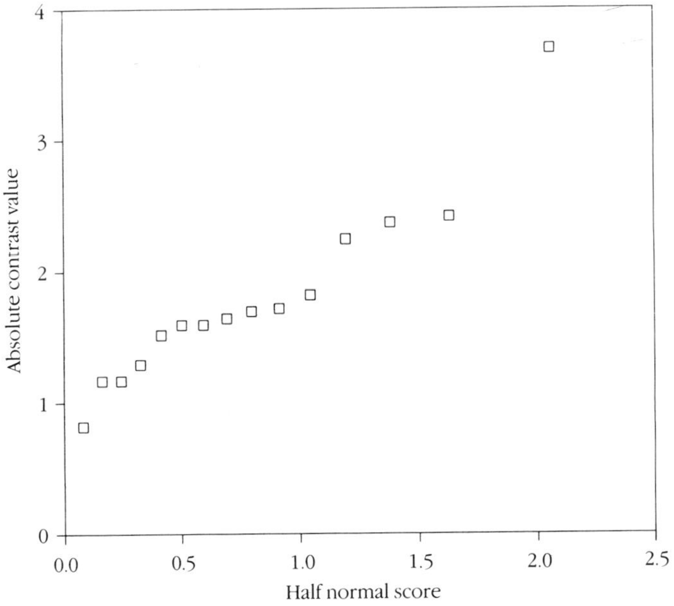


*Fig. A3.4* Glove box lid experiment. The effect of a mis-recorded value on the half normal plot

the right. This often makes half normal plots easier to interpret than their full normal counterparts.

In a half normal plot the effect of a single wild value is to increase all the absolute contrasts. The 'line' will then miss the origin, as shown in Fig. A3.4, which is the half normal version of Fig. A3.3.

## Final remarks on normal plots

As the artificial example in Section 3.1 demonstrates, normal plots are not infallible: real effects may be obscured by random variation, and random variation may also produce spurious points 'off the line'. In our experience the latter error is rare enough for us to suggest that it is better to treat doubtful effects as real, at least provisionally, rather than as noise.

Sometimes the plot will be open to two substantially different interpretations, in which case both should be pursued in further work. Ambiguity of this kind can sometimes be resolved by removing a few very large effects and *re-plotting* the remainder. The re-plotting *must be based on the normal scores appropriate to the number of contrasts left in the plot.* For example, when two effects are removed from a sample of 15, the remainder are plotted against the complete set of normal (or half normal) scores for 13 effects, and *not* against the first 13 of the scores for 15 effects.

In a few cases the plot will look roughly linear but with no obvious outliers. This may indicate either that there are no real effects or that most of the contrasts correspond to real effects. The latter is more likely, given that the experimenters have put considerable effort into choosing sensible factors,

**Normal plots**

One of the main strengths of spreadsheets is their ability to make graphs from data in rows and columns of the worksheet. A normal plot can be constructed as a special type of $x$–$y$ plot. What is required is a set of (either full or half) normal scores in a column of the worksheet. Contrast values need to be ordered from smallest to largest and placed in another column of the worksheet. Do not forget to remove the sign of the contrasts for the Daniel plot *before* sorting.

Construct an $x$–$y$ plot using the appropriate commands, with the normal scores as the $x$ variable and the (sorted) contrasts as the $y$ variable. As an added feature of the plot, each contrast can be labelled with an easy-to-identify abbreviation so that important factors can be quickly spotted from the plot.

All the key strokes that are needed to sort the contrasts and construct the plot could be written as a spreadsheet macro so that normal plots can be constructed automatically within the worksheet.

but it is possible that they have not set the levels far enough apart to generate measurable effects.

## APPENDIX 3.2 NORMAL SCORES

These are shown in Tables A3.2 and A3.3.

*Table A3.2* Full normal scores

| Number of contrasts | | | | | | | |
|---|---|---|---|---|---|---|---|
| 7 | 8 | 9 | 10 | 11 | 12 | 13 | 14 |
| −1.365 | −1.435 | −1.495 | −1.548 | −1.595 | −1.637 | −1.675 | −1.710 |
| −0.756 | −0.850 | −0.930 | −0.999 | −1.059 | −1.113 | −1.161 | −1.204 |
| −0.351 | −0.471 | −0.570 | −0.653 | −0.726 | −0.789 | −0.846 | −0.897 |
| 0.000 | −0.152 | −0.273 | −0.374 | −0.460 | −0.534 | −0.600 | −0.659 |
| 0.351 | 0.152 | 0.000 | −0.122 | −0.224 | −0.311 | −0.386 | −0.453 |
| 0.756 | 0.471 | 0.273 | 0.122 | 0.000 | −0.102 | −0.189 | −0.266 |
| 1.365 | 0.850 | 0.570 | 0.374 | 0.224 | 0.102 | 0.000 | −0.088 |
| | 1.435 | 0.930 | 0.653 | 0.460 | 0.311 | 0.189 | 0.088 |
| | | 1.495 | 0.999 | 0.726 | 0.534 | 0.386 | 0.266 |
| | | | 1.548 | 1.059 | 0.789 | 0.600 | 0.453 |
| | | | | 1.595 | 1.113 | 0.846 | 0.659 |
| | | | | | 1.637 | 1.161 | 0.897 |
| | | | | | | 1.675 | 1.204 |
| | | | | | | | 1.710 |

*Table A3.2* contd

| Number of contrasts | | | | | | | |
|---|---|---|---|---|---|---|---|
| 15 | 16 | 17 | 18 | 19 | 20 | 21 | 22 |
| −1.742 | −1.772 | −1.799 | −1.825 | −1.849 | −1.871 | −1.893 | −1.913 |
| −1.244 | −1.281 | −1.315 | −1.347 | −1.376 | −1.404 | −1.430 | −1.454 |
| −0.944 | −0.986 | −1.026 | −1.062 | −1.095 | −1.127 | −1.156 | −1.184 |
| −0.712 | −0.760 | −0.804 | −0.844 | −0.882 | −0.917 | −0.950 | −0.981 |
| −0.513 | −0.567 | −0.616 | −0.662 | −0.703 | −0.742 | −0.778 | −0.812 |
| −0.333 | −0.394 | −0.449 | −0.499 | −0.545 | −0.587 | −0.627 | −0.664 |
| −0.164 | −0.232 | −0.294 | −0.349 | −0.400 | −0.446 | −0.489 | −0.529 |
| 0.000 | −0.077 | −0.145 | −0.207 | −0.262 | −0.313 | −0.360 | −0.403 |
| 0.164 | 0.077 | 0.000 | −0.068 | −0.130 | −0.186 | −0.237 | −0.284 |
| 0.333 | 0.232 | 0.145 | 0.068 | 0.000 | −0.062 | −0.118 | −0.169 |
| 0.513 | 0.394 | 0.294 | 0.207 | 0.130 | 0.062 | 0.000 | −0.056 |
| 0.712 | 0.567 | 0.449 | 0.349 | 0.262 | 0.186 | 0.118 | 0.056 |
| 0.944 | 0.760 | 0.616 | 0.499 | 0.400 | 0.313 | 0.237 | 0.169 |
| 1.244 | 0.986 | 0.804 | 0.662 | 0.545 | 0.446 | 0.360 | 0.284 |
| 1.742 | 1.281 | 1.026 | 0.844 | 0.703 | 0.587 | 0.489 | 0.403 |
| | 1.772 | 1.315 | 1.062 | 0.882 | 0.742 | 0.627 | 0.529 |
| | | 1.799 | 1.347 | 1.095 | 0.917 | 0.778 | 0.664 |
| | | | 1.825 | 1.376 | 1.127 | 0.950 | 0.812 |
| | | | | 1.849 | 1.404 | 1.156 | 0.981 |
| | | | | | 1.871 | 1.430 | 1.184 |
| | | | | | | 1.893 | 1.454 |
| | | | | | | | 1.913 |

| Number of contrasts | | | | | | | | |
|---|---|---|---|---|---|---|---|---|
| 23 | 24 | 25 | 26 | 27 | 28 | 29 | 30 | 31 |
| −1.932 | −1.950 | −1.967 | −1.984 | −2.000 | −2.015 | −2.029 | −2.043 | −2.057 |
| −1.477 | −1.499 | −1.520 | −1.540 | −1.559 | −1.577 | −1.595 | −1.612 | −1.628 |
| −1.210 | −1.235 | −1.259 | −1.281 | −1.302 | −1.323 | −1.342 | −1.361 | −1.379 |
| −1.010 | −1.037 | −1.063 | −1.087 | −1.111 | −1.133 | −1.154 | −1.175 | −1.194 |
| −0.843 | −0.873 | −0.901 | −0.928 | −0.953 | −0.977 | −1.000 | −1.022 | −1.043 |
| −0.698 | −0.730 | −0.761 | −0.789 | −0.817 | −0.843 | −0.867 | −0.891 | −0.913 |
| −0.566 | −0.601 | −0.634 | −0.665 | −0.694 | −0.722 | −0.748 | −0.773 | −0.797 |
| −0.444 | −0.481 | −0.517 | −0.550 | −0.581 | −0.611 | −0.639 | −0.666 | −0.691 |
| −0.328 | −0.369 | −0.407 | −0.442 | −0.476 | −0.507 | −0.537 | −0.566 | −0.593 |
| −0.216 | −0.260 | −0.301 | −0.339 | −0.375 | −0.409 | −0.441 | −0.471 | −0.500 |
| −0.108 | −0.155 | −0.199 | −0.240 | −0.278 | −0.314 | −0.348 | −0.380 | −0.411 |
| 0.000 | −0.051 | −0.099 | −0.143 | −0.184 | −0.223 | −0.259 | −0.293 | −0.325 |
| 0.108 | 0.051 | 0.000 | −0.048 | −0.092 | −0.133 | −0.171 | −0.208 | −0.242 |
| 0.216 | 0.155 | 0.099 | 0.048 | 0.000 | −0.044 | −0.085 | −0.124 | −0.160 |
| 0.328 | 0.260 | 0.199 | 0.143 | 0.092 | 0.044 | 0.000 | −0.041 | −0.080 |
| 0.444 | 0.369 | 0.301 | 0.240 | 0.184 | 0.133 | 0.085 | 0.041 | 0.000 |
| 0.566 | 0.481 | 0.407 | 0.339 | 0.278 | 0.223 | 0.171 | 0.124 | 0.080 |
| 0.698 | 0.601 | 0.517 | 0.442 | 0.375 | 0.314 | 0.259 | 0.208 | 0.160 |
| 0.843 | 0.730 | 0.634 | 0.550 | 0.476 | 0.409 | 0.348 | 0.293 | 0.242 |
| 1.010 | 0.873 | 0.761 | 0.665 | 0.581 | 0.507 | 0.441 | 0.380 | 0.325 |
| 1.210 | 1.037 | 0.901 | 0.789 | 0.694 | 0.611 | 0.537 | 0.471 | 0.411 |
| 1.477 | 1.235 | 1.063 | 0.928 | 0.817 | 0.722 | 0.639 | 0.566 | 0.500 |
| 1.932 | 1.499 | 1.259 | 1.087 | 0.953 | 0.843 | 0.748 | 0.666 | 0.593 |
| | 1.950 | 1.520 | 1.281 | 1.111 | 0.977 | 0.867 | 0.773 | 0.691 |
| | | 1.967 | 1.540 | 1.302 | 1.133 | 1.000 | 0.891 | 0.797 |
| | | | 1.984 | 1.559 | 1.323 | 1.154 | 1.022 | 0.913 |
| | | | | 2.000 | 1.577 | 1.342 | 1.175 | 1.043 |
| | | | | | 2.015 | 1.595 | 1.361 | 1.194 |
| | | | | | | 2.029 | 1.612 | 1.379 |
| | | | | | | | 2.043 | 1.628 |
| | | | | | | | | 2.057 |

*Table A3.3* Half normal scores (for $n \leq 15$ use the positive half of a set of $2n$ full normal scores)

| Number of contrasts | | | | | | | |
|---|---|---|---|---|---|---|---|
| 16 | 17 | 18 | 19 | 20 | 21 | 22 | 23 |
| 0.039 | 0.036 | 0.034 | 0.033 | 0.031 | 0.030 | 0.028 | 0.027 |
| 0.116 | 0.110 | 0.103 | 0.098 | 0.093 | 0.089 | 0.085 | 0.081 |
| 0.195 | 0.183 | 0.173 | 0.164 | 0.156 | 0.148 | 0.141 | 0.135 |
| 0.274 | 0.258 | 0.243 | 0.230 | 0.219 | 0.208 | 0.199 | 0.190 |
| 0.356 | 0.334 | 0.315 | 0.298 | 0.283 | 0.269 | 0.257 | 0.245 |
| 0.440 | 0.412 | 0.388 | 0.367 | 0.348 | 0.331 | 0.315 | 0.301 |
| 0.527 | 0.493 | 0.464 | 0.438 | 0.415 | 0.394 | 0.375 | 0.358 |
| 0.618 | 0.578 | 0.542 | 0.511 | 0.484 | 0.459 | 0.437 | 0.417 |
| 0.716 | 0.667 | 0.624 | 0.587 | 0.555 | 0.526 | 0.500 | 0.476 |
| 0.820 | 0.761 | 0.711 | 0.667 | 0.629 | 0.595 | 0.565 | 0.538 |
| 0.935 | 0.863 | 0.803 | 0.752 | 0.707 | 0.668 | 0.633 | 0.602 |
| 1.064 | 0.975 | 0.903 | 0.842 | 0.789 | 0.744 | 0.704 | 0.668 |
| 1.213 | 1.102 | 1.013 | 0.940 | 0.878 | 0.825 | 0.778 | 0.738 |
| 1.396 | 1.248 | 1.137 | 1.048 | 0.974 | 0.912 | 0.858 | 0.811 |
| 1.643 | 1.429 | 1.281 | 1.169 | 1.080 | 1.006 | 0.943 | 0.889 |
| 2.070 | 1.672 | 1.459 | 1.312 | 1.200 | 1.110 | 1.036 | 0.973 |
| | 2.094 | 1.700 | 1.487 | 1.340 | 1.229 | 1.139 | 1.064 |
| | | 2.117 | 1.725 | 1.513 | 1.367 | 1.256 | 1.166 |
| | | | 2.139 | 1.749 | 1.538 | 1.393 | 1.281 |
| | | | | 2.159 | 1.772 | 1.562 | 1.417 |
| | | | | | 2.178 | 1.793 | 1.584 |
| | | | | | | 2.196 | 1.813 |
| | | | | | | | 2.213 |

*Table A3.3* contd

| Number of contrasts | | | | | | | |
|---|---|---|---|---|---|---|---|
| 24 | 25 | 26 | 27 | 28 | 29 | 30 | 31 |
| 0.026 | 0.025 | 0.024 | 0.023 | 0.022 | 0.021 | 0.021 | 0.020 |
| 0.078 | 0.075 | 0.072 | 0.069 | 0.067 | 0.064 | 0.062 | 0.060 |
| 0.130 | 0.124 | 0.120 | 0.115 | 0.111 | 0.107 | 0.104 | 0.100 |
| 0.182 | 0.175 | 0.168 | 0.162 | 0.156 | 0.151 | 0.145 | 0.141 |
| 0.235 | 0.225 | 0.217 | 0.209 | 0.201 | 0.194 | 0.187 | 0.181 |
| 0.288 | 0.277 | 0.266 | 0.256 | 0.247 | 0.238 | 0.230 | 0.222 |
| 0.343 | 0.329 | 0.316 | 0.304 | 0.293 | 0.282 | 0.273 | 0.264 |
| 0.398 | 0.382 | 0.366 | 0.352 | 0.339 | 0.327 | 0.316 | 0.305 |
| 0.455 | 0.436 | 0.418 | 0.402 | 0.387 | 0.373 | 0.360 | 0.348 |
| 0.514 | 0.491 | 0.471 | 0.452 | 0.435 | 0.419 | 0.404 | 0.391 |
| 0.574 | 0.548 | 0.525 | 0.504 | 0.485 | 0.467 | 0.450 | 0.435 |
| 0.636 | 0.607 | 0.581 | 0.557 | 0.535 | 0.515 | 0.496 | 0.479 |
| 0.701 | 0.668 | 0.639 | 0.612 | 0.587 | 0.565 | 0.544 | 0.525 |
| 0.769 | 0.732 | 0.699 | 0.669 | 0.641 | 0.616 | 0.593 | 0.572 |
| 0.841 | 0.799 | 0.762 | 0.728 | 0.697 | 0.669 | 0.643 | 0.620 |
| 0.918 | 0.870 | 0.828 | 0.789 | 0.755 | 0.724 | 0.695 | 0.669 |
| 1.001 | 0.946 | 0.897 | 0.854 | 0.816 | 0.781 | 0.749 | 0.721 |
| 1.091 | 1.027 | 0.972 | 0.923 | 0.880 | 0.841 | 0.806 | 0.774 |
| 1.191 | 1.116 | 1.052 | 0.997 | 0.948 | 0.904 | 0.865 | 0.830 |
| 1.305 | 1.215 | 1.140 | 1.076 | 1.021 | 0.971 | 0.927 | 0.888 |
| 1.439 | 1.328 | 1.238 | 1.163 | 1.099 | 1.043 | 0.994 | 0.950 |
| 1.605 | 1.461 | 1.350 | 1.260 | 1.185 | 1.121 | 1.065 | 1.015 |
| 1.832 | 1.625 | 1.481 | 1.371 | 1.281 | 1.206 | 1.142 | 1.085 |
| 2.229 | 1.850 | 1.645 | 1.501 | 1.391 | 1.301 | 1.226 | 1.162 |
| | 2.245 | 1.868 | 1.663 | 1.520 | 1.410 | 1.320 | 1.245 |
| | | 2.259 | 1.885 | 1.680 | 1.538 | 1.428 | 1.338 |
| | | | 2.274 | 1.900 | 1.697 | 1.555 | 1.445 |
| | | | | 2.287 | 1.916 | 1.713 | 1.571 |
| | | | | | 2.300 | 1.930 | 1.729 |
| | | | | | | 2.313 | 1.945 |
| | | | | | | | 2.325 |

## APPENDIX 3.3 CRITICAL VALUES FOR $F$ TESTS

These are listed in Table A3.4.

*Table A3.4* Critical values for $F$ tests (upper 10%, 5% and 1% points of the $F(1,f_\sigma)$ distribution)

| | Critical value | | |
|---|---|---|---|
| $f_\sigma$ | 10% | 5% | 1% |
| 5 | 4.06 | 6.61 | 16.26 |
| 6 | 3.78 | 5.99 | 13.75 |
| 7 | 3.59 | 5.59 | 12.25 |
| 8 | 3.46 | 5.32 | 11.26 |
| 9 | 3.36 | 5.12 | 10.56 |
| 10 | 3.28 | 4.96 | 10.04 |
| 11 | 3.23 | 4.84 | 9.65 |
| 12 | 3.18 | 4.75 | 9.33 |
| 13 | 3.14 | 4.67 | 9.07 |
| 14 | 3.10 | 4.60 | 8.86 |
| 15 | 3.07 | 4.54 | 8.68 |
| 16 | 3.05 | 4.49 | 8.53 |
| 17 | 3.03 | 4.45 | 8.40 |
| 18 | 3.01 | 4.41 | 8.29 |
| 19 | 2.99 | 4.38 | 8.19 |
| 20 | 2.97 | 4.35 | 8.10 |
| 21 | 2.96 | 4.32 | 8.02 |
| 22 | 2.95 | 4.30 | 7.95 |
| 23 | 2.94 | 4.28 | 7.88 |
| 24 | 2.93 | 4.26 | 7.82 |
| 25 | 2.92 | 4.24 | 7.77 |

CHAPTER 4

# Planning a two-level experiment

*In Chapters 2 and 3 we introduced the orthogonal array $L_8(2^7)$ and its larger relative $L_{16}(2^{15})$. In this chapter we tabulate some of the experimental plans that can be based on $L_8(2^7)$ and on $L_{16}(2^{15})$. We also introduce $L_{12}(2^{11})$, which has rather different properties from $L_8(2^7)$ and $L_{16}(2^{15})$. We compare various strategies (including the one favoured by Taguchi) for coping with interactions in two-level experiments, and introduce the idea of augmenting (adding runs to) an experiment to simplify its confounding pattern.*

*We also discuss some other important aspects of planning experiments to cope with non-random sources of background variation: randomization of the run order, and the use of blocks, split plots and plans that are partially orthogonal to simple background trends.*

## 4.1 A SHORT CATALOGUE OF PLANS

All fractional two-level plans have an associated *resolution number*, usually denoted by a Roman numeral. The idea is that plans with higher resolution numbers have simpler confounding patterns and therefore have the potential to generate data that can be interpreted in a more clear-cut fashion. The concept of resolution number can be given a mathematical definition, but it is more useful to explain the implications of the most commonly occurring resolution numbers, which are III, IV and V.

- In a *resolution III* plan some (or all) of the main effects are confounded with one or more two-way interactions.
- In a *resolution IV* plan a main effect can only be confounded with three-way or higher-order interactions ('the main effects are clear of two-way

interactions'). Some (or all) of the two-way interactions are confounded with other two-way interactions.

- In a *resolution V* plan the main effects are clear of two-way interactions, *and* there is no confounding between two-way interactions.

For example, the plan used to study the glove box lids (Chapter 3) has resolution number IV. A plan must be at least resolution V if all the two-way interactions are to be separately estimable.

There is no general mathematical formula that links the number of factors, the number of runs and the resolution number of a plan. For example, given a resolution IV plan it may be possible to add another factor — keeping the number of runs the same — without reducing the resolution number to III. However, adding further factors will eventually reduce the resolution number. *Saturated* designs, in which every contrast measures a main effect, are always resolution III. Table 4.1 shows, for four of the standard two-level arrays, the maximum number of factors that can be allocated subject to achieving a given resolution number.

One of the ways in which Taguchi has had a major impact on the teaching of experimentation is through the use of orthogonal arrays to catalogue the most useful experimental designs. Although Taguchi did not invent the idea of an orthogonal array, and such arrays are used in some books on design of experiments, notably in the work of George Box, Taguchi was the first writer to base his teaching systematically on orthogonal arrays. As we mentioned in Chapter 2, Taguchi's arrays are somewhat different from

*Table 4.1* Maximum number of factors consistent with a given resolution number

| | Resolution number | | |
|---|---|---|---|
| Array | III | IV | V |
| $L_8$ | 7 | 4 | 3* |
| $L_{16}$ | 15 | 8 | 5 |
| $L_{32}$ | 31 | 16 | 6† |
| $L_{64}$ | 63 | 32 | 8 |

*This is a complete factorial plan, and strictly speaking has no resolution number. But since all two-way interactions are separately estimable it has a lot in common with a resolution V plan

†This is actually resolution VI, but the addition of a seventh factor reduces the resolution number to IV

ours. For one thing, he uses the codes (1) and (2) rather than (−) and (+). As an example, his $L_8(2^7)$ is given in Table 1.1.

Another difference between Taguchi's arrays and ours lies in the *column order*. In $L_8(2^7)$ his column 1 is our column 4, his column 3 is our column 5, and so on. Of course, the order in which the columns are written down is of no consequence once the experiment is under way. A further reason for regarding this as a minor issue is that *the patterns of confounding are almost identical* in the two versions of the arrays. A full explanation of what we mean by 'almost identical' would require us to delve more deeply into the structure of Taguchi's arrays than we wish to do, but, as an example, if factors $A$ and $B$ are allocated to the first two columns of Taguchi's $L_8(2^7)$, a contrast based on re-coding the third column (replacing (1) by −1 and (2) by +1) measures *minus* the $A \times B$ interaction as we have defined it. Provided this sign reversal is borne in mind, the tables given in this chapter can be used just as well with Taguchi's arrays as with ours.

Influenced by Taguchi, a number of companies have produced their own catalogues of designs. Several authors, including Wheeler (1989), Bisgaard (1988) and Logothetis and Wynn (1989), have produced tables for publication. We see no point in simply duplicating their efforts. On the other hand we think that a short catalogue of the most useful plans will help to get our readers started on running real experiments.

In the following tables each plan except the first is defined incrementally. For example, in Table 4.2 a seven-factor plan based on $L_8(2^7)$ is defined by taking the six-factor plan and adding a seventh factor ($G$) in column 6. The six-factor plan is itself defined by adding factor $F$ (in $c_5$) to the five-factor plan. It is of course the allocation of individual factors to columns that specifies the experimental plan, and to emphasize this point the main effects are shown in bold type.

To discover the confounding pattern of a particular plan, i.e. to find out which effects are measured by each contrast, read down from the top of the table until you reach the plan in which you are interested. Plus signs are implied throughout. For example, reading down the $c_5$ column in Table 4.2 as far as the seven-factor plan, the following effects are listed: $A \times C$, $B \times D$, $F$, $E \times G$. This implies that in the seven-factor plan the contrast based on $c_5$ measures the following combination of effects: $F + A \times C + B \times D + E \times G$. As usual, we have omitted three-way and higher-order interactions. In some instances a contrast will not be shown as measuring any effect. This means that it actually measures three-way and higher-order interactions, if they are present.

Our method of displaying the plans has the disadvantage that the factors are not allocated to the columns in alphabetical order. In our view this inconvenience is justified by the fact that our tables are a good deal more concise than other versions we are aware of. We have found that in practice most people prefer to use factor labels that are mnemonics for the factor descriptions (as we did in the glove box lid example), rather than the usual alphabet.

## Plans based on $L_8(2^7)$

The $L_8(2^7)$ array was written out several times in Chapter 2: see Tables 2.5 and 2.13. Table 4.2 lists some two-level plans that can be based on this array. These plans are not unique. For example, allocating four factors to the *last four columns* produces a resolution IV plan. This can easily be checked from the multiplication table for $L_8(2^7)$ (Table 2.14). The product of any two of the last four columns is always $c_1$, $c_2$ or $c_3$, and all two-way interactions will be confined to these columns. As another alternative, the four odd-numbered columns form a resolution IV plan. This is again clear from Table 2.14, because the product of two odds is always an even.

*Table 4.2* Plans based on $L_8(2^7)$

| Number of factors | Resolution number | $c_1$ | $c_2$ | $c_3$ | $c_4$ | $c_5$ | $c_6$ | $c_7$ |
|---|---|---|---|---|---|---|---|---|
| 3 | Full factorial | **A** | **B** | $A \times B$ | **C** | $A \times C$ | $B \times C$ | |
| 4 | IV | | | $C \times D$ | | $B \times D$ | $A \times D$ | **D** |
| 5* | III | $B \times E$ | $A \times E$ | **E** | $D \times E$ | | | $C \times E$ |
| 6 | III | $C \times F$ | $D \times F$ | | $A \times F$ | **F** | $E \times F$ | $B \times F$ |
| 7 | III | $D \times G$ | $C \times G$ | $F \times G$ | $B \times G$ | $E \times G$ | **G** | $A \times G$ |

*In a two-block plan use factor $E$ to define the blocks

### Generating the $L_8$ orthogonal array

To generate the $L_8$ orthogonal array (strictly speaking the contrast matrix), three columns of $\pm 1$s are initially needed in the worksheet, which (written as rows rather than columns to save space) are $(-1, +1, -1, +1, -1, +1, -1, +1)$, $(-1, -1, +1, +1, -1, -1, +1, +1)$ and $(-1, -1, -1, -1, +1, +1, +1, +1)$. Call these columns $c_1$, $c_2$, and $c_4$. Then using the formula to multiply columns together cell by cell, generate the other columns of the array according to $c_3 = c_1 \times c_2$, $c_5 = c_1 \times c_4$, $c_6 = c_2 \times c_4$, and $c_7 = c_3 \times c_4 = c_1 \times c_2 \times c_4$. This procedure will generate the matrix in Table 2.13.

To generate a contrast matrix for Taguchi's version of $L_8$, switch the names of $c_1$ and $c_4$. The remaining columns are given by $c_3 = c_1 \times c_2 \times (-1)$, $c_5 = c_1 \times c_4 \times (-1)$, $c_6 = c_2 \times c_4 \times (-1)$ and $c_7 = c_3 \times c_4 \times (-1)$. Recall that Taguchi's column order is different to the one we generally choose and that in effect Taguchi changes the sign when he multiplies two columns together.

## Blocking

All the plans in Table 4.2 can be modified to give a two-block design by allocating a 'block factor' instead of an experimental factor. For an explanation of the concept of blocking, see Section 4.4. In most cases it is not important which column is used for the block factor, but there is one special case, noted in Table 4.2. When there are four genuine factors it is preferable to use $c_3$ (factor $E$) to define the blocks, because it is usual to assume that the block factor does not interact with any of the experimental factors. Deleting all interactions that involve $E$ leaves a relatively simple confounding pattern (shown in Table 4.3).

*Table 4.3* A four-factor plan in two blocks

| $c_1$ | $c_2$ | $c_3$ | $c_4$ | $c_5$ | $c_6$ | $c_7$ |
|---|---|---|---|---|---|---|
| $A$ | $B$ | Blocks<br>$A \times B$<br>$C \times D$ | $C$ | $A \times C$<br>$B \times D$ | $B \times C$<br>$A \times D$ | $D$ |

## Larger arrays

Table 4.4 gives the $L_{12}(2^{11})$ array. Except in the very special case in which only *two* factors are allocated, all plans based on the $L_{12}(2^{11})$ array are resolution III. The fundamental reason for this is that $L_{12}(2^{11})$ *does not have a multiplication table*. As the reader can easily check, the product of any two columns is

- not itself a column of the array, and
- not orthogonal to any columns except the two that were multiplied.

*Table 4.4* The $L_{12}(2^{11})$ array

| Row | | | | | | | | | | | |
|---|---|---|---|---|---|---|---|---|---|---|---|
| 1 | − | − | − | − | − | − | − | − | − | − | − |
| 2 | − | − | − | − | − | + | + | + | + | + | + |
| 3 | − | − | + | + | + | − | − | − | + | + | + |
| 4 | − | + | − | + | + | − | + | + | − | − | + |
| 5 | − | + | + | − | + | + | − | + | − | + | − |
| 6 | − | + | + | + | − | + | + | − | + | − | − |
| 7 | + | − | + | + | − | − | + | + | − | + | − |
| 8 | + | − | + | − | + | + | + | − | − | − | + |
| 9 | + | − | − | + | + | + | − | + | + | − | − |
| 10 | + | + | + | − | − | − | − | + | + | − | + |
| 11 | + | + | − | + | − | + | − | − | − | + | + |
| 12 | + | + | − | − | + | − | + | − | + | + | − |

If factors are allocated to all 11 columns, each column measures a main effect and a combination of no less than 45 interactions! These 'combinations' are more complicated than the sums of effects that we saw in Chapters 2 and 3. For example, contrast 1 measures

$$A - \tfrac{1}{3}(B \times C) - \tfrac{1}{3}(B \times D) - \tfrac{1}{3}(B \times E) - \text{etc.}$$

The list includes all the two-way interactions between factors other than $A$. The multiplier $\tfrac{1}{3}$ applies throughout, but in some cases the minus sign is

*Table 4.5* (a) The $L_{16}(2^{15})$ array

| Row | $c_1$ | $c_2$ | $c_3$ | $c_4$ | $c_5$ | $c_6$ | $c_7$ | $c_8$ | $c_9$ | $c_{10}$ | $c_{11}$ | $c_{12}$ | $c_{13}$ | $c_{14}$ | $c_{15}$ |
|---|---|---|---|---|---|---|---|---|---|---|---|---|---|---|---|
| 1 | − | − | + | − | + | + | − | − | + | + | − | + | − | − | + |
| 2 | + | − | − | − | − | + | + | − | − | + | + | + | + | − | − |
| 3 | − | + | − | − | + | − | + | − | + | − | + | + | − | + | − |
| 4 | + | + | + | − | − | − | − | − | − | − | − | + | + | + | + |
| 5 | − | − | + | + | − | − | + | − | + | + | − | − | + | + | − |
| 6 | + | − | − | + | + | − | − | − | − | + | + | − | − | + | + |
| 7 | − | + | − | + | − | + | − | − | + | − | + | − | + | − | + |
| 8 | + | + | + | + | + | + | + | − | − | − | − | − | − | − | − |
| 9 | − | − | + | − | + | + | − | + | − | − | + | − | + | + | − |
| 10 | + | − | − | − | − | + | + | + | + | − | − | − | − | + | + |
| 11 | − | + | − | − | + | − | + | + | − | + | − | − | + | − | + |
| 12 | + | + | + | − | − | − | − | + | + | + | + | − | − | − | − |
| 13 | − | − | + | + | − | − | + | + | − | − | + | + | − | − | + |
| 14 | + | − | − | + | + | − | − | + | + | − | − | + | + | − | − |
| 15 | − | + | − | + | − | + | − | + | − | + | − | + | − | + | − |
| 16 | + | + | + | + | + | + | + | + | + | + | + | + | + | + | + |

(b) Multiplication table for $L_{16}$

| Column number | Column number | | | | | | | | | | | | | |
|---|---|---|---|---|---|---|---|---|---|---|---|---|---|---|
| | 2 | 3 | 4 | 5 | 6 | 7 | 8 | 9 | 10 | 11 | 12 | 13 | 14 | 15 |
| 1 | 3 | 2 | 5 | 4 | 7 | 6 | 9 | 8 | 11 | 10 | 13 | 12 | 15 | 14 |
| 2 | | 1 | 6 | 7 | 4 | 5 | 10 | 11 | 8 | 9 | 14 | 15 | 12 | 13 |
| 3 | | | 7 | 6 | 5 | 4 | 11 | 10 | 9 | 8 | 15 | 14 | 13 | 12 |
| 4 | | | | 1 | 2 | 3 | 12 | 13 | 14 | 15 | 8 | 9 | 10 | 11 |
| 5 | | | | | 3 | 2 | 13 | 12 | 15 | 14 | 9 | 8 | 11 | 10 |
| 6 | | | | | | 1 | 14 | 15 | 12 | 13 | 10 | 11 | 8 | 9 |
| 7 | | | | | | | 15 | 14 | 13 | 12 | 11 | 10 | 9 | 8 |
| 8 | | | | | | | | 1 | 2 | 3 | 4 | 5 | 6 | 7 |
| 9 | | | | | | | | | 3 | 2 | 5 | 4 | 7 | 6 |
| 10 | | | | | | | | | | 1 | 6 | 7 | 4 | 5 |
| 11 | | | | | | | | | | | 7 | 6 | 5 | 4 |
| 12 | | | | | | | | | | | | 1 | 2 | 3 |
| 13 | | | | | | | | | | | | | 3 | 2 |
| 14 | | | | | | | | | | | | | | 1 |

replaced by a plus. Any given two-way interaction will influence nine contrasts, but this influence is attenuated by the multiplier $\frac{1}{3}$.

With fewer factors, some of the interactions can be deleted, but the confounding pattern remains extremely complicated, and is not affected by the choice of columns.

Unlike $L_{12}(2^{11})$, the $L_{16}(2^{15})$ array (Table 4.5) works very much like the $L_8(2^7)$. For example, it has a multiplication table. Table 4.6 lists some plans that can be derived from $L_{16}(2^{15})$.

The plans based on $L_{16}(2^{15})$ can be modified to incorporate two blocks. Unless Table 4.6 suggests otherwise, it is convenient to use factor $D$ (column 8) to define the blocks, which then consist of rows 1–8 and 9–16. For plans with four or eight blocks, see Bisgaard (1988).

For every $n$ that is a multiple of 4, there is an $n$-run orthogonal array that can be used as the basis of a balanced fractional plan. Most of these were listed by Plackett and Burman (1946). When $n$ is a power of 2, the array always has a multiplication table like those of $L_8(2^7)$ and $L_{16}(2^{15})$. The next array in this sequence is of course $L_{32}(2^{31})$. The intermediate arrays do not have multiplication tables, so they behave more like $L_{12}(2^{11})$ than $L_8(2^7)$, but each has special features of its own. Wheeler (1989) gives $L_{20}$, $L_{24}$ and $L_{28}$ as well as $L_{32}$.

## 4.2 INTERACTIONS AND EXPERIMENTAL STRATEGY

In Table 4.2 we gave a five-factor plan based on columns 1, 2, 3, 4 and 7 of $L_8(2^7)$. Table 4.7 shows an alternative plan based on columns 1, 2, 4, 6 and 7. Although both plans are resolution III, in each case there are two contrasts that do not measure main effects, and it is often argued that a sensible choice can be made between the plans by paying attention to these two 'spare' contrasts. The experimenters should identify the two two-way interactions that they believe are most likely to be important, and if possible arrange for the two spare contrasts to measure this pair of interactions.

Suppose, for example, that the $A \times B$ and $B \times E$ interactions are felt to be the most important *a priori*. The plan in Table 4.7 would be preferred to the one in Table 4.2, because in the latter $A \times B$ is confounded with $E$ and $B \times E$ with $A$. If we were able to justify ignoring the $A \times C$ and $C \times E$ interactions, the third and fifth contrasts would provide estimates of $A \times B$ and $B \times E$ respectively. It is sometimes said that these two interactions have been *allocated* to $c_3$ and $c_5$. This is rather misleading because the appearance of these effects in $c_3$ and $c_5$ is inevitable once the factors have been allocated to columns.

This line of thinking is greatly facilitated if a collection of *linear graphs* is available (see, for example, Taguchi 1986). These diagrams enable the user to ensure that certain specified two-way interactions are not confounded with

*Table 4.6* (a) Plans based on $L_{16}(2^{15})$, four and five factors

| Number of factors | Resolution number | $c_1$ | $c_2$ | $c_3$ | $c_4$ | $c_5$ | $c_6$ | $c_7$ | $c_8$ | $c_9$ | $c_{10}$ | $c_{11}$ | $c_{12}$ | $c_{13}$ | $c_{14}$ | $c_{15}$ |
|---|---|---|---|---|---|---|---|---|---|---|---|---|---|---|---|---|
| 4 | Full factorial | $\boldsymbol{A}$ | $\boldsymbol{B}$ | $A \times B$ | $\boldsymbol{C}$ | $A \times C$ | $B \times C$ | | $\boldsymbol{D}$ | $A \times D$ | $B \times D$ | | $C \times D$ | | | |
| 5 | V | | | | | | | $D \times E$ | | | | $C \times E$ | | $B \times E$ | $A \times E$ | $\boldsymbol{E}$ |

(b) Plans based on $L_{16}(2^{15})$, six to 15 factors

| Number of factors | Resolution number | $c_1$ | $c_2$ | $c_3$ | $c_4$ | $c_5$ | $c_6$ | $c_7$ | $c_8$ | $c_9$ | $c_{10}$ | $c_{11}$ | $c_{12}$ | $c_{13}$ | $c_{14}$ | $c_{15}$ |
|---|---|---|---|---|---|---|---|---|---|---|---|---|---|---|---|---|
| 6 | IV | $\boldsymbol{A}$ | $\boldsymbol{B}$ | $A \times B$<br>$C \times E$<br>$D \times F$ | $\boldsymbol{C}$ | $A \times C$<br>$B \times E$ | $A \times E$<br>$B \times C$ | $\boldsymbol{E}$ | $\boldsymbol{D}$ | $A \times D$<br>$B \times F$ | $A \times F$<br>$B \times D$ | $\boldsymbol{F}$ | $C \times D$<br>$E \times F$ | | | $C \times F$<br>$D \times E$ |
| 7 | IV | | | | | $D \times G$ | $F \times G$ | | | $C \times G$ | $E \times G$ | | $A \times G$ | $\boldsymbol{G}$ | | $B \times G$ |
| 8 | IV | | | $G \times H$ | | $F \times H$ | $D \times H$ | | | $E \times H$ | $C \times H$ | | $B \times H$ | | $\boldsymbol{H}$ | $A \times H$ |
| 9* | III | $H \times I$ | $G \times I$ | | $F \times I$ | | | $D \times I$ | $E \times I$ | | | $C \times I$ | | $B \times I$ | $A \times I$ | $\boldsymbol{I}$ |
| 10* | III | $B \times J$ | $A \times J$ | $\boldsymbol{J}$ | $E \times J$ | | | $C \times J$ | $F \times J$ | | | $D \times J$ | $I \times J$ | $H \times J$ | $G \times J$ | |
| 11* | III | $C \times K$ | $E \times K$ | | $A \times K$ | $\boldsymbol{K}$ | $J \times K$ | $B \times K$ | $G \times K$ | | $I \times K$ | $H \times K$ | | $D \times K$ | $F \times K$ | |
| 12 | III | $E \times L$ | $C \times L$ | $K \times L$ | $B \times L$ | $J \times L$ | $\boldsymbol{L}$ | $A \times L$ | $H \times L$ | $I \times L$ | | $G \times L$ | | $F \times L$ | $D \times L$ | |
| 13 | III | $D \times M$ | $F \times M$ | | $G \times M$ | | $I \times M$ | $H \times M$ | $A \times M$ | $\boldsymbol{M}$ | $J \times M$ | $B \times M$ | $K \times M$ | $C \times M$ | $E \times M$ | $L \times M$ |
| 14 | III | $F \times N$ | $D \times N$ | $M \times N$ | $H \times N$ | $I \times N$ | | $G \times N$ | $B \times N$ | $J \times N$ | $\boldsymbol{N}$ | $A \times N$ | $L \times N$ | $E \times N$ | $C \times N$ | $K \times N$ |
| 15 | III | $G \times O$ | $H \times O$ | $I \times O$ | $D \times O$ | $M \times O$ | $N \times O$ | $F \times O$ | $C \times O$ | $K \times O$ | $L \times O$ | $E \times O$ | $\boldsymbol{O}$ | $A \times O$ | $B \times O$ | $J \times O$ |

*In a two-block plan use factor $I$ to define the blocks

### Generating the $L_{16}$ orthogonal array

$L_{16}$ can be generated directly from $L_8$. Reproduce the $L_8$ cell for cell into a position directly below it in the worksheet using the copy command. There are now two $L_8$ arrays in the worksheet, one on top of the other (seven columns and 16 rows). Then type a new eighth column immediately to the right of this $7 \times 16$ array consisting of eight $-1$s followed by eight $+1$s. Finally multiply each of the original seven columns by the new eighth column in turn. The final array will be a $15 \times 16$ array of $\pm 1$s and will mimic Table 4.5.

To generate $L_{16}$ from scratch, four columns are needed initially, these (written as rows to save space) being
$c_1 = (-1, +1, -1, +1, -1, +1, -1, +1, -1, +1, -1, +1, -1, +1, -1, +1)$,
$c_2 = (-1, -1, +1, +1, -1, -1, +1, +1, -1, -1, +1, +1, -1, -1, +1, +1)$,
$c_4 = (-1, -1, -1, -1, +1, +1, +1, +1, -1, -1, -1, -1, +1, +1, +1, +1)$ and
$c_8 = (-1, -1, -1, -1, -1, -1, -1, -1, +1, +1, +1, +1, +1, +1, +1, +1)$.
Then the other columns can be generated according to $c_3 = c_1 \times c_2$, $c_5 = c_1 \times c_4$, $c_6 = c_2 \times c_4$, $c_7 = c_3 \times c_4$, $c_9 = c_1 \times c_8$, $c_{10} = c_2 \times c_8$, $c_{11} = c_3 \times c_8$, $c_{12} = c_4 \times c_8$, $c_{13} = c_5 \times c_8$, $c_{14} = c_6 \times c_8$ and $c_{15} = c_7 \times c_8$.

To generate Taguchi's version of $L_{16}$, reverse the ordering of $c_1$, $c_2$, $c_4$ and $c_8$, and change the sign when multiplying two columns together.

*Table 4.7* An alternative plan for five factors in eight runs

| $c_1$ | $c_2$ | $c_3$ | $c_4$ | $c_5$ | $c_6$ | $c_7$ |
|---|---|---|---|---|---|---|
| $A$ | $B$ | $A \times B$ | $C$ | $A \times C$ | $D$ | $E$ |
| $D \times E$ | $C \times D$ | $C \times E$ | $B \times D$ | $B \times E$ | $A \times E$ | $A \times D$ |
| | | | | | $B \times C$ | |

each other or with any main effect. However, they do not give complete information about confounding between main effects and interactions, so that for example the linear graph corresponding to the plan in Table 4.7 would not warn us that the estimated main effect of $A$ will be biased if the $D \times E$ interaction should (unexpectedly) prove to be substantial. For further information about linear graphs, see Sections 7.6 and 10.1.

Linear graphs were given a lot of attention when Taguchi's ideas were first publicized in the West by the American Supplier Institute. In his recent writing Taguchi has modified — or possibly merely clarified — his earlier discussions of interaction. He recommends that only main effects be considered when a plan is chosen. This is not because he believes that it is safe to ignore interactions. On the contrary, he acknowledges that important interactions very often exist and points out the difficulties that they cause. However, he believes that given sufficient understanding and ingenuity it is usually possible to eliminate interactions. According to Taguchi, the sole purpose of an orthogonal array experiment is to check whether additivity has been achieved, using the following strategy:

(i) Run an orthogonal array experiment (usually of resolution III) and estimate the main effect of each factor.
(ii) Using the estimated main effects, select the best configuration and predict the response for that configuration. Run the configuration — Taguchi calls this a *confirmation run* — and check the actual result against the prediction.
(iii) If the actual result fails to confirm the prediction, assume that interactions have biased the estimated main effects. Take steps to eliminate these interactions and run a new experiment. (Of course, some allowance for random variation must be made when comparing predicted and actual values, but exactly how much allowance to make is a very difficult question to which we cannot give a definite answer.)

Taguchi argues that the best type of orthogonal array to use for this purpose is one like $L_{12}$, because any one interaction will bias all but two of the main effects, making it more likely to be detected.

Taguchi says very little *in detail* about how to go about removing interactions. We shall discuss some ideas in Chapter 11, but as far as the present chapter is concerned, the important point is that Taguchi does not regard experimentation as a generator of the knowledge and understanding necessary to eliminate interactions. Instead, he uses the experimental data simply as a numerical check for the presence of interaction. We find this hard to accept, and recommend that experiments be used to obtain as much information about interactions as resources will allow.

On the other hand, we see little merit in trying to make use of a few spare contrasts in a resolution III plan by guessing the important interactions. A resolution III experiment should normally be seen as the first stage of a sequence of experiments, and the following strategy will often be appropriate when a large number of factors must be screened initially:

- Stage 1: A resolution III plan using as many runs as is necessary to accommodate the factors of interest.
- Stage 2: An experiment using a smaller number of factors, selected on the basis of the stage 1 results. This plan should be resolution IV.
- Stage 3: If necessary, some extra runs designed to resolve any ambiguities in the interpretation of stage 2.

It is helpful if stage 1 includes enough runs to make a viable normal plot. From this point of view the $L_8$ array is rather too small, though our experience suggests that Daniel plots will still be effective provided there are only one or two 'real' effects.

Stage 2 can be thought of as a 'confirmation experiment'. We can compare *predicted effects*, calculated from the main effects at stage 1, with the actual effects observed at stage 2, and obtain some idea of the importance of interactions. If the stage 2 plan is resolution IV, it will also enable the direct measurement of combinations of interactions. Any combinations that stand out can be further investigated at stage 3. Clearly, this strategy requires substantial resources to be held back rather than invested in the initial experiment.

Taguchi's single confirmation run can be thought of as a way of (potentially) reducing the amount of experimentation by showing that stages 2 and 3 are unnecessary because interactions are small enough to be ignored. However, it puts a lot of weight on a single result. In general it is safer to try to confirm *effects* rather than individual results. In two-level experiments, effects are differences between averages, and less uncertainty is attached to effects than to individual observations, except in very small experiments. Having discussed these points with Taguchi we believe that he too would prefer to confirm effects rather than individual predictions, when this is feasible.

There is another rather more technical problem with single confirmation runs, which we will explain by means of a hypothetical example. Table 4.8(a) shows the calculations involved in predicting for the configuration $A+$, $B+$, $C+$, $D+$, based on estimated main effects for these four factors. We suppose that in the experiment that produced these estimates, $A$ was confounded with $C \times D$. We take $\bar{y}$ to be 4.0. Note that since all the main effects are positive, $A+$, $B+$, $C+$, $D+$ is predicted to give the highest response. Even if this prediction were confirmed exactly, it would not lend support to the idea that $C$ and $D$ do not interact. Since $A$ and $C \times D$ were confounded in the original experiment, the results of that experiment are consistent with the possibility that the main effect of $A$ is zero, and that the $C \times D$ interaction is actually 1.0.

*Table 4.8* (a) Hypothetical example of prediction

| | $A$ | $B$ | $C$ | $D$ |
|---|---|---|---|---|
| | [ +1 | +1 | +1 | +1 ] |
| Estimated main effects | 1.0 | 0.8 | 2.4 | 1.2 |

Prediction $= 4.0 + \frac{1}{2}(1.0 + 0.8 + 2.4 + 1.2)$
$= 7.2$

(b) Identical prediction from a different hypothesis

| | $B$ | $C$ | $D$ | $C \times D$ |
|---|---|---|---|---|
| | [ +1 | +1 | +1 | +1 ] |
| Estimated effects | 0.8 | 2.4 | 1.2 | 1.0 |

Prediction $=$ 7.2 as before

Table 4.8(b) shows that the prediction based on this hypothesis is identical to the previous one.

The reader can verify that the same problem will not arise if the prediction is made for the 'worst' configuration $A-$, $B-$, $C-$, $D-$. This example shows that if confirmation is to be based on individual results, it should involve at least two predictions; confirming the 'best' and the 'worst' is a convenient general method. The difference between the two predictions is the combined effect of all the factors whose signs have been switched.

## Augmentation

The idea of a *follow-up experiment* covers any situation in which an experiment is planned on the basis of the results of a previous experiment. This is a very general concept, and to narrow it down a bit we assume in this discussion that no changes are made to the list of factors or their levels. The purpose of the follow-up experiment is to evaluate some configurations that have not previously been tried, and so help to resolve any ambiguities in the interpretation of the previous experiment — see for example stage 3 of the three-stage scheme suggested above. These added runs are called an *augmentation* of the original experiment.

In the glove box lid experiment (Table 3.6 and Fig. 3.5) it would be very interesting to know whether the relatively large contrast for $c_6$ primarily reflects interaction between the melt and mould temperatures, two of the three factors whose main effects stand out in the Daniel plot. The $c_6$ contrast actually measures a sum of four two-factor interactions, but in principle only three further runs are required to provide separate estimates of each of these interactions.

For a substantial discussion of augmentation runs see Cuthbert Daniel's book (Daniel 1976), in which he warns that adding only the minimum number of runs produces estimates that make very inefficient use of the available results. The reason for this is that the complete experimental plan (original plus added runs) is not sufficiently well balanced. For this particular augmentation problem Daniel recommends an additional eight runs.

## Reflection

Reflection, also known as fold-over, is an extreme example of an augmentation method, in which the number of runs in the follow-up experiment is equal to the size of the original experiment. This is accomplished by re-running the experiment with all signs reversed: wherever a factor was previously at level $(-)$, it is now set at $(+)$, and vice versa. An extra factor can be added to the experiment at this point without upsetting the balance. In other words, a factor that was held constant throughout the original experiment can be set at some other level throughout the reflection.

If no extra factor is included, the contrast can be used to measure a time effect. This may be substantial if the two halves of the experiment are run a long time apart.

If a resolution III plan is reflected, the plan and its reflection together make up a resolution IV plan. For example, reflecting the seven-factor plan in Table 4.2 produces the plan shown in Table 4.9. There is a good reason why we have written the column for the 'extra factor' in an unusual way. If rows 9–16 of the table are written *above* rows 1–8, this produces the last eight columns of $L_{16}(2^{15})$ — except that $c_8$ of $L_{16}(2^{15})$ now appears as the last column. We showed in Section 4.1 that the last four columns of $L_8(2^7)$ form a resolution IV plan, and the same is true of the last eight of $L_{16}(2^{15})$, the last 16 of $L_{32}(2^{31})$, and so on.

*Table 4.9* Reflecting a resolution III plan

| | *A* | *B* | *E* | *C* | *F* | *G* | *D* | Extra factor *H* |
|---|---|---|---|---|---|---|---|---|
| *Original experiment* | − | − | + | − | + | + | − | + |
| | + | − | − | − | − | + | + | + |
| | − | + | − | − | + | − | + | + |
| | + | + | + | − | − | − | − | + |
| | − | − | + | + | − | − | + | + |
| | + | − | − | + | + | − | − | + |
| | − | + | − | + | − | + | − | + |
| | + | + | + | + | + | + | + | + |
| *Reflection* | + | + | − | + | − | − | + | − |
| | − | + | + | + | + | − | − | − |
| | + | − | + | + | − | + | − | − |
| | − | − | − | + | + | + | + | − |
| | + | + | − | − | + | + | − | − |
| | − | + | + | − | − | + | + | − |
| | + | − | + | − | + | − | + | − |
| | − | − | − | − | − | − | − | − |

Reflection of the $L_{12}(2^{11})$ array is a convenient way to generate a resolution IV plan for 12 factors in 24 runs.

Reflection is worth consideration when the original experiment suggests that most or all of the factors affect the response, or it is impossible to separate effects into 'noise' and 'real' with any degree of confidence. It may also be used if the experimenters have 'second thoughts', when an experiment is already under way. They may become concerned that the experiment originally planned is too small, in which case reflection provides a convenient way of doubling the number of runs. For another type of application of reflection, see Section 10.2.

*Partial reflection* is similar to reflection but the signs of only one or two

**Reflection**

To achieve reflection, the plan matrix needs to be displayed in the worksheet in terms of $\pm 1$s rather than $\pm$s. Copy the array of $\pm 1$s directly below itself in the worksheet, multiplying each cell by $-1$. Hence what was a $+1$ becomes a $-1$ and vice versa. Type in the new column consisting of $+1$s for the original array and $-1$s for the reflected array immediately to the right in the worksheet.

To generate the full set of *contrasts*, multiply each column of the larger main/reflected array by the new column.

factors are switched in the added runs. For example, reflecting a single factor $A$ allows separate estimation of all two-way interactions involving $A$. A further variant of this idea is to apply partial reflection to only a part of the first experimental plan. For example, if the original experiment had 16 runs, partial reflection might be applied to generate another eight.

Wheeler (1988) discusses several examples of the use of reflection and partial reflection.

## 4.3 RANDOMIZATION OF THE RUN ORDER

Books on the planning of experiments have traditionally made a strong recommendation that the run order should be chosen at random. Suppose, for example, that the experimental plan were based on the $L_8(2^7)$ array. The eight different configurations would not be run in the *standard order* in which they have appeared in all our tables, but in a new order selected at random. Recently there has been a noticeable shift in opinion among statisticians, and many — including ourselves — now take the view that in the type of experiment described in this book randomization of run order is not as crucial as is sometimes claimed. In the remainder of this section we will briefly discuss the benefits and drawbacks of randomization. Randomization represents an attempt to get round the difficulties caused by sources of variation that are neither within the control of the experimenters nor of the type that can sensibly be thought of as random. In the language of statistical process control, these are 'special causes'. For example, an increase in the voltage input to a machine, occurring part-way through an experiment, may remain undetected and raise all the subsequent results by a fixed amount. Table 4.10 shows some hypothetical results.

Factors have been allocated to all the columns of the array, but we imagine that *none* of them has an effect on $y$. Apart from random variation,

*Table 4.10* $L_8(2^7)$ in standard order, with hypothetical results

| *A* | *B* | *C* | *D* | *E* | *F* | *G* | Response (*y*) |
|---|---|---|---|---|---|---|---|
| − | − | + | − | + | + | − | 8.92 |
| + | − | − | − | − | + | + | 10.96 |
| − | + | − | − | + | − | + | 9.49 |
| + | + | + | − | − | − | − | 10.54 |
| − | − | + | + | − | − | + | 14.33 |
| + | − | − | + | + | − | − | 13.61 |
| − | + | − | + | − | + | − | 14.13 |
| + | + | + | + | + | + | + | 14.38 |

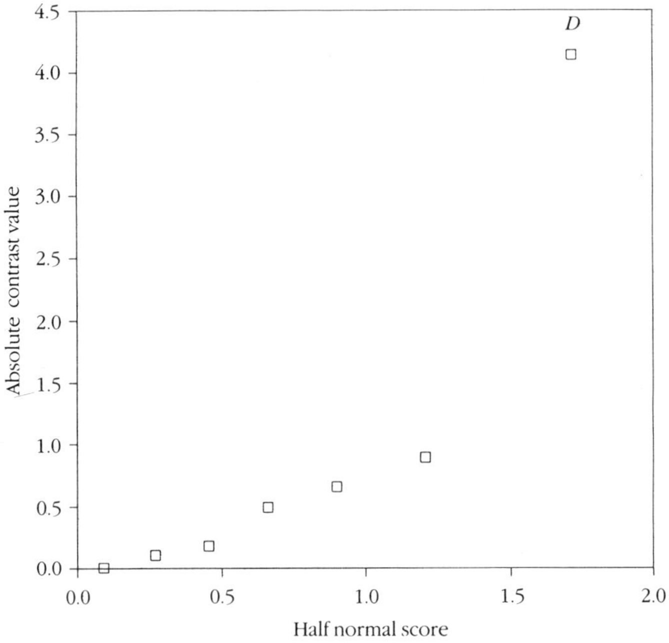


*Fig. 4.1* Daniel plot for data influenced by a 'special cause' of variation. Apparently factor *D* has an effect

the only factor affecting the *y* values is a voltage change that adds 4 units to rows 5–8. Of course, this gives exactly the same results as we would have got if factor *D* had had a real effect of 4 units. The value of the $c_4$ contrast will be roughly 4, and because the columns of the array are orthogonal, all the other contrasts measure only the 'background' random variation. Figure 4.1 shows the Daniel plot; seeing this in practice, we would be led to the erroneous belief that *D* probably has a real effect.

Now suppose that the run order is selected at random, and that the actual order is the one shown in Table 4.11. The *y* values remain exactly as

*Table 4.11* $L_8(2^7)$ in haphazard order

| $A$ | $B$ | $C$ | $D$ | $E$ | $F$ | $G$ | Response ($y$) |
|---|---|---|---|---|---|---|---|
| + | − | − | + | + | − | − | 8.92 |
| − | + | − | − | + | − | + | 10.96 |
| + | + | + | − | − | − | − | 9.49 |
| + | − | − | − | − | + | + | 10.54 |
| − | + | − | + | − | + | − | 14.33 |
| + | + | + | + | + | + | + | 13.61 |
| − | − | + | − | + | + | − | 14.13 |
| − | − | + | + | − | − | + | 14.38 |

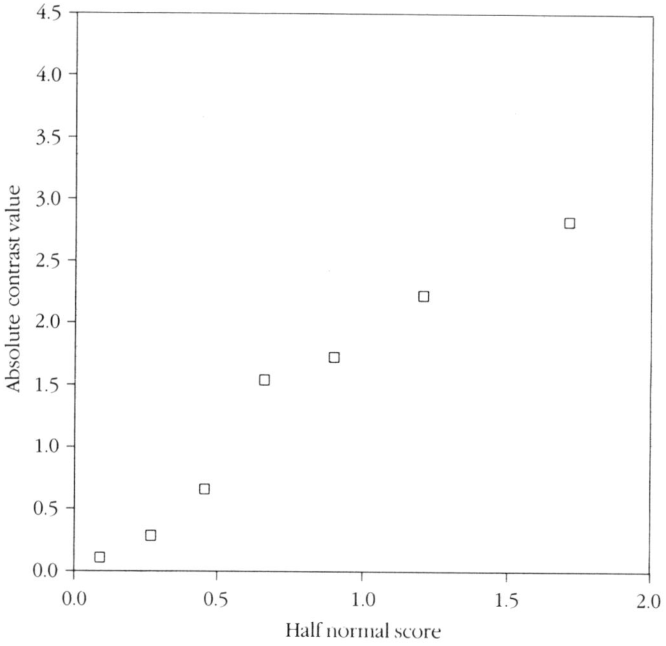


*Fig. 4.2* Daniel plot showing the benefit of randomization. Now, no effect appears off the line

before, because we have supposed that they are in no way affected by the factor levels in each run. The new Daniel plot is in Fig. 4.2. This time, all the contrasts behave like noise, and the plot would not mislead us.

The reason why Fig. 4.2 gives a correct impression is that the patterns of signs in the columns of the new array are fairly irregular (except that the new $G$ column is identical to the old $A$ column!), whereas the effect of the imagined special cause had a very simple pattern. As far as its effect on the data is concerned, this special cause is now indistinguishable from random variation. Although the use of a haphazard array *cannot* be relied on to neutralize the effect of all kinds of systematic extraneous variation, it usually works quite well. There is, however, a price to be paid. The total amount of background variation has increased, and this reduces the chance of detecting small but genuine effects.

The carburettor experiment in Chapter 1 was actually run in a random order (not the order implied by Table 1.1) as a guard against influence from different operators and analysts responsible for assembling the carburettors and measuring the contamination levels. This was a sensible precaution to take, but in general we would argue that randomization is less important in many industrial, as opposed to agricultural, experiments because it is relatively quick and easy to check the soundness of our conclusions by making changes to the process or product. In this context, statistical methods act as a focusing or prioritizing tool: they narrow the range of product or process changes that are thought to be worth further investigation. In terms of the PDCA cycle (Fig. 1.1), Fig. 4.1 would lead us to make, at stage 4 of the cycle, an erroneous prediction about the effect of changing factor $D$, but the error should quickly become obvious when we go round the cycle again to test out this change.

Another reason for reducing the emphasis on randomization is that arrays in non-standard order can create practical difficulties. In most experiments there are some factors that are difficult to change, and it is very convenient to allocate them to columns that have only a few switches of sign. Moreover, if a spreadsheet is to be used to calculate contrasts, draw normal plots and so on, it is necessary to type in the results in a pre-specified order. In our examples we have envisaged the use of standard order. Unless it is carried out by the computer program, the process of sorting the results to fit the standard order is time-consuming and prone to error.

However, there is a way round this particular difficulty. It should be clear from our discussion so far that it is the *product* of the randomization process — an irregular array — and not the fact of having used randomization to which we attach importance. We believe it would be legitimate for an experimenter to adopt the same haphazard order in a sequence of experiments. In effect, this would become the experimenter's standard order and the software could easily be adapted to receive the results in this form.

**Arrays in a haphazard order**

Most spreadsheets generate random numbers, usually between 0 and 1. Generate a set of random numbers in a column adjacent to the array in the worksheet that is required to be haphazard. Then use the sort command to rearrange the whole array based on the column of random numbers as the 'primary sort key'. This will result in an array in haphazard order, with each row intact.

To sum up, we believe that because of the haphazard arrays that it usually produces, randomization is in principle a good idea. However, its benefits are not guaranteed and it should not be used if it creates serious practical difficulties in running the experiment or analysing the results. The use of randomization does not provide an excuse for the experimenters to ignore the need to prepare properly for the experiment by doing their best to eliminate extraneous sources of variation.

## 4.4 BLOCKS, SPLIT PLOTS AND SIMPLE TRENDS

Randomization is used as a defence against systematic sources of variation that may or may not be present. When such an effect is *strongly* suspected, it is better to modify the experimental plan. In engine testing, time constraints may make it necessary to employ two or more test rigs; despite calibration, there may remain a systematic difference between results on the two rigs. In many cases there is a very simple solution to this problem. Suppose, for example, that there are two rigs. We can treat 'rigs' as a two-level factor to be allocated to a column of the orthogonal array in exactly the same way as we allocate the factors in which we are really interested. If there is a 'rigs main effect' it will not be confounded with any other main effect. Depending on the plan chosen, it *may* be confounded with a two-way interaction.

Systematic background effects are often suspected when experiments are conducted over an extended time period, because this gives an opportunity for so many possible changes in background variables. In this case, the time available can be divided into two halves or *blocks*, producing a 'time factor' with two levels. Table 4.12 shows an example in which three experimental factors and 'time' have been allocated to four columns of $L_8(2^7)$. This particular plan is very convenient because the first four runs in the standard order all have 'time' at the (−) level. In other words, these four runs should

*Table 4.12* An experimental plan incorporating two blocks

| *A* | *B* | Time | *C* |
|---|---|---|---|
| − | − | − | − |
| + | − | − | + |
| − | + | − | + |
| + | + | − | − |
| − | − | + | + |
| + | − | + | − |
| − | + | + | − |
| + | + | + | + |

all be made in the first time block, and runs 5–8 in the second time block. Within these time blocks, the run order could be randomized.

In Table 4.13 the $L_8(2^7)$ array has been divided into four blocks by allocating three block factors $B_1$, $B_2$ and $B_3$ to $c_2$, $c_4$ and $c_6$. Block 1 corresponds to the configuration $B_1-$, $B_2-$, $B_3+$, block 2 to $B_1+$, $B_2-$, $B_3-$, and so on. In order to implement this method one of the columns must be the product of the other two (e.g. $c_2 \times c_4 = c_6$). Between them, the $c_2$, $c_4$ and $c_6$ contrasts account for all the differences between the blocks. Experimental factors can be allocated to any or all of the remaining columns.

*Table 4.13* Using three block factors to define four blocks

| | $B_1$ | | $B_2$ | | $B_3$ | | |
|---|---|---|---|---|---|---|---|
| − | − | + | − | + | + | − | Block 1 |
| + | − | − | − | − | + | + | |
| − | + | − | − | + | − | + | Block 2 |
| + | + | + | − | − | − | − | |
| − | − | + | + | − | − | + | Block 3 |
| + | − | − | + | + | − | − | |
| − | + | − | + | − | + | − | Block 4 |
| + | + | + | + | + | + | + | |

The word *block* originated in agricultural experiments, where it refers to an area of land, but it is now used to mean any group of experimental runs that are believed to be homogeneous, or relatively homogeneous, with respect to some source of background variation. It is usual to assume that the effect of moving from one block to another does not interact with any of the experimental factors. This means, for example, that the long-run main effect of factor $A$ is the same in every block. This special assumption about blocks can sometimes be exploited to improve the experimental plan, by careful choice of the columns to which the block factors are allocated. Some two-block plans were suggested in Section 4.1, but for plans with four or more blocks the reader should consult Bisgaard (1988).

## Split plot experiments

When it appears that several blocks will be required, the number of contrasts available to study the experimental factors is correspondingly reduced. However, a large number of blocks can sometimes be turned into an advantage by thinking about them in a different way. What is required is that the differences between blocks should be capable of being modelled as random (this might be achieved in practice by running the blocks in a random order). If so, the experiment can be planned in a completely different manner. As an example, the experimental plan in Table 4.14 is obtained by

*Table 4.14* Example of a split plot layout

| *A* | *B* | *C* | *D* | *E* | *F* |
|---|---|---|---|---|---|
| − | − | − | + | − | + |
| + | − | − | + | − | + |
| − | + | − | − | − | − |
| + | + | − | − | − | − |
| − | − | + | − | − | + |
| + | − | + | − | − | + |
| − | + | + | + | − | − |
| + | + | + | + | − | − |
| − | − | − | + | + | − |
| + | − | − | + | + | − |
| − | + | − | − | + | + |
| + | + | − | − | + | + |
| − | − | + | − | + | − |
| + | − | + | − | + | − |
| − | + | + | + | + | + |
| + | + | + | + | + | + |

allocating factors to $c_1$, $c_2$, $c_4$, $c_6$, $c_8$ and $c_{10}$ in the $L_{16}(2^{15})$ array. The runs have been divided into eight blocks, but no block factors have been allocated to columns. It is clear that the main effect contrast for *A* will not be affected by block differences, because it has different signs for the two runs in each block, so the block differences cancel out. Inspection of the full $L_{16}$ array will reveal that all the *odd*-numbered contrasts have this property. However, all the *even*-numbered contrasts have the same sign within each block. As a result, all of these contrasts (including the main effects of *B*, *C*, *D*, *E* and *F*) will be affected by the block differences.

The usual methods can be applied, provided it is sensible to think of the differences between blocks as random and we are careful to keep track of which contrasts are in the odd set and which are in the even. For example, Fig. 4.3 shows the half normal plot for a set of data in Cuthbert Daniel's original paper (Daniel 1959) on the use of normal plots to analyse experiments. The odd and even contrasts form two lines with different slopes. The odd-numbered contrasts measure *within-block* variation and the even contrasts *between-block* variation. The line corresponding to the even set has a higher slope, indicating that random variation between blocks is greater than within, a very common situation. Sometimes, however, the two sets of contrasts appear to form a single line, and can be treated as one homogeneous set.

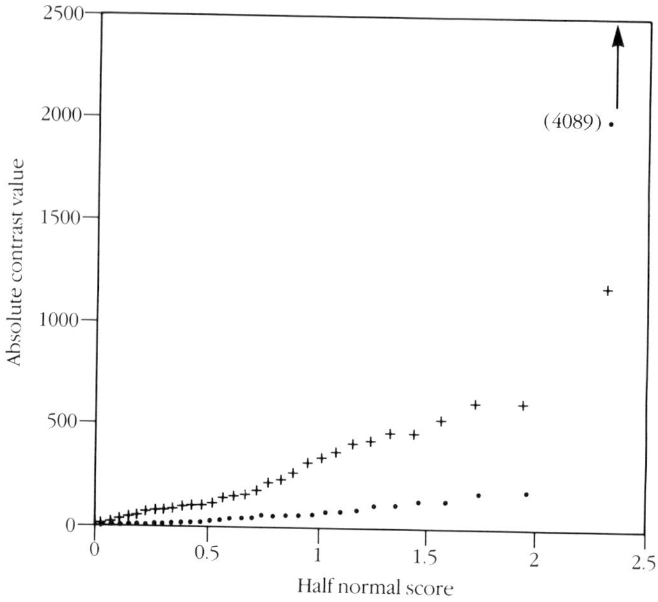


*Fig. 4.3* Daniel's half normal plot. Contrasts shown as dots measure variation within blocks; contrasts shown as plus signs measure variation between blocks. The largest within-block contrast has a value of 4089, and is not shown in the correct position, to help scaling

Although we are continuing to call them blocks, these groups of runs are now playing a new role. In agricultural applications this type of design and analysis is called a split plot experiment. In the plan shown in Table 4.14 each pair of runs would occupy a plot (sometimes called a main plot) and each run would occupy a subplot.

As we noted above, any factor allocated to an even-numbered column takes only one level on each plot, which can be convenient when running the experiment.

There are many situations in which this kind of thinking is useful even though the idea of a block or plot seems to have no obvious relevance. In the example that produced Fig. 4.3 the response was the tensile strength of steel. There were five factors concerned with the chemical composition of the steel, and one process factor. The most convenient way to run the experiment was to make some steel with a specific chemical composition (a *heat*) and divide the heat into two halves, which are subjected to different process conditions. This is then repeated with steel of a different composition. Differences between heats can be expected to be larger than between the two halves of a heat, even in the absence of factor effects, so the heats correspond to main plots and the two halves correspond to subplots. Daniel's example is typical of an experiment on a *multi-stage* process.

The actual experiment was a full factorial, but it would have been possible to use the plan in Table 4.14 by allocating the process factor to $c_1$ and the composition factors to the five remaining columns. Each pair of runs then corresponds to one heat. The data can be analysed as we suggested above, making sure that the odd and even contrasts are carefully distinguished.

## Linear and quadratic trends

It is sometimes plausible to assume that the variation in a background variable takes a simple form, for example a linear or quadratic trend. We can then exploit the fact that in some orthogonal arrays — when written out in standard order — some of the contrasts are unaffected by such trends. For example, Table 4.15 shows four columns taken from $L_8(2^7)$, and two hypothetical background variables. One of them is simply equal to the run number, the other is the square of the run number. When applied to the linear variable, all four contrasts take the value zero. This remains true for *any* variable that is linearly related to the run number, and these columns are said to be orthogonal to a linear trend. Column $c_7$ is also orthogonal to the quadratic trend, and hence to any trend that is the sum of linear and quadratic components.

In $L_{16}(2^{15})$, columns $c_3$, $c_5$ to $c_7$ and $c_9$ to $c_{15}$ are orthogonal to a linear trend, so it is possible to allocate 11 factors to $L_{16}(2^{15})$ in such a way that the main effects (and the interactions that are confounded with the main effects) are unaffected by this type of background variation.

As in the case of $L_8(2^7)$, the odd-numbered columns of $L_{16}(2^{15})$ generate a resolution IV plan, and if we leave $c_1$ empty we get a seven-factor resolution IV plan in which all the main effects are orthogonal to a linear trend. However, some of the columns that measure interaction ($c_2$, $c_4$, $c_8$) will be affected. If we require all two-way interactions to be orthogonal to a linear trend, at most four columns can be used, so we end up with a complete $2^4$ experiment.

*Table 4.15* Linear and quadratic trends in $L_8(2^7)$

| $c_3$ | $c_5$ | $c_6$ | $c_7$ | Background variables | |
|---|---|---|---|---|---|
| + | + | + | − | 1 | 1 |
| − | − | + | + | 2 | 4 |
| − | + | − | + | 3 | 9 |
| + | − | − | − | 4 | 16 |
| + | − | − | + | 5 | 25 |
| − | + | − | − | 6 | 36 |
| − | − | + | − | 7 | 49 |
| + | + | + | + | 8 | 64 |

In $L_8(2^7)$ there are only four columns that are orthogonal to a linear trend (the ones shown in Table 4.15), so it is not possible to run a complete $2^3$ plan in which all two-way interactions are unaffected.

In $L_{12}(2^{11})$ there are only two columns ($c_3$ and $c_7$) that are orthogonal to a linear trend, though $c_4$, $c_7$, $c_{10}$ and $c_{11}$ come close.

P W M John (1990) discusses some rules for detecting columns that are orthogonal to linear and quadratic trends, in two- and three-level orthogonal arrays. It turns out that the idea of reflection plays a key role. For example, in Table 4.15 the last four entries in $c_5$ are the reflection of the first four.

## SUMMARY OF CHAPTER 4

Plans with higher resolution numbers have simpler confounding patterns. In resolution III plans, main effects are confounded with two-way interactions. In resolution IV plans, main effects are clear of two-way interactions. In resolution V plans, there is no confounding between two-way interactions. We give a short catalogue of some useful plans based on $L_8(2^7)$ and $L_{16}(2^{15})$. These plans can be modified to give a two-block design with one less factor. Whenever $n$ is a power of 2 there is an $n$-row array that behaves like $L_8$ and $L_{16}$.

$L_{12}(2^{11})$ is an example of an array that has no multiplication table. All plans based on it are resolution III, with a complicated confounding pattern in which each two-way interaction biases most of the main effects.

One way of trying to cope with interactions is to guess which ones are likely to be important and use Taguchi's 'linear graphs' to ensure that these are not confounded with any main effect. However, in his recent work Taguchi has argued against this strategy, suggesting instead that a prediction of the best result achievable should be made from main effects only. If this prediction cannot be confirmed, interactions are probably present and the experimenters should re-think their approach to the problem so as to eliminate interactions.

We take a different view and recommend that experiments be used to obtain as much information about interactions as resources permit. Resolution III experiments should normally be regarded as the first stage in a multi-stage strategy. The first-stage experiment would be used to select the variables in a follow-up investigation, which might itself be augmented by further runs.

Taguchi's prediction/confirmation method is an attempt to save resources by showing that interactions are negligible, but puts a lot of weight on a single confirmation run. In general, it is preferable to try to confirm effects rather than individual predictions in a follow-up experiment. There is a technical flaw in the argument that if a prediction based only on main effects is confirmed in a further run, interactions can be ignored. Confirming the 'best' and 'worst' would avoid this flaw.

There are techniques for selecting the best configurations to add to an experiment to reduce the complexity of the confounding pattern and clarify the interpretation of the results. The reflection (or fold-over) method doubles the size of the experiment by reversing the signs of all factor levels. Resolution III experiments then become resolution IV.

Randomization of the run order has the potential to prevent systematic sources of background variation from producing misleading experimental results, but its benefits are not guaranteed and it can create practical difficulties in running the experiment. When such 'special causes' are strongly suspected, the experimental plan should be modified. It can be arranged in blocks by introducing one or more block factors. These block factors can be treated exactly like the experimental factors, except that it is usual to assume that there is no interaction between the two types of factor, and this assumption can sometimes be exploited to improve the plan.

In an alternative type of plan some of the experimental factors are not orthogonal to the block differences. It is then necessary to keep track of which contrasts are affected by between-block differences and which by within-block differences. In an agricultural context this type of experiment is called a split plot plan. It is often applicable to multi-stage industrial processes with several sources of variation.

When arrays are run in standard order some of the contrasts are unaffected by a linear trend in a background variable, and a few are unaffected by a quadratic trend. These properties can sometimes be used as an alternative to randomization or blocking.

# CHAPTER 5

# Experiments with factors at three levels

*Many of the ideas that we have introduced in previous chapters, including orthogonal contrasts, orthogonal arrays, main effects, interactions, confounding, normal plots and analysis of variance, are applicable when the factors have three levels rather than two, and the details will be found in this chapter. Three-level experiments also have some special features arising from the fact that in the case of quantitative factors we are now able to measure curvature and fit non-linear prediction equations.*

*There are several types of fractional three-level plan. Two are introduced in this chapter: plans based on three-level orthogonal arrays, and plans given by adding one run to a two-level design. We discuss the role that such experiments should play in a sensible experimentation strategy.*

## 5.1 ORTHOGONAL ARRAYS FOR THREE-LEVEL FACTORS

The array in Table 5.1 can be used as an experimental plan for four factors, each with three levels, in nine runs. We use Taguchi's terminology and call it the $L_9(3^4)$ orthogonal array. Unlike Taguchi we code the levels using (−), (0) and (+) rather than 1, 2 and 3. Note that, like the previous two-level arrays ($L_8$, $L_{12}$, $L_{16}$, etc.), this array has the property of balance. For any and every pair of columns, each combination of symbols occurs the same number of times (just once each in this case). $L_9$ is the smallest orthogonal array for three-level factors. Larger arrays that accommodate three-level factors have 18, 27, 36, etc., runs, and we touch on some of these in this and later chapters.

In order to keep the introduction to three-level factors as simple as

*Table 5.1* The $L_9(3^4)$ orthogonal array

| Row | | | | |
|---|---|---|---|---|
| 1 | − | − | − | − |
| 2 | − | 0 | 0 | 0 |
| 3 | − | + | + | + |
| 4 | 0 | − | 0 | + |
| 5 | 0 | 0 | + | − |
| 6 | 0 | + | − | 0 |
| 7 | + | − | + | 0 |
| 8 | + | 0 | − | + |
| 9 | + | + | 0 | − |

possible, we stay with $L_9$ and discuss an example concerning the dimensional instability of cast metal flywheels.

The process engineers wanted to improve stability because flywheels rotate at high speed when a car engine is running, and any out-of-balance may cause vibration. The measure of instability was taken to be the difference between the 'high' and 'low' spots, measured between the faces of the wheel — a perfect flywheel would not have a high or low spot and would record zero on this scale, while an unbalanced wheel would have a large value for this measurement.

The engineers chose to investigate four factors, each at three levels, as follows:

| | Level | | |
|---|---|---|---|
| Factor | (−) | (0) | (+) |
| (*A*) Cavity | 1 | 2 | 3 |
| (*B*) Pre-fill level of sand | Minimum | $\frac{1}{4}$ full | $\frac{1}{2}$ full |
| (*C*) Squeeze pressure (psi) | 60 | 75 | 90 |
| (*D*) Cooling time in mould | 10% less | Current setting | 10% more |

The cavity identifies the casting site, the pre-fill level of sand is the amount of sand in the mould prior to casting, the squeeze pressure is the pressure under which the mould is clamped, and the cooling time is how long the casting is left in the mould before it is removed.

Each factor was allocated to a column of the $L_9$ array, and the experiment yielded the results shown in Table 5.2. The instability was originally measured in millimetres. The data are multiplied by 100 in Table 5.2 to remove the decimal places.

The definition of a *main effect* of a three-level factor is not quite as straightforward as in the two-level case. For the moment, we will talk about two parts of a main effect: the effect of changing the factor from level (−) to

*Table 5.2* Results of the flywheel experiment

| Run | *A* | *B* | *C* | *D* | Instability |
|---|---|---|---|---|---|
| 1 | − | − | − | − | 26 |
| 2 | − | 0 | 0 | 0 | 30 |
| 3 | − | + | + | + | 39 |
| 4 | 0 | − | 0 | + | 35 |
| 5 | 0 | 0 | + | − | 41 |
| 6 | 0 | + | − | 0 | 48 |
| 7 | + | − | + | 0 | 30 |
| 8 | + | 0 | − | + | 31 |
| 9 | + | + | 0 | − | 35 |

level (0), and the effect of changing from level (0) to level (+). Later we will explain the nature of an effect for a three-level factor in a more precise way, but at this point the reader needs to be aware that, however the effects are defined, the main effect of a three-level factor has *two* components.

We can calculate a three-level version of the response table, by looking at the average instability for each factor level. This is valid because of the balance in the experiment with regard to factor changes. The effects as defined above are then easily calculated as the differences between these averages. Table 5.3 has the response table for the flywheel data. By allocating four factors to the $L_9$ array, we are *saturating* the design. This may seem an odd statement at first, since we said in Chapter 2 for the two-level case that a saturated design had one less factor than the number of runs. Here, though, each factorial effect has *two* components, and since there are four factors, this means we are estimating $4 \times 2 = 8$ 'bits' of information from the experiment. The number of runs is nine and we say the design is saturated because $9 - 1 = 8$. This is a more general definition of saturation than in the two-level case. The practical consequence of this is that if any two factors exhibit an interaction this will bias the main effects of the other two factors. In larger three-level arrays, interactions often bias many main effects. At this stage we ask the reader to bear in mind the possibility of interactions — we return to the topic in more detail later in the chapter.

*Table 5.3* Response table for the flywheel experiment

| | *A* | *B* | *C* | *D* |
|---|---|---|---|---|
| Average of level (−) | 31.7 | 30.3 | 35.0 | 34.0 |
| Average of level (0) | 41.3 | 34.0 | 33.3 | 36.0 |
| Average of level (+) | 32.0 | 40.7 | 36.7 | 35.0 |
| Effect ( ) to (0) | 9.6 | 3.7 | −1.7 | 2.0 |
| Effect (0) to (+) | −9.3 | 6.7 | 3.4 | −1.0 |

The effects can be presented graphically, by plotting the average response for each level of each factor. The effects plot for the flywheel data is given in Fig. 5.1.

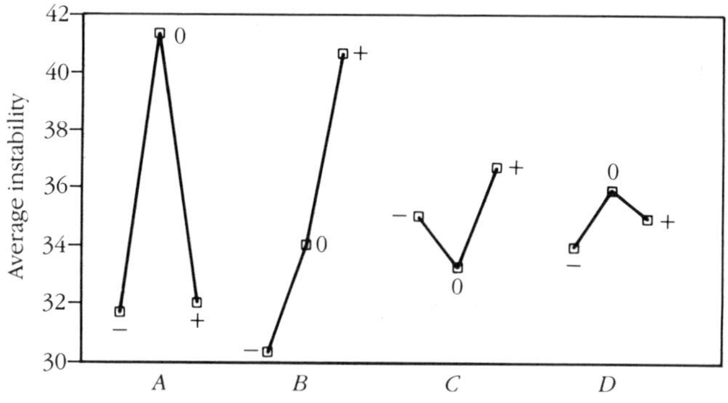


*Fig. 5.1* Flywheel experiment. Effects plot

Factor $D$ (cooling time) does not, comparatively, have much effect on dimensional instability, since all three levels give similar averages. For factor $A$ the labelling of the cavities is purely arbitrary since this is a qualitative factor. Cavity 2 gave much worse results than the others. Both factors $B$ (pre-fill level) and $C$ (squeeze pressure) are quantitative, and so there is a hierarchy in the levels. For factor $B$ the instability increases with the level of sand: both components of the main effect are positive. For factor $C$, the effects change sign, and the flywheel stability is best for a squeeze pressure around level (0). As for the two-level case in Chapter 2, we will defer the application of statistical methods to assess the effects relative to 'noise' until later in this chapter, and talk first about prediction.

## Prediction in experiments with three-level factors

When it is required to predict the response *only at factor levels used in the experiment*, the form of the prediction equation given as [2.9] can be used with three-level factors just as easily as with two-level factors. For the flywheel example the effects plot suggests that to achieve the best stability we need to choose factor $A$ at level (−) (just!), factor $B$ at level (−), factor $C$ at (0) and factor $D$ at (−). To predict the instability we have

$$\text{prediction} = \bar{y} + (\bar{y}_{A-} - \bar{y}) + (\bar{y}_{B-} - \bar{y}) + (\bar{y}_{C0} - \bar{y}) + (\bar{y}_{D-} - \bar{y}) \quad [5.1]$$

where $\bar{y}_{A-}$ denotes the average instability measurement when factor $A$ is at the (−) level, $\bar{y}_{B-}$ likewise for factor $B$, and so on. Substituting these numbers into [5.1] gives

$$\text{prediction} = 35.0 + (31.7 - 35.0) + (30.3 - 35.0) + (33.3 - 35.0) + (34.0 - 35.0) = 24.3$$

As in the two-level case, if this prediction cannot be confirmed, we might conclude that some interactions are active, and that what we *thought* was a main effect was really an interaction.

However, there will often be situations where we need to predict at levels in between those used in the experiment. Of course, this applies only to quantitative factors. The form of the prediction equation [5.1] cannot be used for this purpose, and a more general equation is required.

A very crude way to predict at intermediate values of factor levels is just to interpolate along the straight lines shown in the effects plot, Fig. 5.1, but this makes a strong and probably unrealistic assumption that a sharp change in effect occurs at level (0).

Usually it makes more sense to assume that the response $y$ changes in a *smooth* way as a factor is varied between (−) and (+). That is, if we took measurements corresponding to factor $C$, say, at many pressures between 60 and 90 psi, we would get a curve like the one illustrated in Fig. 5.2, rather than the straight lines implied by the effects plot.

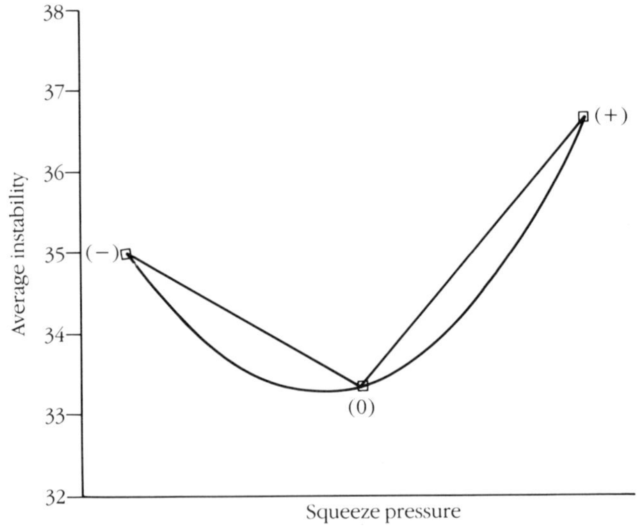


*Fig. 5.2* Flywheel experiment. Interpolating between levels

The straight lines provide a first approximation to the true $y$ values, but we can get a better approximation if we are prepared to take the trouble to describe the curvature, or more generally the non-linearity. This is the advantage of three-level experiments over two-level ones. We will pursue this idea, but with a different case study, in Section 5.2.

## 5.2 EXAMPLE — ENGINE MAPPING

In order to explain the use of three-level experiments to measure curvature and construct prediction equations, it is helpful to start by looking at a *complete* factorial experiment in which the problem of confounding does not arise. Our example is concerned with engine mapping, an activity in which experiments are carried out on an engine by varying several factors, for example speed, load and spark advance, and measuring several responses, for example fuel consumption and exhaust gas emissions. We would like to thank Martin Herbert of the Ford Motor Co. Ltd for this experiment.

Generally, many hundreds of experimental runs are conducted on one engine at various factor configurations. The equations derived from the data are used to give instructions to electronic engine management systems that control the engine while in use, so that fuel consumption and emissions can be kept to a minimum.

Figure 5.3 is an illustration of the points chosen in a recent map for two factors, engine speed and torque (load). These points are certainly not randomly chosen — they are *designed* in some way, but there are rather a lot of them. As the number of factors increases to typically five, up to 4000 runs

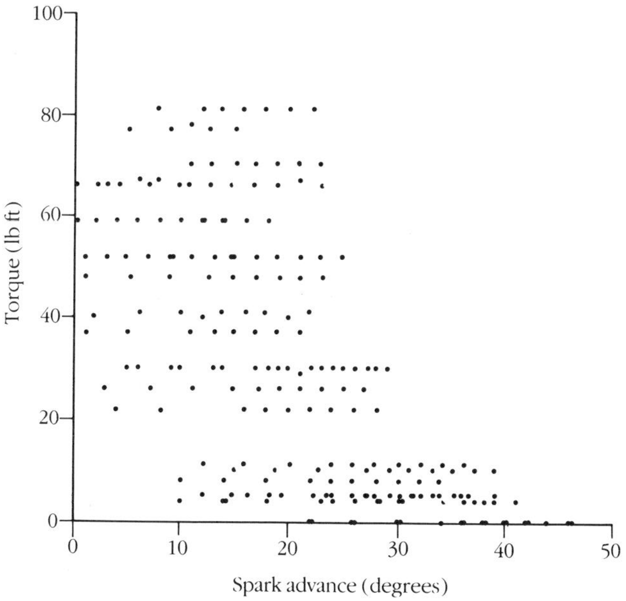


*Fig. 5.3* Factor combinations used in a typical engine map

may be made. A natural question to ask is — can the number of map points be reduced to a much smaller number in such a way that a reliable equation can still be obtained for prediction?

To answer this question, we need to understand something of the nature of the relationship between the responses (denoted by $y$) and the factors. Let us consider just one factor to start with, which we will denote by $x$. The *real* functional relationship between $y$ and $x$ is generally unknown, say $y = f(x)$. The object of the engine map in this case is to *approximate* this equation by conducting experiments. Taylor's theorem says that any function $y = f(x)$ can be approximated in the neighbourhood of a specified $x$ value by a polynomial in $x$. In the context of an experiment it is useful to take the specified $x$ value to be the one coded as (0), leading to the following equation:

$$y = f(0) + xf^{(1)}(0) + x^2f^{(2)}(0)/2! + x^3f^{(3)}(0)/3! + \ldots$$

where $f^{(i)}(0)$ is the $i$th derivative of $f(x)$ at zero. Therefore, any function can be expressed approximately as a polynomial as long as it can be differentiated. One important question is — to what degree (power) does the polynomial have to be taken so that it gives a useful approximation to the unknown function $f(x)$ over the range of $x$ values of interest to the experimenters? There is no hard-and-fast answer to this question, but as long as $f(x)$ is 'well behaved', that is smooth with at most one turning point, then quadratic approximation is usually a good starting point. Taylor's theorem can be extended to several factors (several $x$s) to say that any smooth, well behaved *surface* can be approximated by a generalization of the simple quadratic equation known as a *complete second-order equation*.

In order to make $f(x)$ well behaved so that a second-order equation is adequate for the approximation, we might have to consider transformation of the response (e.g. to $\log(y)$ or $1/y$) or a transformation of the $x$ variables (e.g. from cartesian to polar co-ordinates) or both. These issues are discussed in later chapters.

To estimate second-order equations we need to experiment with each factor at only three levels, at least initially. Reducing the number of levels for investigation greatly reduces the number of experimental runs needed, but we need to be sure that a quadratic approximation will be good enough.

We will confine our discussion of the engine mapping experiment to just three factors, namely engine speed ($R$, measured as rpm), spark angle ($S$, measured in degrees) and torque ($T$, measured in lb ft), and two responses, namely fuel flow rate ($y$, measured in $\text{lb h}^{-1}$) and exhaust emissions consisting of oxides of nitrogen, called $NO_x$ for short ($z$, measured in $\text{g h}^{-1}$).

In order to investigate the possibility of being able to reduce the number of experiments and still obtain a reliable engine map, the engineers decided on the levels shown at the top of page 105.

A new map was conducted with these new levels, and every combination of $R$, $T$ and $S$ was tested, totalling only $3^3 = 27$ points. The original map on this engine had 584 points. Note that each factor has its levels equally spaced on a linear scale. The reason for this is that quadratic equations can be most

| Factor | Level (−) | (0) | (+) |
|---|---|---|---|
| Engine speed ($R$) | 2000 | 3500 | 5000 |
| Engine torque ($T$) | 8 | 30 | 52 |
| Spark angle ($S$) | 10 | 20 | 30 |

easily and efficiently derived when the factors have equally spaced levels. At first glance, the rule of having equally spaced levels for the factors appears restrictive, but this equal spacing does not have to be on a linear scale. For example the numbers 10, 100 and 1000 are equally spaced on a *logarithmic* scale, so that if these were the required levels for the factor, we would work in the logarithmic scale.

The coding −, 0, +, and its numerical counterpart −1, 0, +1, is very convenient for estimating quadratic equations using orthogonal contrasts, as we shall see. In order to introduce a variety of new ideas in a gradual way, we will discuss the fuel flow response only, and start with a small subset of the data. As we deal with more aspects of three-level experimentation we will introduce more data accordingly.

Table 5.4 gives the results of just nine runs in the total experiment of 27 runs. In these nine runs all possible combinations of $R$ and $T$ were tried, with factor $S$ fixed at its middle level of 20 degrees.

*Table 5.4* Part of the engine mapping experiment

| Speed $R$ | Torque $T$ | Fuel flow rate |
|---|---|---|
| − | − | 4.2 |
| − | 0 | 6.5 |
| − | + | 9.3 |
| 0 | − | 7.3 |
| 0 | 0 | 11.8 |
| 0 | + | 16.9 |
| + | − | 13.0 |
| + | 0 | 19.7 |
| + | + | 26.1 |

We begin the analysis by looking at the three results for $R$ at the (−) level, which are plotted in Fig. 5.4. We have used a coded scale for $T$ in which the equally spaced levels are represented by −1, 0 and +1. A useful way of summarizing this diagram numerically is to calculate:

- the *slope* of the straight line joining the two outer points, and
- the *vertical distance* from this line to the middle point.

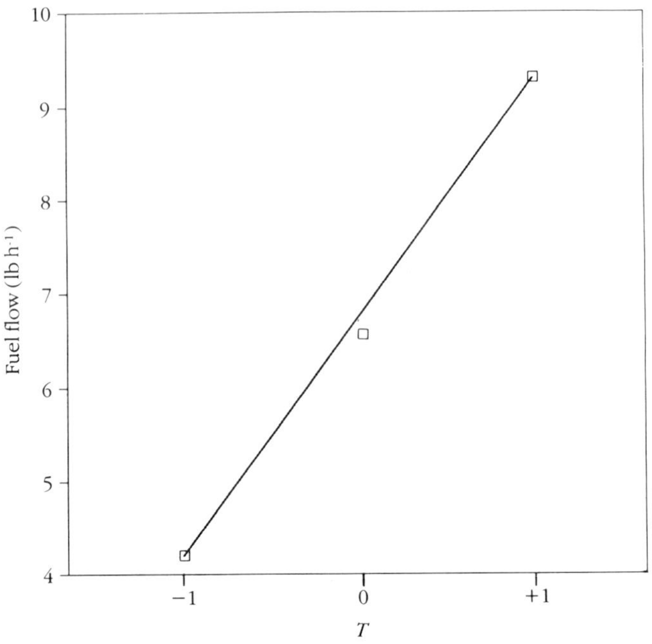


*Fig. 5.4* Engine mapping. The first three runs in Table 5.4

The slope is just

$$\tfrac{1}{2}(9.3 - 4.2) = 2.55$$

It can sensibly be thought of as a measure of the 'linear effect of $T$ on $y$'. The vertical distance from the line to the middle point is calculated as

$$\tfrac{1}{2}(4.2 + 9.3) - 6.5 = 0.25$$

It is clearly a measure of the extent to which the three points are not collinear, since an exact straight line would give zero. In fact this quantity is said to measure the 'quadratic effect of $T$ on $y$'. This interpretation deserves a closer look, but we first summarize our calculations in Table 5.5. This shows that both the quantities we have calculated are *contrasts* (their coefficients sum to zero), and that these contrasts are *orthogonal* (the sum of products of their coefficients — their *inner product* – is zero).

To see why the second contrast is called 'quadratic', note that there is a unique quadratic curve (parabola) that passes through any given set of three points. For the points in Fig. 5.4 the equation of the curve turns out to be

$$y = 6.50 + 2.55T + 0.25T^2 \qquad [5.2]$$

so the linear and quadratic contrasts above supply the coefficients of $T$ and $T^2$. This is always so when the three levels of $T$ are equally spaced and coded $-1$, 0 and $+1$, so this is one good reason for choosing this particular coding scheme.

*Table 5.5* A useful pair of contrasts

| | Linear | Quadratic | Fuel flow |
|---|---|---|---|
| | −1 | +1 | 4.2 |
| | 0 | −2 | 6.5 |
| | +1 | +1 | 9.3 |
| Divisor | 2 | 2 | |
| Value | 2.55 | 0.25 | |

**Linear and quadratic contrasts**

Generating quadratic contrasts from linear ones already in the worksheet can be achieved by using the 'if' logical operator in the column of cells reserved for the quadratic contrasts. In words, the logical operator says 'if the linear contrast coefficient is ±1, then write a +1, else write a −2'.

To calculate the contrast values for a particular set of data, generate new columns whose cell entries are the contrast cells multiplied by the data cells. Summing these new columns and dividing by the appropriate divisors gives the required contrast values.

The linear and quadratic contrast values can also be calculated using the regression facility (if the spreadsheet has one). The 'dependent' or $y$ variable is the column of data, and the 'independent' or $x$ variables consist — for each factor — of the linear contrast column, and a column of numbers that are the *squares* of the linear contrast column (*not* the quadratic contrast column). The regression output will return 'regression coefficients', one of which will be equivalent to the linear contrast and one the quadratic contrast.

Equation [5.2] summarizes the effect of $T$ on fuel flow when $R$ is at the (−) level. If we had only the data in Fig. 5.4 available to us, the quadratic equation could be used to predict fuel flow for intermediate levels of $T$. In practice we would need to consider whether there is sufficient evidence of non-linearity to justify using the quadratic equation rather than a simple straight line. We will not dwell on this point here because the same type of question will arise when we consider the engine mapping data as a whole.

We end this section with another look at the linear contrast. Since it is half the difference between the results at the (−) and (+) levels, we write it as $\frac{1}{2}(y_+ - y_-)$. If we had run a two-level experiment, using only the (−) and (+) levels, then in the language of Chapter 2 the quantity $(y_+ - y_-)$ would measure *the* effect of $T$ on $y$. The reader may wonder whether it is worth maintaining a distinction between two such closely related quantities. It would be possible to abolish the distinction by, for example, *defining* the effect of $T$ in a two-level experiment to be $\frac{1}{2}(y_+ - y_-)$. However, it is important not to lose sight of the differences between the two- and three-level cases. The key difference is that, in the two-level case, just knowing the *size* and *direction* of an effect was adequate for an understanding of the factors, while with three levels we are able to measure non-linearity and so begin to ask questions about the *shape* of the relationship between $y$ and the factors, and this is facilitated by fitting a simple equation such as a quadratic. Hence, when factors are at three levels, we define the contrasts to provide the coefficients for this equation.

## Main effects and interactions

We now move on to consider the complete set of results in Table 5.4. As in the case of two-level factors, there are two different sorts of effect to be considered, namely main effects and interactions.

Because another factor ($R$) has to be taken account of, the linear main effect of $T$ is now calculated as an *average*:

(i) find the linear effect of $T$ *for each level of* $R$;
(ii) take the *average* of these linear effects.

The individual linear effects are, for $R$ at levels −, 0 and +, $\frac{1}{2}(9.36 - 4.2)$, $\frac{1}{2}(16.9 - 7.3)$ and $\frac{1}{2}(26.1 - 13.0)$, respectively, with values 2.55, 4.80 and 6.55. Their average is 4.63, which can be formally written out as

$$\tfrac{1}{6}(-4.2 + 9.3 - 7.3 + 16.9 - 13.0 + 26.1)$$

The same idea is used to calculate the quadratic effect of $T$, that is the average is taken of the quadratic effects of $T$ at each level of $R$, which are $\frac{1}{2}(4.2 + 9.3) - 6.5$, $\frac{1}{2}(7.3 + 16.9) - 11.8$ and $\frac{1}{2}(13.0 + 26.1) - 19.7$, respectively. Their average can be formally written out as

$$\tfrac{1}{6}(4.2 - 2 \times 6.5 + 9.3 + 7.3 - 2 \times 11.8 + 16.9 + 13.0 - 2 \times 19.7 + 26.1)$$

The same procedures are applied to calculate the linear and quadratic effects of $R$, and we get the four main effect contrasts shown in Table 5.6 with abbreviated labels. The values of the contrasts can be interpreted as coefficients in a quadratic equation for fuel flow as a function of $R$ and $T$. We will discuss this interpretation below, but for the moment we note that the contrast values for $T_\ell$ and $T_q$ are somewhat different from the linear and quadratic coefficients in equation [5.2], because there is an interaction between $R$ and $T$ in this set of data. We will discuss this interaction in more detail shortly.

From a practical point of view the main effect contrast coefficients can be thought of as re-coded versions of the columns in the plan in Table 5.4. The linear contrasts are given by applying [5.3] and the quadratic contrasts by [5.4].

*Table 5.6* Main effect contrasts for the results in Table 5.4

| | $R_\ell$ | $T_\ell$ | $R_q$ | $T_q$ | Fuel flow |
|---|---|---|---|---|---|
| | −1 | −1 | +1 | +1 | 4.2 |
| | −1 | 0 | +1 | −2 | 6.5 |
| | −1 | +1 | +1 | +1 | 9.3 |
| | 0 | −1 | −2 | +1 | 7.3 |
| | 0 | 0 | −2 | −2 | 11.8 |
| | 0 | +1 | −2 | +1 | 16.9 |
| | +1 | −1 | +1 | +1 | 13.0 |
| | +1 | 0 | +1 | −2 | 19.7 |
| | +1 | +1 | +1 | +1 | 26.1 |
| Divisor | 6 | 6 | 6 | 6 | |
| Value | 6.47 | 4.63 | 1.13 | 0.13 | |

| Coded factor level | Coefficient in linear contrast |
|---|---|
| − | −1 |
| 0 | 0 |
| + | +1 |

[5.3]

| Coded factor level | Coefficient in quadratic contrast |
|---|---|
| − | +1 |
| 0 | −2 |
| + | +1 |

[5.4]

The divisor is now 6, which is just the total number of −1s and +1s in each contrast column. This simple rule to determine the divisor works for all three-level orthogonal plans when the proportions of levels (−), (0) and (+) are equal. This includes all plans based on the $L_9(3^4)$ array in Table 5.1 — the plan in Table 5.4 is just the first two columns of $L_9(3^4)$.

We now look at the interaction that we hinted at above by developing *interaction contrasts*. We found previously that, at the three levels of $R$, the linear effect of $T$ was 2.55, 4.80 and 6.55, respectively. An interaction is evident here because these effects change with the level of $R$. Plotting these values against the levels of $R$ gives Fig. 5.5.

By analogy with Fig. 5.1, we can calculate the linear effect of $R$ *on the linear effect of* $T$ to be

$$\tfrac{1}{2}(6.55 - 2.55) = 2.00$$

In general we have

$$\begin{matrix}\text{linear effect of } R \\ \text{on linear effect of } T\end{matrix} = \frac{1}{2}\left\{\begin{pmatrix}\text{linear effect of } T \\ \text{when } R \text{ is at level } (+)\end{pmatrix} - \begin{pmatrix}\text{linear effect of } T \\ \text{when } R \text{ is at level } (-)\end{pmatrix}\right\}$$

$$= \tfrac{1}{2}\{\tfrac{1}{2}(y_{++} - y_{+-}) - \tfrac{1}{2}(y_{-+} - y_{--})\}$$

$$= \tfrac{1}{4}(y_{--} - y_{-+} - y_{+-} + y_{++}) \qquad [5.5]$$

where $y_{--}$ is the response when both factors are at the (−) level, and so on. Formula [5.5] is known as the *linear by linear interaction*, abbreviated to $R_\ell \times T_\ell$. A similar argument can be used to generate linear by quadratic ($R_\ell \times T_q$), quadratic by linear ($R_q \times T_\ell$) and quadratic by quadratic ($R_q \times T_q$) contrasts, each measuring a different aspect of the $R \times T$ interaction. The coefficients for each of the interaction contrasts are shown in Table 5.7.

*Table 5.7* Interaction contrasts for the results in Table 5.4

| | $R_\ell \times T_\ell$ | $R_\ell \times T_q$ | $R_q \times T_\ell$ | $R_q \times T_q$ | Fuel flow |
|---|---|---|---|---|---|
| | +1 | −1 | −1 | +1 | 4.2 |
| | 0 | +2 | 0 | −2 | 6.5 |
| | −1 | −1 | +1 | +1 | 9.3 |
| | 0 | 0 | +2 | −2 | 7.3 |
| | 0 | 0 | 0 | +4 | 11.8 |
| | 0 | 0 | −2 | −2 | 16.9 |
| | −1 | +1 | −1 | +1 | 13.0 |
| | 0 | −2 | 0 | −2 | 19.7 |
| | +1 | +1 | +1 | +1 | 26.1 |
| Divisor | 4 | 4 | 4 | 4 | |
| Value | 2.00 | −0.20 | −0.25 | −0.25 | |

**Interaction contrasts for three-level factors**

Interaction contrasts for three-level factors can, as in the case of two-level factors, simply be obtained by multiplying together main effect contrasts. For example, if Table 5.6 is already in the worksheet, Table 5.7 can be obtained by multiplying the relevant columns cell by cell in the usual manner. Hence the total of eight contrasts in this example can easily be constructed prior to calculating the contrast values themselves. The same principle can be followed for larger arrays.

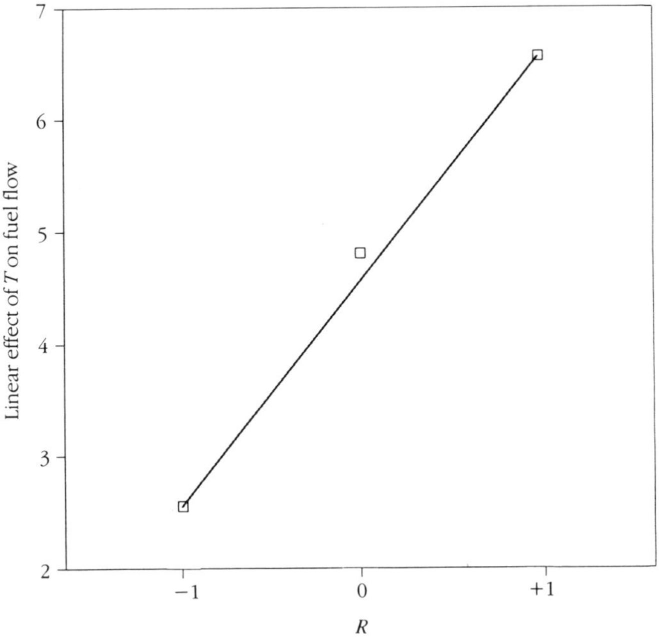


*Fig. 5.5* Engine mapping data in Table 5.4. The linear effect of $R$ on the linear effect of $T$

As in the case of two-level experiments, the quickest way of finding the coefficients in the interaction columns is to multiply together coefficients of pairs of main effects. For example, multiplying the $R_\ell$ and $T_\ell$ columns in the matrix part of Table 5.6 gives the coefficients in $R_\ell \times T_\ell$ in Table 5.7. This multiplication rule does *not* apply to the divisor though; these are given by counting the total number of $-1$s and $+1$s in the column, just as for main effects.

Figure 5.6 helps in the interpretation of the coefficients in the $R_\ell \times T_\ell$ contrast. It shows the nine configurations in Table 5.4 as nine points in a plane. Next to each point (in *italics*) is its coefficient in $R_\ell \times T_\ell$. Note that only the four corner points contribute to the contrast, and that exactly the same coefficients would have been used to form the $R \times T$ contrast if we had run just a two-level experiment using only the four corner points (see Chapter 2). In this new context the divisor is 4 rather than 2.

All the contrasts in Tables 5.6 and 5.7 are orthogonal to each other, and eight orthogonal contrasts is the most that can be calculated from nine results.

The last line of Table 5.7 gives the values of the interaction contrasts for our example. Note that the linear by linear contrast is much larger than the others. Graphically, some light is thrown on these values by Fig. 5.7, which is another way of plotting all the data in Table 5.4. There is very little non-linearity at any level of $R$, so the linear effect of $R$ on the quadratic effect of $T$

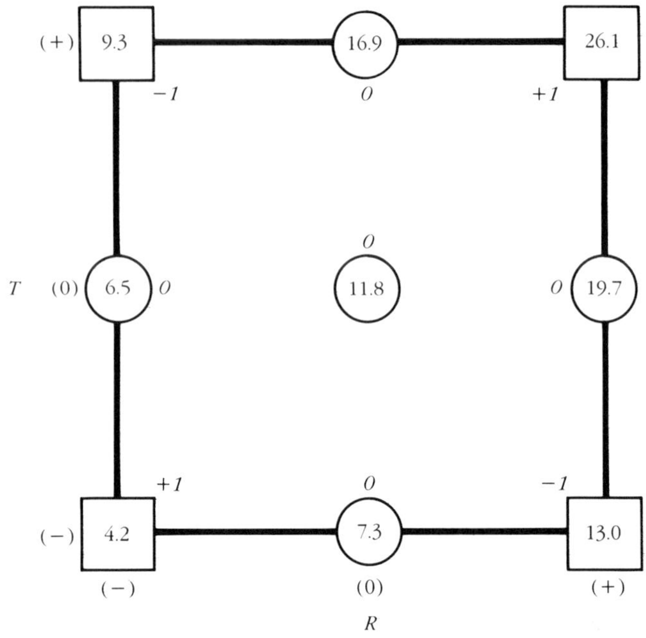


*Fig. 5.6* Engine mapping. Coefficients in the linear by linear interaction contrast, shown by italic numbers. The results in the circles do not contribute to the contrast value

**Checking orthogonality**

Most spreadsheets have commands to transpose ranges of numbers (that is, change rows to columns and columns to rows) and to multiply matrices. To check orthogonality of a set of contrasts, first make a transposed copy of the contrasts so that the contrasts appear as rows rather than columns. Then, using the matrix multiplication command, multiply the transposed contrasts by the original contrasts (the ones written as columns). If all the contrasts are orthogonal, the result will be a square matrix (range) of numbers that will be zero everywhere except down the leading diagonal.

($R_\ell \times T_q$) and the quadratic effect of $R$ on the quadratic effect of $T$ ($R_q \times T_q$) must be small. The slopes of the lines increase markedly with $R$, and this increase appears to be roughly linear, so the interaction is mainly linear by linear, and the quadratic effect of $R$ on the linear effect of $T$ ($R_q \times T_\ell$) must be small.

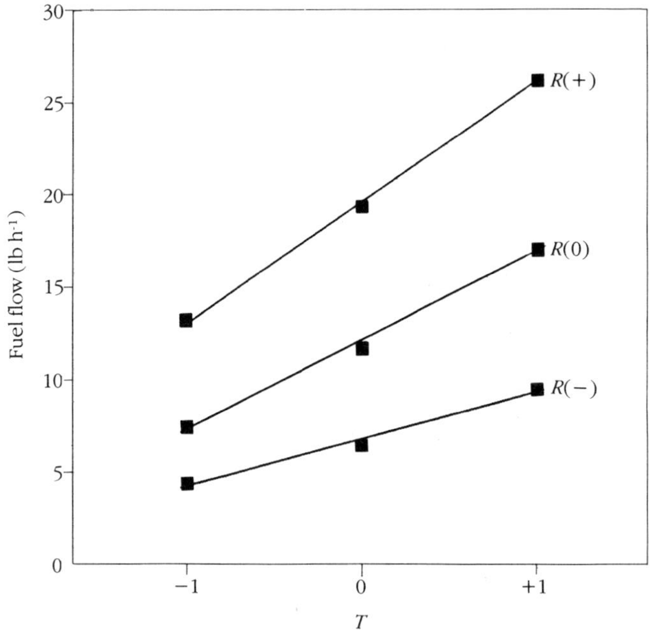


*Fig. 5.7* Engine mapping. Another representation of the data in Table 5.4

## Fitting a response surface

Figure 5.8 is another picture of the plan and results given in Table 5.4, this time represented as a set of points in three dimensions. The points have been connected by a smooth surface, called a *response surface* because it shows how the fuel flow might change in response to changes in $R$ and $T$. One particular smooth surface that passes through all nine points can be described by equation [5.6], where as usual $R$ and $T$ should be interpreted in coded (−1, 0, +1) form:

$$y = 12.76 + 6.47R + 4.63T + 1.13(R^2 - \tfrac{2}{3}) + 0.13(T^2 - \tfrac{2}{3}) + 2.00RT - 0.20R(T^2 - \tfrac{2}{3}) - 0.25(R^2 - \tfrac{2}{3})T - 0.25(R^2 - \tfrac{2}{3})(T^2 - \tfrac{2}{3}) \qquad [5.6]$$

Putting $R = T = 0$ into the right-hand side gives

$$y = 12.76 - (1.13 \times \tfrac{2}{3}) - (0.13 \times \tfrac{2}{3}) - (0.25 \times \tfrac{4}{9}) = 11.8$$

the observed value for fuel flow when $R$ and $T$ were at level (0). As another example, putting $R = T = +1$ gives

$$y = 12.76 + 6.47 + 4.63 + 1.13 \times \tfrac{1}{3} + 0.13 \times \tfrac{1}{3} + 2.00 - 0.20 \times \tfrac{1}{3} - 0.25 \times -0.25 \times \tfrac{1}{9}$$
$$= 26.1$$

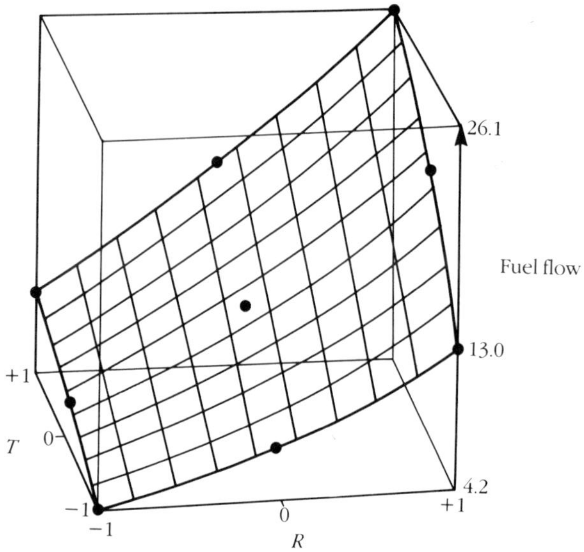


*Fig. 5.8* Engine mapping. The data in Table 5.4 with fitted response surface

as observed when $R$ and $T$ were at level $(+)$.

Equation [5.6] may appear to be rather complicated, and indeed it can be mathematically 'simplified' by collecting together the terms in $R$, terms in $T$, etc. However, the particular form we have used in [5.6] has several advantages, the most obvious one being that all the coefficients apart from the first *are given by the contrast values in Tables 5.6 and 5.7*. The first coefficient, which is the intercept on the $y$ axis, is given by $\bar{y}$, the mean of the response values. The number $\frac{2}{3}$ that appears several times in [5.6] is actually the average value of $R^2$ (and of $T^2$) over the nine runs of the experiment:

$$\begin{array}{c}\text{average (coded)}\\ \text{value of } R^2\end{array} = \frac{9 \times (-1)^2 + 9 \times (0)^2 + 9 \times (+1)^2}{27} = \frac{2}{3}$$

and it needs to be included if all the coefficients are to be derived directly from orthogonal contrasts.

In practice the equation that defines the response surface would be used to predict the response for configurations that were not used in the experiment. From this point of view it is a disadvantage rather than an advantage to have a surface that passes *exactly* through all of the observed points. Each observed $y$ value is, we assume, affected by random noise, and if we choose a surface that exactly interpolates the points we are forcing it to reproduce the pattern of noise that we happened to experience in the experiment. It is far better to have a surface (equation) that *smooths out* the noise. Such an equation would have fewer terms than [5.6] while still passing close to the data points. One convenient form of equation is given by dropping from [5.6] the terms of order higher than two, i.e. those which involve $RT^2$, $R^2T$ (third order) and $R^2T$ (fourth order), leaving

$$y = 12.76 + 6.47R + 4.63T + 1.13(R^2 - \tfrac{2}{3}) + 0.13(T^2 - \tfrac{2}{3}) + 2.00RT \quad [5.7]$$

Equation [5.7] is known as a *complete second-order equation* because it contains all possible second-order terms in $R$ and $T$ (that is $R^2$, $T^2$ and $RT$). The only interaction of which it can take account is the linear by linear type.

Second-order equations are also called *second-degree* equations. The use of the term 'second-order' rather than 'second-degree' is common in statistical applications.

Table 5.8 shows that the $y$ values produced by this simplified equation match the *actual* $y$ values very well. In fact it may be possible to simplify the equation even further, using statistical analysis to determine which terms (if any) might be dropped, but we defer this question until the next section.

*Table 5.8* Comparison of actual and predicted fuel flow

| Actual fuel flow | Fuel flow calculated from equation [5.7] |
|---|---|
| 4.2 | 4.1 |
| 6.5 | 6.6 |
| 9.3 | 9.3 |
| 7.3 | 7.4 |
| 11.8 | 11.9 |
| 16.9 | 16.7 |
| 13.0 | 13.0 |
| 19.7 | 19.5 |
| 26.1 | 26.3 |

## 5.3 ENGINE MAPPING — MORE DATA

Table 5.9 gives the complete set of fuel flow results from the engine mapping experiment, with one run for every possible combination of $R$, $T$ and $S$. A glance at the data reveals the strong positive effect that both $R$ and $T$ have on fuel flow, and within each group of three runs we see a negative correlation with the level of $S$.

A total of 26 orthogonal contrasts can be calculated from this experiment, comprising:

- a linear and quadratic main effect contrast for each factor;
- for each pair of factors, four contrasts that measure different aspects of their two-way interaction; and

*Table 5.9* Full plan and results (fuel flow) of the engine mapping experiment

| Run | Speed $R$ | Torque $T$ | Spark $S$ | Fuel flow |
|---|---|---|---|---|
| 1 | − | − | − | 4.5 |
| 2 | − | − | 0 | 4.2 |
| 3 | − | − | + | 3.7 |
| 4 | − | 0 | − | 7.1 |
| 5 | − | 0 | 0 | 6.5 |
| 6 | − | 0 | + | 6.4 |
| 7 | − | + | − | 9.8 |
| 8 | − | + | 0 | 9.3 |
| 9 | − | + | + | 9.1 |
| 10 | 0 | − | − | 8.2 |
| 11 | 0 | − | 0 | 7.3 |
| 12 | 0 | − | + | 7.2 |
| 13 | 0 | 0 | − | 12.7 |
| 14 | 0 | 0 | 0 | 11.8 |
| 15 | 0 | 0 | + | 12.0 |
| 16 | 0 | + | − | 17.8 |
| 17 | 0 | + | 0 | 16.9 |
| 18 | 0 | + | + | 16.6 |
| 19 | + | − | − | 15.5 |
| 20 | + | − | 0 | 13.0 |
| 21 | + | − | + | 12.5 |
| 22 | + | 0 | − | 22.1 |
| 23 | + | 0 | 0 | 19.7 |
| 24 | + | 0 | + | 19.0 |
| 25 | + | + | − | 29.0 |
| 26 | + | + | 0 | 26.1 |
| 27 | + | + | + | 25.8 |

- eight contrasts that measure different aspects of the three-way interaction $R \times T \times S$, like $R_\ell \times T_\ell \times S_\ell$, $R_q \times T_\ell \times S_\ell$, $R_q \times T_q \times S_\ell$, and so on.

The coefficients for the main effect contrasts can be found by applying the re-coding rules in [5.3] and [5.4] to the columns of the experimental plan. The divisor is now 18 in each case. To get the coefficients in the interaction contrasts, the main effect columns are multiplied in pairs (for two-factor interactions) and in threes (for three-factor interactions). The divisor is 12 for all of the two-way interaction contrasts and 8 for the three-way interactions. In all cases, to determine the divisor count the number of $\pm 1$s in the contrast column.

If we were interested in the three-way interactions, then, as an example, multiplying the $R_\ell$, $T_\ell$ and $S_\ell$ columns gives the coefficients in the $R_\ell \times T_\ell \times S_\ell$ contrast, which measures the linear effect of $S$ on the $R_\ell \times T_\ell$ effect, or equivalently the linear effect of $T$ on the $R_\ell \times S_\ell$ effect, and so on. Although three-way interactions do not occur in second-order equations, if they are calculated they can be useful for model checking, i.e. making a check on the adequacy of the second-order equation. We will call any contrast that can be used to check the adequacy of the second-order model a *checking contrast*, so all the third- and higher-order interactions are checking contrasts in this example. We will make some use of checking contrasts below, and talk more about them in Chapter 6.

## Prediction equation and normal plot

When there are three factors the second-order prediction equation has a linear and quadratic term in each factor separately and a product term for each pair of factors — nine terms, excluding the intercept. The constants in the second-order equation are given by $\bar{y}$ and the values of the following contrasts: $R_\ell$, $T_\ell$, $S_\ell$, $R_q$, $T_q$, $S_q$, $R_\ell \times T_\ell$, $R_\ell \times S_\ell$ and $T_\ell \times S_\ell$.

Of course, some of these contrasts could be measuring random noise rather than real effects, in which case the corresponding term could be deleted from the equation. We can form a Daniel plot from all the 26 contrast values, and if any of these plot 'on the line' it suggests that the corresponding term might be deleted. Also, if any of the other 17 contrasts — the checking contrasts — are clearly off the line, it suggests that there are important interaction effects that are not allowed for in the second-order equation.

Construction of the Daniel plot is a little more complicated for experiments with three-level factors than for the two-level factors discussed in Chapter 3 because the coefficients in these contrasts are very varied, and not merely patterns of $-1$s and $+1$s. Even if there are no real effects, and all the contrasts measure random noise, they will not behave like a set of random values from a single distribution. For example, the quadratic contrasts are inherently more variable than the linear ones. As a counter-measure we can standardize the contrast values before plotting, by calculating

$$\text{standardized contrast value} = \frac{\text{contrast value}}{k} \qquad [5.8]$$

where

$$k = \sqrt{\left(\frac{\text{sum of squares of coefficients in the contrast column}}{\text{divisor}^2}\right)}$$

The standardized contrast values given by equation [5.8] provide a set of numbers to use in a full or half normal plot. Table 5.10 summarizes the calculations for the fuel flow data in Table 5.9. For example, to standardize the quadratic contrast for factor $R$ ($R_q$), the sum of squares of the coefficients in the $R_q$ column is given by $9 \times (-1)^2 + 9 \times (-2)^2 + 9 \times (+1)^2 = 54$. The divisor is 18, so $k = \surd(54/324) = 0.408$. The standardized contrast for $R_q$ is then $1.24/0.408 = 3.04$. This differs slightly from the number in Table 5.10

*Table 5.10* Standardized contrast values for the fuel flow data

| Contrast name | Contrast value | $k$ | Standardized value | Contrast name | Contrast value | $k$ | Standardized value |
|---|---|---|---|---|---|---|---|
| $R_\ell$ | 6.78 | 0.236 | 28.78 | $T_q \times S_\ell$ | −0.07 | 0.5 | −0.15 |
| $T_\ell$ | 4.68 | 0.236 | 19.87 | $R_\ell \times S_q$ | 0.48 | 0.5 | 0.95 |
| $S_\ell$ | −0.80 | 0.236 | −3.39 | $T_\ell \times S_q$ | 0.08 | 0.5 | 0.15 |
| $R_q$ | 1.24 | 0.408 | 3.03 | $R_q \times T_q$ | −0.09 | 0.866 | −0.11 |
| $T_q$ | 0.11 | 0.408 | 0.26 | $R_q \times S_q$ | 0.16 | 0.866 | 0.18 |
| $S_q$ | 0.52 | 0.408 | 1.28 | $T_q \times S_q$ | −0.04 | 0.866 | −0.05 |
| $R_\ell \times T_\ell$ | 2.01 | 0.289 | 6.96 | $R_q \times T_\ell \times S_\ell$ | 0.04 | 0.612 | 0.06 |
| $R_\ell \times S_\ell$ | −0.59 | 0.289 | −2.05 | $R_\ell \times T_q \times S_\ell$ | 0.01 | 0.612 | 0.02 |
| $T_\ell \times S_\ell$ | −0.03 | 0.289 | −0.09 | $R_\ell \times T_\ell \times S_q$ | 0.01 | 0.612 | 0.02 |
| $R_\ell \times T_\ell \times S_\ell$ | −0.04 | 0.354 | −0.11 | $R_q \times T_q \times S_\ell$ | 0.19 | 1.061 | 0.18 |
| $R_q \times T_\ell$ | −0.13 | 0.5 | −0.25 | $R_q \times T_\ell \times S_q$ | 0.19 | 1.061 | 0.18 |
| $R_q \times S_\ell$ | −0.48 | 0.5 | −0.95 | $R_\ell \times T_q \times S_q$ | 0.26 | 1.061 | 0.25 |
| $R_\ell \times T_q$ | −0.03 | 0.5 | −0.05 | $R_q \times T_q \times S_q$ | 0.24 | 1.837 | 0.13 |

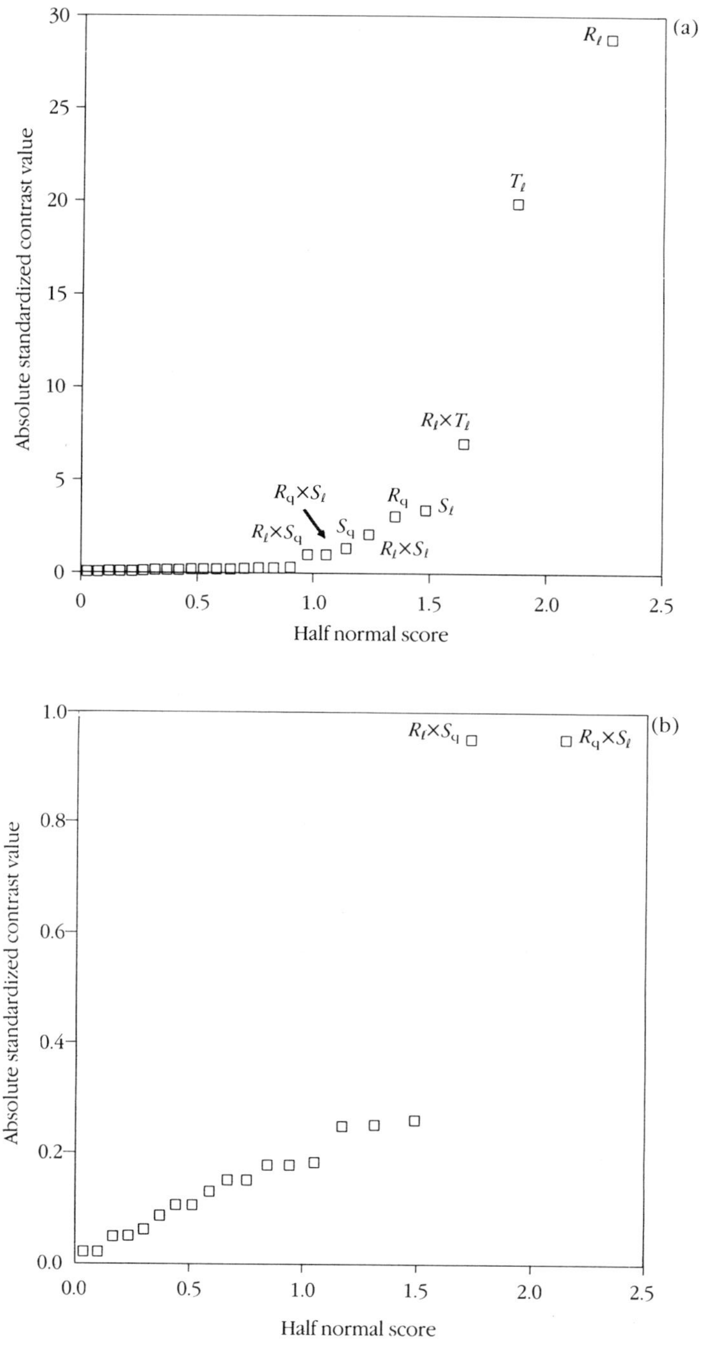


*Fig. 5.9* The fuel flow data in Table 5.9. (a) Daniel plot of 26 contrasts; (b) Daniel plot of 19 contrasts

because of rounding error in this simple illustration. The $k$ values vary quite considerably, showing how important it is to standardize before plotting.

A Daniel plot of the 26 standardized contrasts is shown in Fig. 5.9(a). Figure 5.9(b) results from removing the largest nine contrasts and re-plotting (see Appendix 3.1 for important remarks about re-plotting). Our interpretation of the plots is as follows:

- Of the effects that appear in the second-order equation, $R_\ell$, $T_\ell$, $R_\ell \times T_\ell$, $S_\ell$, $R_q$, $R_\ell \times S_\ell$, and $S_q$ appear to be active.
- The $T_q$ and $T_\ell \times S_\ell$ contrasts plot 'on the line' so the terms in $(T^2 - \frac{2}{3})$ and $TS$ could probably be omitted from the second-order equation.
- All eight components of the three-way interaction fall 'on the line'. This is a relief, because three-way effects are very difficult to interpret in a useful way.
- Because the $R_q \times S_\ell$ and $R_\ell \times S_q$ effects appear to be active, there is evidence that the second-order equation could be improved as a predictor of fuel flow.

Following on from the last point, one modification to the equation that would be simple to make is the addition of terms in $R^2S$ and $RS^2$. However, before making the equation more complicated (i.e. increasing from second to third order), we would prefer to explore the possibility of *transforming* either the response $y$ or the factors $R$, $T$ and $S$. We will look at the idea of transforming the response in Chapters 8 and 10 and discuss transforming the factors generally in Chapter 11.

## Analysis of variance

It is possible to construct an analysis-of-variance table for factors at three levels in much the same way as was done for the two-level case in Chapter 3. It is very convenient that each contrast has an associated contribution to $SS_T$ given by the formula

$$\text{contribution to } SS_T = (\text{standardized contrast})^2 \qquad [5.9]$$

where the standardized contrast is given by equation [5.8]. In fact, calculating the contribution from a two-level contrast using equation [3.2] is a special case of equation [5.9].

Since in the three-level case we plot the *standardized* contrast values rather than the *actual* contrast values, the normal plots can be considered as graphical analysis of variance. As in the two-level case we can use the normal plot to guide us as to which contrasts to use to estimate $\sigma$, the standard deviation of the random part of the data. As before, these contrasts are the ones that form a straight line pointing at the origin. In Fig. 5.9(b), 17 contrasts form a reasonable straight line, and these are good candidates to 'pool' to form the sum of squares $SS_\sigma$. The numerical values of the standardized contrasts were given in Table 5.10, and if we square and sum the smallest 17 of them we get a total of 0.3876. An estimate of $\sigma$ is given as usual (see equation [3.3]) by $\hat{\sigma} = \sqrt{(0.3876/17)} = 0.151$.

The contributions of the other standardized contrasts can be calculated from [5.9] and then measured against $\sigma$ using an $F$ ratio defined as

$$F \text{ ratio} = \frac{(\text{standardized contrast})^2}{SS_\sigma/f_\sigma} = \frac{(\text{standardized contrast})^2}{\hat{\sigma}^2}$$

This is exactly the equation we had in Chapter 3.

The calculations are summarized (to two decimal places) in Table 5.11. The 5% critical value for the $F(1,17)$ distribution is 4.45, and the nine $F$ ratios in Table 5.11 easily exceed this number.

*Table 5.11* Analysis of variance for the fuel flow data

| Source | Degrees of freedom | Contribution to $SS_T$ | $F$ ratio |
|---|---|---|---|
| $R_\ell$ | 1 | 828.25 | 36327 |
| $T_\ell$ | 1 | 394.81 | 17316 |
| $R_\ell \times T_\ell$ | 1 | 48.40 | 2123 |
| $S_\ell$ | 1 | 11.52 | 505 |
| $R_q$ | 1 | 9.21 | 404 |
| $R_\ell \times S_\ell$ | 1 | 4.20 | 184 |
| $S_q$ | 1 | 1.64 | 72 |
| $R_q \times S_\ell$ | 1 | 0.90 | 40 |
| $R_\ell \times S_q$ | 1 | 0.90 | 40 |
| Contrasts 'on the line' | 17 | 0.39 | |
| Total | 26 | 1300.21 | |

**Standardizing contrasts**

Standardizing contrasts is an easy development within the worksheet. The contrast coefficients, the divisor and the contrast values all play a part. To establish the constant $k$ in equation [5.8], proceed as follows. The sum of squares of coefficients in the contrast column can be calculated easily if the spreadsheet has the ability to calculate a *variance* of a set of numbers. Since the coefficients in a contrast *always* sum to zero, then the 'average contrast coefficient' is zero. Hence the variance of the contrast coefficients is equal to the sum of squares divided by $n$ or $(n - 1)$, where $n$ is the number of coefficients in the contrast (the number of runs in the experiment). With the divisor, $k$ can now be calculated and each contrast standardized accordingly.

Calculating the contribution that each contrast makes to the total sum of squares, equation [5.9], is then a simple matter of squaring the standardized contrast value.

## The fitted second-order equation

Using the unstandardized contrast values from Table 5.10, the full second-order equation is

$$y = 13.10 + 6.78R + 4.68T - 0.80S + 1.24(R^2 - \tfrac{2}{3}) + 0.11(T^2 - \tfrac{2}{3}) + 0.52(S^2 - \tfrac{2}{3}) + 2.01RT - 0.59RS - 0.03TS \qquad [5.10]$$

which can be tidied up to look like this:

$$y = 11.85 + 6.78R + 4.68T - 0.80S + 1.24R^2 + 0.11T^2 + 0.52S^2 + 2.01RT - 0.59RS - 0.03TS \qquad [5.11]$$

It is possible to go directly from the contrasts to [5.11], using the fact that in the tidied-up equation the intercept is

$$\bar{y} - \tfrac{2}{3}(\text{sum of quadratic contrasts})$$

The one disadvantage of [5.11] is that it is easy to forget that if a term is dropped it may be necessary to re-calculate the intercept. Suppose, for example, that we are guided by the normal plot and drop the terms in $(T^2 - \frac{2}{3})$ and $TS$. Working from [5.10], the correctly simplified equation is

$$y = 13.10 + 6.78R + 4.68T - 0.80S + 1.24(R^2 - \tfrac{2}{3}) + 0.52(S^2 - \tfrac{2}{3}) + 2.01RT - 0.59RS$$

or

$$y = 11.93 + 6.78R + 4.68T - 0.80S + 1.24R^2 + 0.52S^2 + 2.01RT - 0.59RS \qquad [5.12]$$

Simply dropping $T^2$ and $TS$ from [5.11] will not produce the correct intercept, although the difference is of no great importance in this case.

## Analysis of residuals

Although the Daniel plot suggested that two terms could be omitted from the complete second-order equation, the ultimate test of any prediction equation is its performance in predicting the response at factor levels that were not used in the experiment. In Chapter 6 we will present some additional fuel flow data, which can be used to compare the predictions from different equations. Meanwhile, there is one further method of using the data from the experiment to assess the equation. For any configuration included in the experiment the *residual* is defined as

(actual $y$ value) − (predicted $y$ value)

When looked at in detail, residuals have quite complicated statistical properties. In particular:

- The residuals are correlated with each other, because all the data contribute to the calculation of predicted values.
- Some residuals are inherently more variable than others, just like contrasts.

Roughly speaking, the correlation between residuals is a function of the ratio of the number of terms in the prediction equation to the amount of data available for fitting the equation. We are not in a position to state a general rule of thumb, but we are wary of plotting residuals when the number of terms in the equation is more than 25% of the number of distinct configurations in the experiment. In the case of equation [5.12] there are eight terms and 27 configurations, so we must proceed with caution.

The second problem with residuals can be overcome by standardization (see, for example, Ryan *et al.* 1985). For the types of experimental plan in this book, standardization does not make a great deal of difference to the plots and we will ignore this complication.

In general statistical work residual plots are used for many different purposes, including:

- identification of individual points for which prediction is particularly poor — this may indicate a problem with the data rather than with the equation (see Section 6.3 for an example);
- detection of systematic lack of fit, for example a tendency for over-prediction of low and high $y$ values, with under-prediction in between.

The latter problem would show up in a scatter plot of residuals versus predicted values. For a successful equation the bulk of the points form a horizontal band across the plot. Systematic lack of fit is indicated when the band seems to have a curve in it. No such problem is evident in Fig. 5.10, which is based on equation [5.12].

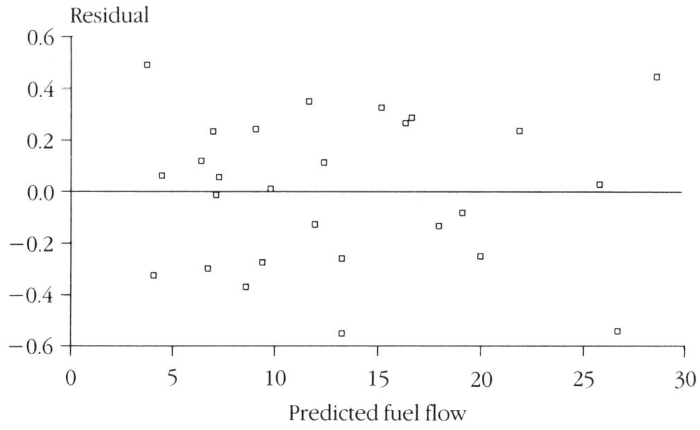


*Fig. 5.10* The fuel flow data in Table 5.9. Plot of residuals against predictions from equation [5.12]

A connection between the analysis of residuals and the methods of statistical process control is made in Section 6.3.

## 5.4 FRACTIONAL PLANS FOR THREE-LEVEL FACTORS

The ideas introduced in Sections 5.2 and 5.3 can be applied to any number of factors at three levels, provided every possible combination is run. For $k$ factors, $3^k$ runs are needed, so, even with only four factors, 81 runs are required. The incentive to use a *fractional* plan is even stronger here than it is in the two-level case. There are several distinct types of three-level fractional plan; in this chapter we discuss plans based on three-level orthogonal arrays and plans given by taking a two-level design and adding a run (or runs) with all factors at level (0).

The simplest three-level orthogonal array is the $L_9(3^4)$ array in Table 5.1. Another is the $L_{27}(3^{13})$ array, which is given in Table 5.12. It has 13 columns and can therefore be used to study up to 13 three-level factors. The complete factorial plan shown in Table 5.9 can be seen as a simple example of the use of this array, with the three factors $R$, $T$ and $S$ allocated to columns 1, 2 and 5, respectively. If a fourth factor is allocated we have a one-third fraction of a full $3^4$ plan. If the fourth factor is allocated to column 9, it can be shown that all main effects and linear by linear interactions are separately estimable, in other words that $L_{27}(3^{13})$ provides enough information to fit a second order prediction equation in four factors. This point is taken up in Chapter 6.

If a fifth factor is added it is no longer possible to estimate all the terms in the second-order equation. As with all orthogonal arrays, the pattern of confounding becomes more complicated as further factors are added. Moreover $L_{27}(3^{13})$ shares with the Plackett–Burman arrays $L_{12}(2^{11})$, $L_{20}(2^{19})$, etc., the characteristic that any one interaction may be confounded with several main effects, so disentangling the information is virtually impossible.

As a specific comparison we note that when there are seven factors some main effects are confounded with three interaction terms, whereas the much smaller $L_{16}(2^{15})$ array can accommodate eight factors while keeping all main effects clear of interactions. The three-level array has the potential to provide information about non-linear effects, but at the cost of a much higher degree of confounding, as well as a larger number of runs. For this reason, a two-level array would normally be preferred for screening purposes, reserving the three-level plans for situations in which the experimenters have had the chance to screen out the unimportant factors, leaving a short list (generally not more than five) of factors that deserve closer study at three or more levels. It is then easier to justify the relatively high ratio of runs to factors that is required to fit a second-order equation. For further details of fitting prediction equations from three-level (and some five-level) fractional plans, see Chapter 6.

*Table 5.12* The $L_{27}(3^{13})$ array

| Row | | | | | | | | | | | | | |
|---|---|---|---|---|---|---|---|---|---|---|---|---|---|
| 1 | − | − | − | − | − | − | − | − | − | − | − | − | − |
| 2 | − | − | − | − | 0 | 0 | 0 | 0 | 0 | 0 | 0 | 0 | 0 |
| 3 | − | − | − | − | + | + | + | + | + | + | + | + | + |
| 4 | − | 0 | 0 | 0 | − | − | − | 0 | 0 | 0 | + | + | + |
| 5 | − | 0 | 0 | 0 | 0 | 0 | 0 | + | + | + | − | − | − |
| 6 | − | 0 | 0 | 0 | + | + | + | − | − | − | 0 | 0 | 0 |
| 7 | − | + | + | + | − | − | − | + | + | + | 0 | 0 | 0 |
| 8 | − | + | + | + | 0 | 0 | 0 | − | − | − | + | + | + |
| 9 | − | + | + | + | + | + | + | 0 | 0 | 0 | − | − | − |
| 10 | 0 | − | 0 | + | − | 0 | + | − | 0 | + | − | 0 | + |
| 11 | 0 | − | 0 | + | 0 | + | − | 0 | + | − | 0 | + | − |
| 12 | 0 | − | 0 | + | + | − | 0 | + | − | 0 | + | − | 0 |
| 13 | 0 | 0 | + | − | − | 0 | + | 0 | + | − | + | − | 0 |
| 14 | 0 | 0 | + | − | 0 | + | − | + | − | 0 | − | 0 | + |
| 15 | 0 | 0 | + | − | + | − | 0 | − | 0 | + | 0 | + | − |
| 16 | 0 | + | − | 0 | − | 0 | + | + | − | 0 | 0 | + | − |
| 17 | 0 | + | − | 0 | 0 | + | − | − | 0 | + | + | − | 0 |
| 18 | 0 | + | − | 0 | + | − | 0 | 0 | + | − | − | 0 | + |
| 19 | + | − | + | 0 | − | + | 0 | − | + | 0 | − | + | 0 |
| 20 | + | − | + | 0 | 0 | − | + | 0 | − | + | 0 | − | + |
| 21 | + | − | + | 0 | + | 0 | − | + | 0 | − | + | 0 | − |
| 22 | + | 0 | − | + | − | + | 0 | 0 | − | + | + | 0 | − |
| 23 | + | 0 | − | + | 0 | − | + | + | 0 | − | − | + | 0 |
| 24 | + | 0 | − | + | + | 0 | − | − | + | 0 | 0 | − | + |
| 25 | + | + | 0 | − | − | + | 0 | + | 0 | − | 0 | − | + |
| 26 | + | + | 0 | − | 0 | − | + | − | + | 0 | + | 0 | − |
| 27 | + | + | 0 | − | + | 0 | − | 0 | − | + | − | + | 0 |

If the reader is in the unusual situation of being able to ignore interactions with a high level of confidence, or wishes to use the array in the prediction/confirmation mode that we attributed to Taguchi in Section 4.2, a set of main effect contrasts, both linear and quadratic, is given by applying the re-coding formulae [5.3] and [5.4] to each column of $L_{27}(3^{13})$ in turn. Rather than write out all 26 contrasts, we will apply the same idea to the smaller array $L_9(3^4)$ given in Table 5.1. If factors $A$, $B$, $C$, and $D$, say, are allocated to the four columns of the array, [5.3] and [5.4] generate the set of contrasts shown in Table 5.13.

The columns in Table 5.13 are all orthogonal, so we have used our full 'allowance' of eight orthogonal contrasts from nine runs. We have labelled the contrasts $A_\ell$, $A_q$, etc., but as with any three-level saturated plan, an active interaction will bias several main effects. The divisor is 6 here, calculated in the usual way by counting the number of $\pm 1$s. The reader may like to apply these contrasts to the flywheel data, as an exercise. In that example factor $A$ was qualitative, but its 'linear' and 'quadratic' contrasts can still be given sensible interpretations. $A_\ell$ measures the difference between cavities 1 and 3,

*Table 5.13* Eight contrasts for the $L_9(3^4)$ array

| | $A_\ell$ | $B_\ell$ | $C_\ell$ | $D_\ell$ | $A_q$ | $B_q$ | $C_q$ | $D_q$ |
|---|---|---|---|---|---|---|---|---|
| | −1 | −1 | −1 | −1 | +1 | +1 | +1 | +1 |
| | −1 | 0 | 0 | 0 | +1 | −2 | −2 | −2 |
| | −1 | +1 | +1 | +1 | +1 | +1 | +1 | +1 |
| | 0 | −1 | 0 | +1 | −2 | +1 | −2 | +1 |
| | 0 | 0 | +1 | −1 | −2 | −2 | +1 | +1 |
| | 0 | +1 | −1 | 0 | −2 | +1 | +1 | −2 |
| | +1 | −1 | +1 | 0 | +1 | +1 | +1 | −2 |
| | +1 | 0 | −1 | +1 | +1 | −2 | +1 | +1 |
| | +1 | +1 | 0 | −1 | +1 | +1 | −2 | +1 |
| Divisor | 6 | 6 | 6 | 6 | 6 | 6 | 6 | 6 |

and $A_q$ compares cavity 2 with the average of 1 and 3.

Plans based on the $L_9(3^4)$ array can be laid out in the shape of a square and are often known as Latin squares or Graeco-Latin squares.

## Two levels plus centre point

Table 5.14 consists of five rows from the complete $3^2$ experiment shown in Table 5.4. Because it forms a subset of a complete $3^2$, Table 5.14 is technically a fractional three-level experiment. However, it is more natural to think of it as consisting of the four rows of a complete $2^2$ plan with an additional run made with both factors set midway between their low and high levels, i.e. at the origin or *centre point* of the plan.

*Table 5.14* A small part of the engine mapping experiment

| $R$ | $T$ | Fuel flow |
|---|---|---|
| − | − | 4.2 |
| − | + | 9.3 |
| + | − | 13.0 |
| + | + | 26.1 |
| 0 | 0 | 11.8 |

Table 5.15 shows a set of four orthogonal contrasts. The first three are the contrasts we would have used if there had been no run at the centre point, except that their divisors are now 4 rather than 2 because we are working within the framework of second-order prediction equations. With divisor 4 (number of ±1s) we can compare these contrast values with the $R$, $T$ and $RT$ terms in equation [5.6] (they are quite similar).

The last contrast is labelled 'curvature' because it measures the sum of the quadratic effects of each factor: $R_q + T_q$. Based on the 27 runs in Table 5.9, our estimates of the quadratic effects were 1.24 and 0.11 (see Table 5.10). The value of the curvature contrast is (to two decimal places) just the sum of these, but the *exact* agreement here is a coincidence.

*Table 5.15* Four contrasts for the plan in Table 5.14

| | $R$ | $T$ | $RT$ | Curvature | |
|---|---|---|---|---|---|
| | −1 | −1 | +1 | +1 | 4.2 |
| | −1 | +1 | −1 | +1 | 9.3 |
| | +1 | −1 | −1 | +1 | 13.0 |
| | +1 | +1 | +1 | +1 | 26.1 |
| | 0 | 0 | 0 | −4 | 11.8 |
| Divisor | 4 | 4 | 4 | 4 | |
| Value | 6.40 | 4.55 | 2.00 | 1.35 | |

In other situations, there is no reason why the $R_q$ and $T_q$ effects should not be of roughly equal magnitude but have opposite signs and more or less cancel out, but in some important cases they will have the same sign. Figure 5.11 shows the results of a hypothetical experiment with two factors $x_1$ and $x_2$ which is 'sitting on the top of a hill' in the underlying response surface. Both the quadratic effects are negative in this example. The curvature contrast can be written as

$$\begin{pmatrix}\text{average result at the}\\ \text{four corner points}\end{pmatrix} - \begin{pmatrix}\text{result at}\\ \text{the centre}\end{pmatrix} \qquad [5.13]$$

and in Fig. 5.11 can be expected to be much larger than the other three contrasts.

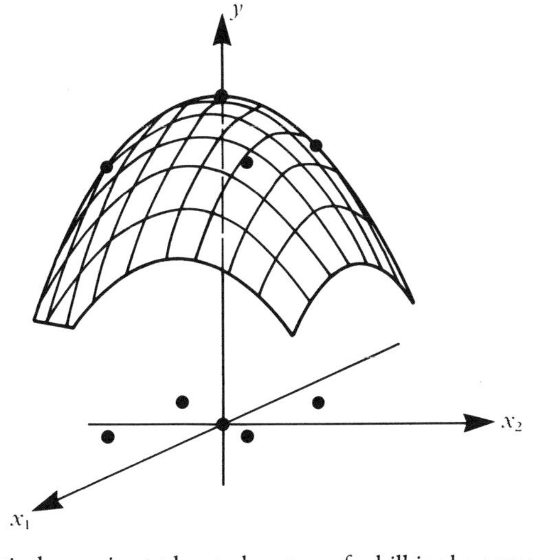


*Fig. 5.11* Hypothetical experiment located on top of a hill in the response surface

We have used a very simple example to introduce this new type of plan but [5.13] is applicable whenever a run at the centre point is added to a two-level plan. As Fig. 5.11 suggests, if the usual two-level contrasts fail to identify any active factors, the experiment may be sitting on the top of a hill or at the bottom of a hollow in terms of the response surface. It will usually be worth making an extra run (or runs) at the centre point to check this out. Note that if the curvature contrast is to be included with the others in a normal plot it is necessary to standardize the contrasts before plotting, using equation [5.8].

Adding an extra run or runs to a basic plan is another example of the idea of *sequential experimentation*, introduced in Chapter 4. The addition of a centre point gives us an indication of whether it is worth continuing experimentation to establish curvature by expanding the experiment from the basic two-level framework to the three-level one. We would do this if a contrast like [5.13] was large.

## Use of the centre point in the engine mapping experiment

In order to illustrate the usefulness of the centre point as a check on quadratic curvature, we return to the engine map experiment, but this time pay attention to the $NO_x$ data. The results are given in Table 5.16, but we have rearranged the rows of the plan for a reason that we will explain later.

Now suppose that we only had the first nine rows in Table 5.16, that is the runs above the horizontal space. This is a full factorial two-level experiment in $R$, $T$, and $S$, *plus* a centre point. These nine runs can be used to generate the eight orthogonal contrasts in Table 5.17.

A formal statistical analysis is unlikely to be successful, because we have only nine contrasts and most of these are likely to measure real effects, leaving very few for 'error'. But since the curvature contrast has the smallest standardized value, smaller even than the third-order effect $R_\ell \times T_\ell \times S_\ell$, we could tentatively fit the following second-order equation, based on the data in the first eight rows of Table 5.16:

$$z = 299.9 + 158.6R + 215.9T + 95.1S + 94.6RT + 60.9RS + 56.1TS$$

Because there are no quadratic terms the intercept is calculated as the average of the first eight results in Table 5.16. The only second-order effects are two-way interactions.

In this particular example we happen to have another 18 runs that can be used to look for evidence of quadratic effects. Figure 5.12 is a half normal plot of the 26 contrasts available from the data in Table 5.16. In this plot only the linear main effects and linear by linear interactions fall a long way off the line. Interestingly, the next largest contrast is associated with the $R_\ell \times T_\ell \times S_\ell$ interaction. Four other contrasts also appear to be slightly off the line, these being, in order of magnitude, $T_q \times S_\ell$, $R_q \times T_\ell$, $R_q$, and $T_\ell \times S_q$. Although these all involve quadratic effects in some way, their magnitude relative to the linear and linear by linear interaction contrasts is very small. The linear and linear

*Table 5.16* The $NO_x$ emission data from the engine mapping experiment

| Original run order | $R$ | $T$ | $S$ | $NO_x$ |
|---|---|---|---|---|
| 1 | − | − | − | 13 |
| 3 | − | − | + | 27 |
| 7 | − | + | − | 201 |
| 9 | − | + | + | 324 |
| 19 | + | − | − | 77 |
| 21 | + | − | + | 219 |
| 25 | + | + | − | 528 |
| 27 | + | + | + | 1010 |
| 14 | 0 | 0 | 0 | 317 |
| 5 | − | 0 | 0 | 126 |
| 23 | + | 0 | 0 | 422 |
| 11 | 0 | − | 0 | 57 |
| 17 | 0 | + | 0 | 598 |
| 13 | 0 | 0 | − | 191 |
| 15 | 0 | 0 | + | 439 |
| 2 | − | − | 0 | 18 |
| 20 | + | − | 0 | 115 |
| 8 | − | + | 0 | 270 |
| 26 | + | + | 0 | 801 |
| 4 | − | 0 | − | 84 |
| 22 | + | 0 | − | 242 |
| 6 | − | 0 | + | 182 |
| 24 | + | 0 | + | 654 |
| 10 | 0 | − | − | 37 |
| 16 | 0 | + | − | 433 |
| 12 | 0 | − | + | 113 |
| 18 | 0 | + | + | 696 |

by linear contrast values are given in Table 5.18. We have also included the $R_\ell \times T_\ell \times S_\ell$ contrast even though it does not contribute to the second-order equation.

The closeness of these contrast values indicates that, if we are going to ignore the quadratic effects, not much is gained by doing a three-level experiment to predict $NO_x$. For completeness, Table 5.19 is the analysis-of-variance table for the 27-run $NO_x$ data. Fifteen contrasts have been judged to lie 'on the line' and pooled to form $SS_\sigma$. The critical 5% point of the $F(1,15)$ distribution is 4.54, and all of the calculated $F$ ratios are bigger than this number. The $F$ tests, like the Daniel plot, suggest the presence of real, but small, quadratic effects.

To recap, the function of the centre point here is to give an early indication of the existence of quadratic curvature, *before* resources are committed to comprehensive experimentation with a third level. Used in this way, centre points can save a lot of experimental time.

*Table 5.17* Eight contrasts based on the first nine rows of the $NO_x$ data

| | $R_\ell$ | $T_\ell$ | $S_\ell$ | $R_\ell \times T_\ell$ | $R_\ell \times S_\ell$ | $T_\ell \times S_\ell$ | $R_\ell \times T_\ell \times S_\ell$ | Curvature | $NO_x$ |
|---|---|---|---|---|---|---|---|---|---|
| | −1 | −1 | −1 | +1 | +1 | +1 | −1 | +1 | 13 |
| | −1 | −1 | +1 | +1 | −1 | −1 | +1 | +1 | 27 |
| | −1 | +1 | −1 | −1 | +1 | −1 | +1 | +1 | 201 |
| | −1 | +1 | +1 | −1 | −1 | +1 | −1 | +1 | 324 |
| | +1 | −1 | −1 | −1 | −1 | +1 | +1 | +1 | 77 |
| | +1 | −1 | +1 | −1 | +1 | −1 | −1 | +1 | 219 |
| | +1 | +1 | −1 | +1 | −1 | −1 | −1 | +1 | 528 |
| | +1 | +1 | +1 | +1 | +1 | +1 | +1 | +1 | 1010 |
| | 0 | 0 | 0 | 0 | 0 | 0 | 0 | −8 | 317 |
| Divisor | 8 | 8 | 8 | 8 | 8 | 8 | 8 | 8 | |
| Value | 158.63 | 215.88 | 95.13 | 94.63 | 60.88 | 56.13 | 28.88 | −17.13 | |
| Standardized value | 448.66 | 610.59 | 269.05 | 267.64 | 172.18 | 158.75 | 81.67 | −16.15 | |

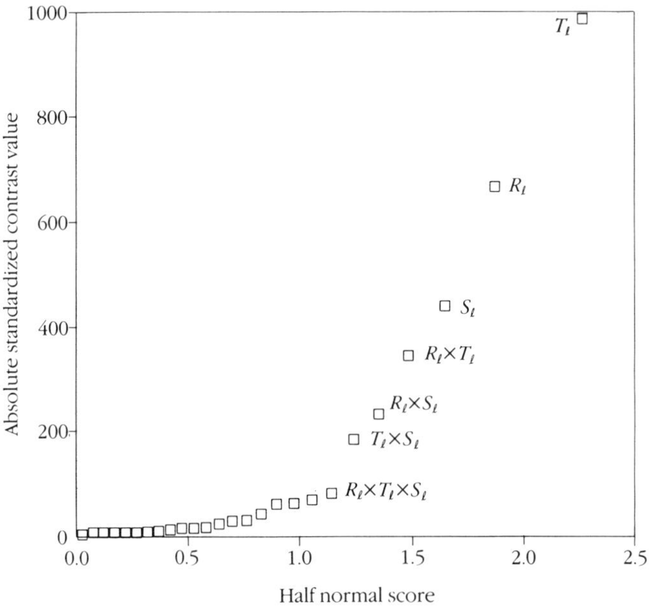


*Fig. 5.12* $NO_x$ data in Table 5.16. Daniel plot of 26 contrasts

*Table 5.18* A comparison of contrast values for the $NO_x$ data

| Contrast name | Calculated from the first nine runs | Calculated from all 27 runs |
|---|---|---|
| $R_\ell$ | 158.63 | 156.83 |
| $T_\ell$ | 215.88 | 232.50 |
| $S_\ell$ | 95.13 | 103.22 |
| $R_\ell \times T_\ell$ | 94.63 | 99.25 |
| $R_\ell \times S_\ell$ | 60.88 | 66.75 |
| $T_\ell \times S_\ell$ | 56.13 | 53.00 |
| $R_\ell \times T_\ell \times S_\ell$ | 28.88 | 28.88 |
| (Intercept | 299.87 | 303.48) |

## Hill climbing

In some applications our purpose is not simply to *map* and predict the response over a pre-specified region. We may want to be able to locate a maximum or a minimum on the surface, starting with only a vague idea of where this point is. We will have to *move* to the maximum after doing some experiments to establish the nature of the surface in the surrounding region.

Suppose we are experimenting on the surface whose contours are

*Table 5.19* Analysis-of-variance table for the $NO_x$ data

| Source | Degrees of freedom | Contribution to $SS_T$ | $F$ ratio |
|---|---|---|---|
| $T_\ell$ | 1 | 973012.50 | 4080.8 |
| $R_\ell$ | 1 | 442740.50 | 1856.8 |
| $S_\ell$ | 1 | 191786.89 | 804.4 |
| $R_\ell \times T_\ell$ | 1 | 118206.75 | 495.8 |
| $R_\ell \times S_\ell$ | 1 | 53466.75 | 224.2 |
| $T_\ell \times S_\ell$ | 1 | 33708.00 | 141.4 |
| $R_\ell \times T_\ell \times S_\ell$ | 1 | 6670.13 | 28.0 |
| $T_q \times S_\ell$ | 1 | 4807.11 | 20.2 |
| $R_q \times T_\ell$ | 1 | 3906.25 | 16.4 |
| $R_q$ | 1 | 3373.35 | 15.7 |
| $T_\ell \times S_q$ | 1 | 1764.00 | 7.4 |
| Contrasts 'on the line' | 15 | 3576.51 | $\Rightarrow \hat{\sigma} = 15.4$ |
| Total | 26 | 1837378.74 | |

illustrated in Fig. 5.13(a), and we wish to locate the maximum by varying the two factors $x_1$ and $x_2$. The first experiment is conducted, say, in the bottom left of the picture. This initial experiment might well be a complete $2^2$ with a centre point. The $2^2$ part of the experiment will show up strong main effects and an interaction but the centre point will indicate that quadratic curvature is slight, which in turn implies that we are a long way from the top of the hill.

Now, given that we are on the side of the hill, the shortest distance to the top is to follow a path at right angles to the contours — this means doing a sequence of 'single-run experiments' along the straight line indicated in Fig. 5.13(b). This is the hill climbing aspect of experimentation. As we follow this path, the response will initially increase, and then, as we pass close to the maximum, start to decrease. At this point, we can conduct further experimentation to examine the surface in detail, for example a $3^2$ experiment to produce a prediction equation for $y$ in this region (Fig. 5.13(c)). The maximum can then be located fairly accurately.

Further details of hill climbing are given by Box *et al.* (1978) and by Box and Draper (1987).

## SUMMARY OF CHAPTER 5

Response tables and plots can be constructed from balanced three-level experiments. The main effect of each factor now has two components. When a factor is quantitative these two components can be characterized in terms of linear and non-linear (quadratic) effects. The corresponding contrasts provide

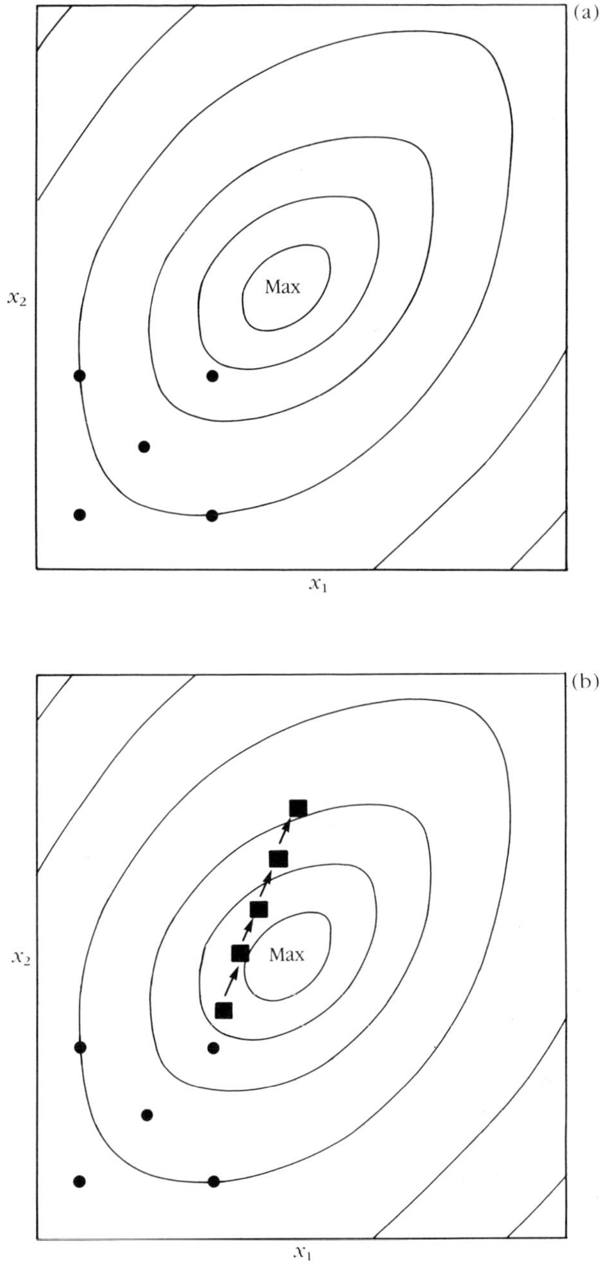


*Fig. 5.13* Hill climbing. (a) Initial experiment; (b) a sequence of single runs; (c) locating the maximum

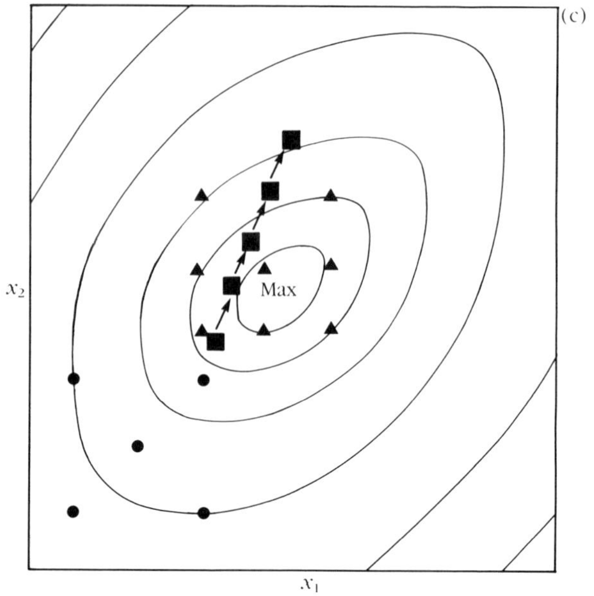


*Fig. 5.13* contd

the coefficients in a quadratic prediction equation.

When the experiment is a complete factorial, different aspects of each two-way interaction can be measured by four separate contrasts. A prediction equation and response surface can be constructed that exactly reproduce the data, but a simpler second-order (quadratic) equation is often found to fit the data reasonably well and to give effective predictions at intermediate points. The only form of interaction allowed for in a second-order prediction equation is linear by linear. The coefficients are generated by a subset of the contrasts, and the remaining contrasts can be used to check the adequacy of the second-order model. A Daniel plot of all the contrasts helps us to decide whether any terms could be removed from the prediction equation, and provides a way of judging the size of the checking contrasts.

Contrasts must be standardized before plotting. The analysis of variance introduced in Chapter 3 can easily be extended to the three-level case, and the contribution to $SS_T$ from an individual contrast is the square of the standardized contrast.

Second-order equations can be written in two alternative forms. If the 'tidy' form is used it must be remembered that the deletion of any of the quadratic terms will affect the intercept.

Residual plots are another useful method of model checking. If residuals are plotted against predictions the ideal plot would have points scattered at random in a horizontal band.

Complete three-level experiments for four or more factors are very large. Fractional plans can be based on the orthogonal arrays $L_9(3^4)$ and $L_{27}(3^{13})$.

The patterns of confounding are very complicated and for this reason it is usually better to employ two-level factors in screening experiments. If a run at the centre point is added to a two-level plan a 'curvature' contrast is available, which measures the sum of the quadratic main effects of all the factors. If this is the largest absolute effect it suggests that the experiment may be located at a local maximum or minimum of the response surface. If the curvature contrast is small it may not be worth committing resources to a comprehensive three-level experiment. These ideas are useful in hill climbing problems.

CHAPTER 6

# Plans for fitting second-order equations

*In Chapter 5 we introduced the idea of fitting a response surface and prediction equation to a set of experimental data, and we suggested that the* second-order *equations are particularly useful in practice. In this chapter we present some plans that provide all the information required to fit a second-order equation, as well as some third-order checking contrasts, using fewer runs than a full three-level experiment. We briefly describe the situations in which five-level factors are useful. These topics are often referred to as* response surface methods.

*The other main purpose of this chapter is to explain how the method of* multiple regression *can be used as a short-cut to some of the statistical output. It provides the coefficients for the prediction equation, and can be adapted to provide standardized contrasts for plotting. It can be used to* re-fit *the prediction equation, omitting either selected terms or selected data values, or both. We show how the analysis of residuals, introduced in Chapter 5, can be helpful in pointing to individual response values that may be in error, and in deciding whether or not to include a particular term in the prediction equation.*

*Some readers may feel that, in comparison with other chapters, this one represents a 'change of gear'. The reader who has no immediate need to understand this material can safely pass over it, with very little effect on their appreciation and understanding of subsequent chapters.*

## 6.1 A PLAN FOR THREE FACTORS

When there are three three-level factors we can picture the 27 runs of the full $3^3$ experiment as in Fig. 6.1, with each factor defining one dimension of the three-dimensional *factor space*. Thinking of the experimental region as a shape in three dimensions provides a geometric perspective to the idea of

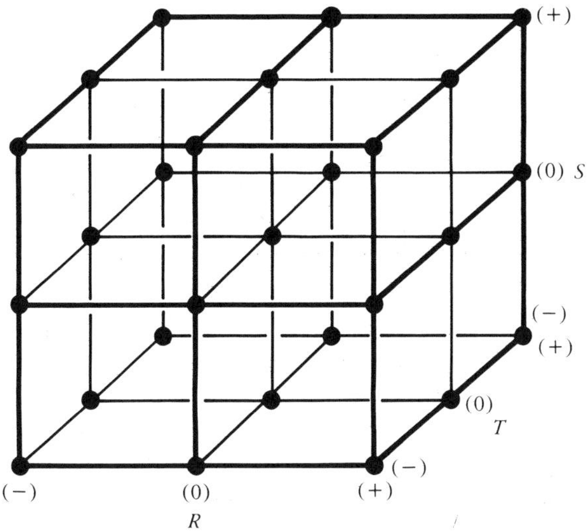


*Fig. 6.1* A full $3^3$ design pictured in three dimensions. The engine mapping factors are shown as an example

experimental design. Of course, for the case of more than three factors it is difficult to imagine the experimental region as a shape, but the principles remain the same.

Choosing a fractional plan means deleting certain points from the full 27, and the theory of experimental design is concerned with ensuring that this deletion is done in a systematic and balanced way. Figure 6.2 shows the set of points that remain if we delete the point in the middle of each of the 12 edges of the cube. It consists of (i) the eight corners of the cube, (ii) the centre point and (iii) a point in the middle of each face; when these latter points are joined together in pairs, as shown in the picture, they form a shape akin to a three-dimensional *star*. They are also known as axial points because the lines joining them, when extended, form a set of three orthogonal axes for the figure.

The 15-point plan is called *composite* because it can be built up from more than one regular geometrical figure. The plan as a whole has a pleasing symmetry and balance, and like the full cube its centre of gravity is at the origin; it is known as a *central* composite plan or design.

## Engine mapping example (continued from Chapter 5)

To illustrate the practical application of the composite plan we return to the engine mapping data. The 15 points shown in Fig. 6.2 are listed in Table 6.1 with a value for fuel flow. These are a subset of the 27 runs shown in Table 5.9, but written in a different order to show the composite structure of the design.

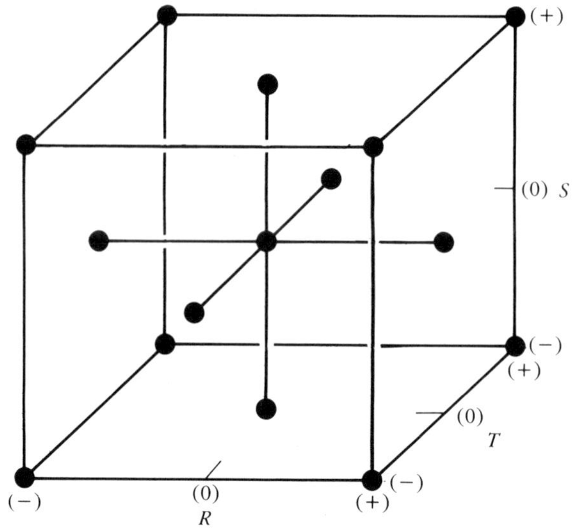


*Fig. 6.2* Central composite plan for three factors. Again, the engine mapping factors are shown as an example

The second-order equation based on just these 15 configurations is given by

$$y = 11.87 + 6.89R + 4.71T - 0.84S + 1.21R^2 + 0.21T^2 + 0.46S^2 + 2.01RT - 0.59RS - 0.01TS \qquad [6.1]$$

*Table 6.1* A 15-run fractional three-factor (central composite) plan

| Speed R | Torque T | Spark S | Fuel flow |
|---|---|---|---|
| − | − | − | 4.5 |
| + | − | − | 15.5 |
| − | + | − | 9.8 |
| + | + | − | 29.0 |
| − | − | + | 3.7 |
| + | − | + | 12.5 |
| − | + | + | 9.1 |
| + | + | + | 25.8 |
| 0 | 0 | 0 | 11.8 |
| − | 0 | 0 | 6.5 |
| + | 0 | 0 | 19.7 |
| 0 | − | 0 | 7.3 |
| 0 | + | 0 | 16.9 |
| 0 | 0 | − | 12.7 |
| 0 | 0 | + | 12.0 |

*Table 6.2* Nine contrasts for the plan in Table 6.1

| | $R_\ell$ | $T_\ell$ | $S_\ell$ | $R_q$ | $T_q$ | $S_q$ | $R_\ell \times T_\ell$ | $R_\ell \times S_\ell$ | $T_\ell \times S_\ell$ |
|---|---|---|---|---|---|---|---|---|---|
| | −1 | −1 | −1 | +1 | +1 | +1 | +1 | +1 | +1 |
| | +1 | −1 | −1 | +1 | +1 | +1 | −1 | −1 | +1 |
| | −1 | +1 | −1 | +1 | +1 | +1 | −1 | +1 | −1 |
| | +1 | +1 | −1 | +1 | +1 | +1 | +1 | −1 | −1 |
| | −1 | −1 | +1 | +1 | +1 | +1 | +1 | −1 | −1 |
| | +1 | −1 | +1 | +1 | +1 | +1 | −1 | +1 | −1 |
| | −1 | +1 | +1 | +1 | +1 | +1 | −1 | −1 | +1 |
| | +1 | +1 | +1 | +1 | +1 | +1 | +1 | +1 | +1 |
| | 0 | 0 | 0 | −2 | −2 | −2 | 0 | 0 | 0 |
| | −1 | 0 | 0 | +5 | −4 | −4 | 0 | 0 | 0 |
| | +1 | 0 | 0 | +5 | −4 | −4 | 0 | 0 | 0 |
| | 0 | −1 | 0 | −4 | +5 | −4 | 0 | 0 | 0 |
| | 0 | +1 | 0 | −4 | +5 | −4 | 0 | 0 | 0 |
| | 0 | 0 | −1 | −4 | −4 | +5 | 0 | 0 | 0 |
| | 0 | 0 | +1 | −4 | −4 | +5 | 0 | 0 | 0 |
| Divisor | 10 | 10 | 10 | 18 | 18 | 18 | 8 | 8 | 8 |
| Value | 6.89 | 4.71 | −0.84 | 1.21 | 0.21 | 0.46 | 2.01 | −0.59 | −0.01 |
| Standardized value | 21.79 | 14.89 | −2.66 | 1.93 | 0.33 | 0.73 | 5.66 | −1.66 | −0.04 |

Notice that equation [6.1] is very similar to [5.11], which was derived from the full set of 27 runs. Apart from the intercept, the coefficients in [6.1] are given by the values of the nine contrasts in Table 6.2. As in Chapter 5, the intercept is given by

$$\bar{y} - \tfrac{2}{3}(\text{sum of quadratic coefficients})$$

The linear and interaction contrasts are given by the same rules as in Chapter 5, but the quadratic contrasts are not. We will not attempt to prove that the $R_q$, $T_q$ and $S_q$ contrasts given in Table 6.2 are the best ones to use in this new type of plan, or even that they provide valid measures of the different quadratic effects. The columns in Table 6.2 can be derived from the general theory of least squares — in other words, it can be proved that of all the possible second-order equations the one with coefficients generated by Table 6.2 has *the smallest sum of squared residuals*, and therefore fits the data best in a well defined mathematical sense.

If we were to follow the pattern of analysis set out in Section 5.3 we would form a normal plot from a set of 14 (number of runs minus one) orthogonal contrasts: the nine contrasts in Table 6.2 and five contrasts that measure effects which are not included in the second-order equation [6.1]. These extra contrasts allow us to check the usefulness of the second-order model — if any of them are large, this is an indication that the second-order model could be improved.

Note, however, that in this new example the contrasts in Table 6.2 do not form an orthogonal set. In fact, each of the three 'quadratic' contrast columns is correlated with the other two. This can be checked as usual by computing the inner product of one of the quadratic contrasts with all the other columns. The result is zero for all columns *except another quadratic contrast* when the answer is −36. Because of this, it is said that the plan in Table 6.1 is not completely orthogonal with respect to the second-order model. The normal plot method is then, strictly speaking, invalid. For the moment we choose to ignore this complication on the grounds that the non-orthogonality affects only a small group of contrasts.

Despite the non-orthogonality among three of the nine contrasts of Table 6.2 it is still true that at most five extra contrasts — checking contrasts (CC) — can be chosen so that they are orthogonal to each other and to those in Table 6.2. One set is shown in Table 6.3 and interpreted as follows.

$CC_1/CC_2/CC_3$: These contrasts look very similar to the plan matrix itself, and the linear contrasts of Table 6.2, with the sign of the ±1s matching the first eight rows of the plan. The 'star' points are taken with weight 4 and with the signs reversed. This ensures that $CC_1/CC_2/CC_3$ are orthogonal to the linear contrasts and all the others. These contrasts actually measure combinations of third-order effects. For example, $CC_1$ can be thought of as measuring $R_\ell \times T_q + R_\ell \times S_q$. As a more direct interpretation, it looks for a difference between the linear effect of $R$ calculated from the corners of the plan, and the linear effect calculated from the star points. For a detailed explanation of how checking contrasts are constructed, see Box and Draper (1987).

**Detecting non-orthogonality of contrasts**

Non-orthogonality between contrasts can easily be detected by performing the transposition and matrix multiplication procedures detailed in Section 5.2. If any contrasts are not orthogonal, this will show in the final matrix as a non-zero number off the leading diagonal. The position of the non-zero entry indicates which two contrasts are not orthogonal. For example, if the third row of the fifth column of the final matrix (also the fifth row of the third column because the final matrix is symmetrical) is non-zero then the third and fifth contrasts, counting from the left, of the contrast set as written in the worksheet, are not orthogonal. Thus the set of non-orthogonal contrasts can be identified very quickly.

This method is also a useful way of checking whether or not a mistake has been made in typing in the contrasts in the first place.

*Table 6.3* Five checking contrasts for the plan in Table 6.1

| | $CC_1$ | $CC_2$ | $CC_3$ | $CC_4$ | $CC_5$ |
|---|---|---|---|---|---|
| | −1 | −1 | −1 | −1 | −1 |
| | +1 | −1 | −1 | +1 | −1 |
| | −1 | +1 | −1 | +1 | −1 |
| | +1 | +1 | −1 | −1 | −1 |
| | −1 | −1 | +1 | +1 | −1 |
| | +1 | −1 | +1 | −1 | −1 |
| | −1 | +1 | +1 | −1 | −1 |
| | +1 | +1 | +1 | +1 | −1 |
| | 0 | 0 | 0 | 0 | −16 |
| | +4 | 0 | 0 | 0 | +4 |
| | −4 | 0 | 0 | 0 | +4 |
| | 0 | +4 | 0 | 0 | +4 |
| | 0 | −4 | 0 | 0 | +4 |
| | 0 | 0 | +4 | 0 | +4 |
| | 0 | 0 | −4 | 0 | +4 |
| Divisor | 8 | 8 | 8 | 8 | 8 |
| Value | 0.36 | −0.11 | −0.61 | −0.04 | 0.21 |
| Standardized value | 0.46 | −0.14 | −0.77 | −0.11 | 0.09 |

$CC_4$: This contrast is obtained directly by multiplying the contrast coefficients of $A_\ell$, $B_\ell$ and $C_\ell$ from Table 6.2, and so $CC_4$ measures the three-factor $A_\ell \times B_\ell \times C_\ell$ interaction.

$CC_5$: This is likely to be the least useful checking contrast, partly because it is a measure of $A_q \times B_q \times C_q$, a *sixth-order* effect, and also because it gives so much weight to a single result (the run at the centre point).

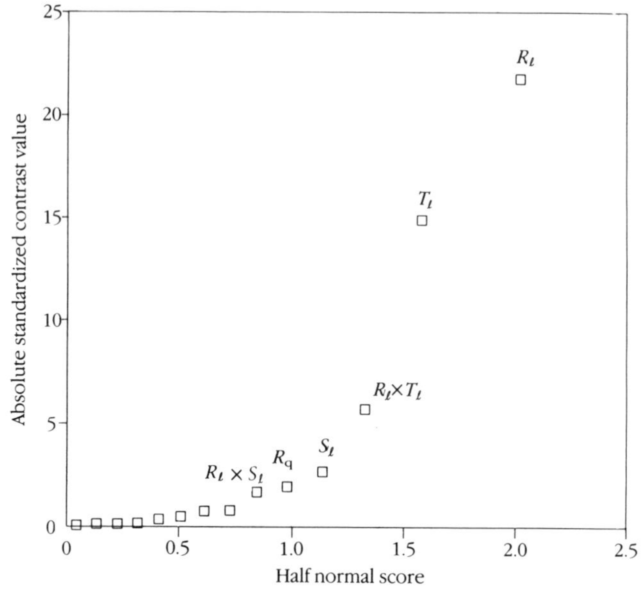


*Fig. 6.3* The fuel flow data in Table 6.1. Daniel plot of 14 standardized contrasts

After standardization using equation [5.8] we get the Daniel plot shown in Fig. 6.3. Three points clearly stand away from the line. Removing them and re-plotting gives Fig. 6.4(a), and removing a further three points gives Fig. 6.4(b). We still do not have a convincing straight line and we will comment on this below. Comparing Fig. 6.4(b) with Fig. 5.9(a) we see that when we look at only 15 of the 27 runs the evidence for a quadratic effect of $S$ is much less clear, and the message of the two prominent checking contrasts is more ambiguous. In general, reducing the number of runs carries the possible penalty that we may not be able to detect some of the smaller effects, but this has to be weighed against the gain of having to do less experimentation.

## Estimating σ

In Chapters 3 and 5 we were able to calculate an estimate of σ by *analysis of variance*, which involved calculating a quantity called $SS_\sigma$ by adding together the contributions to the total sum of squares ($SS_T$) made by a set of orthogonal contrasts that we believed to measure only random variation. The set of contrasts was chosen either by assuming *a priori* that certain effects are negligible or by examining a normal plot. In this section we concentrate on the normal plot, deferring the more formal *a priori* method to Section 6.2. Unfortunately the normal plot method runs into a snag in this example. The set of 'random' contrasts identified by Fig. 6.3 includes both $T_q$ and $S_q$, which

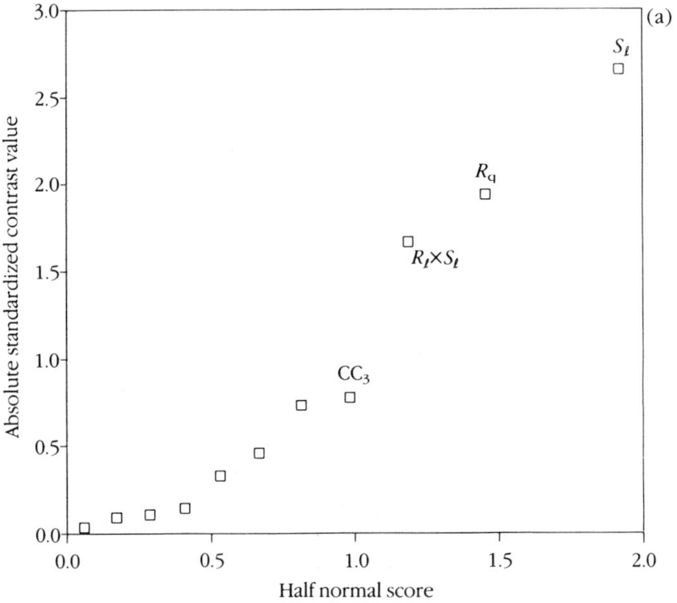


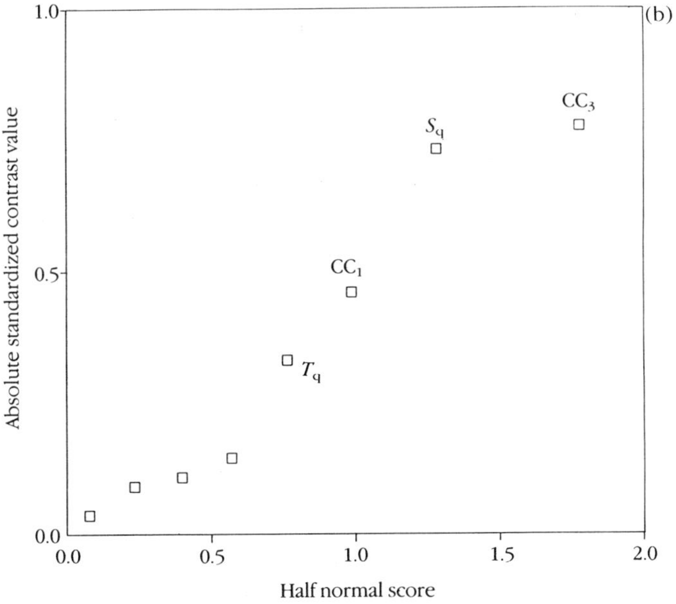


*Fig. 6.4* The fuel flow data in Table 6.1. Re-plots of Fig. 6.3. (a) Three contrasts removed; (b) three more contrasts removed

are not orthogonal. When contrasts are not orthogonal it is impossible to measure their individual contributions to $SS_T$. In Section 6.3 we will show that this difficulty can be avoided by the use of multiple regression. However, it is still possible to derive a rough estimate of $\sigma$ directly from the normal plot.

The method is as follows: plot, and if necessary remove points and re-plot, until all the remaining points appear to form a straight line. *Provided the contrast values have been standardized*, the slope of a line fitted to these points (by eye is adequate) is an estimate of $\sigma$. In Fig. 6.4(b) the slope is about 0.5, but, as we have already remarked, the 'line' is not well defined. In Chapter 5 we obtained an estimate of 0.15 from the complete 27-run experiment. It could be argued that the first four points in Fig. 6.4(b) form a line with slope approximately 0.15, but this observation clearly benefits from hindsight. Another estimate will be derived by analysis of variance in the next section.

## An alternative fractional plan for three factors

The central composite design is not the only fractional plan we can use to fit a second-order equation. Appendix 6.1 includes a *Box–Behnken design* in three factors. It is made up of the 12 edge points in Fig. 6.1, plus three runs at the centre. The composite and Box–Behnken plans are complementary in the sense that, when they are put together, the result is the full $3^3$ plan (with extra runs at the centre). This is the reason why we presented the $NO_x$ data (Table 5.16) in a non-standard order. The first 15 rows make up a three-level composite design and the last 12 are the 'Box–Behnken' points, which form three groups of four. Each group consists of a full $2^2$ plan (at the $(-)$ and $(+)$ levels) in two out of the three factors, with the third factor fixed at (0).

A large amount has been written in books and journals about the merits of alternative response surface plans. Many methods of comparison have been suggested — for a discussion see Box and Draper (1987, p. 502), who list seven criteria by which plans can be compared. When the purpose of the experiment is to map and predict the response over a region of the factor space, one obviously relevant criterion is the *variance function*, $V(\hat{y})$, where $\hat{y}$ is a predicted $y$ value. Because $\hat{y}$ is a function of the data, a standard deviation can be attached to $\hat{y}$ to express the amount of uncertainty associated with the prediction. $V(\hat{y})$, the square of the standard deviation, is more convenient for theoretical investigation than the standard deviation itself.

$V(\hat{y})$ is a function of the factor levels for which $\hat{y}$ is calculated. This function can be very complicated, but it is clear that on the whole $V$ will be larger for points outside the region covered by the experimental runs than for those inside — this reflects the common sense notion that *extrapolation* carries the penalty of greater uncertainty.

The central composite and Box–Behnken plans have similar variance functions over a large part of the interior of the cubic experimental region. Close to the corners the central composite gives more reliable predictions, which is not surprising, but prediction in these rather extreme regions may not be of great interest to the experimenters. Indeed, the Box–Behnken plan may be preferred on the grounds that it does not ask us to test any configuration in which all three factors are simultaneously at the ends of their ranges.

Like the central composite, the three-factor Box–Behnken plan is not fully orthogonal with respect to the second-order model. However, it can be made orthogonal by adding one further run at the centre.

## 6.2 MULTIPLE REGRESSION

The technique of multiple regression is a general method for fitting an equation of the form

$$y = b_0 + b_1x_1 + b_2x_2 + b_3x_3 + \dots \qquad [6.2]$$

where $x_1$, $x_2$, $x_3$, etc., are variables and $b_0$, $b_1$, $b_2$, etc., are coefficients to be determined. Values of the coefficients are usually chosen by the method of least squares. The selected equation is then the one for which the sum of squares of the residuals is minimized. The method is flexible enough to cope with dependence between some of the $x$ variables. For example, the three-factor second-order equation from the engine mapping experiment can be written

$$y = b_0 + b_1R + b_2T + b_3S + b_{11}R^2 + b_{22}T^2 + b_{33}S^2 + b_{12}RT + b_{13}RS + b_{23}TS$$

and treated as an example of [6.2], with the $x$ variables being factors, squares of factors and products of factors that express interactions. We have used the simplified form of the equation, with for example a term in $R^2$ rather than $(R^2 - \frac{2}{3})$. We noted in Chapter 5 that, with the equation in this form, dropping one of the quadratic terms will change the value of $b_0$, the estimate of the intercept. However, this is easily handled within the multiple regression framework, as we will show below.

### Multiple regression input

A multiple regression analysis requires the following input:

(i) A *matrix*, usually called $X$, in which each *column* is a list of the values taken by one of the $x$ variables in the different experimental runs.
(ii) A *column* of response values.

To apply multiple regression to the three-factor second-order equation we need nine $x$ variables: $R$, $T$, $S$, $R^2$, $T^2$, $S^2$, $RT$, $RS$ and $TS$, where $R$, $T$ and $S$ take the levels $-1$, 0 or $+1$, and $R^2$, $T^2$, $S^2$, $RT$, $RS$ and $TS$ are generated directly by squaring or multiplying the relevant columns for $R$, $T$ and $S$. Table 6.4 shows the $X$ matrix.

*Table 6.4* The $X$ matrix for the plan in Table 6.1

| $R$ | $T$ | $S$ | $R^2$ | $T^2$ | $S^2$ | $RT$ | $RS$ | $TS$ |
|---|---|---|---|---|---|---|---|---|
| −1 | −1 | −1 | 1 | 1 | 1 | 1 | 1 | 1 |
| 1 | −1 | −1 | 1 | 1 | 1 | −1 | −1 | 1 |
| −1 | 1 | −1 | 1 | 1 | 1 | −1 | 1 | −1 |
| 1 | 1 | −1 | 1 | 1 | 1 | 1 | −1 | −1 |
| −1 | −1 | 1 | 1 | 1 | 1 | 1 | −1 | −1 |
| 1 | −1 | 1 | 1 | 1 | 1 | −1 | 1 | −1 |
| −1 | 1 | 1 | 1 | 1 | 1 | −1 | −1 | 1 |
| 1 | 1 | 1 | 1 | 1 | 1 | 1 | 1 | 1 |
| 0 | 0 | 0 | 0 | 0 | 0 | 0 | 0 | 0 |
| −1 | 0 | 0 | 1 | 0 | 0 | 0 | 0 | 0 |
| 1 | 0 | 0 | 1 | 0 | 0 | 0 | 0 | 0 |
| 0 | −1 | 0 | 0 | 1 | 0 | 0 | 0 | 0 |
| 0 | 1 | 0 | 0 | 1 | 0 | 0 | 0 | 0 |
| 0 | 0 | −1 | 0 | 0 | 1 | 0 | 0 | 0 |
| 0 | 0 | 1 | 0 | 0 | 1 | 0 | 0 | 0 |

Table 6.4 looks very much like Table 6.2, and in fact differs from Table 6.2 only in the quadratic columns. Starting from the matrix $X$, a multiple regression program will in effect calculate the contrasts shown in Table 6.2; we say 'in effect' because such programs do not normally work directly with contrasts — they obtain the same answers by a different route.

## Multiple regression output

Multiple regression programs differ in the amount and type of output that they produce, but to be useful they must make the following information available:

(i) A list of the chosen coefficients in the equation, probably labelled as *regression coefficients*.

(ii) A standard deviation (often called the standard error) for each coefficient, together with a $t$ ratio, where

$$t \text{ ratio} = \frac{\text{coefficient}}{\text{standard deviation}} \qquad [6.3]$$

(iii) An estimate of $\sigma$.

*Table 6.5* Multiple regression output for the data in Table 6.1

| Term in second-order model | Coefficient | Standard deviation | *t* ratio |
|---|---|---|---|
| Intercept | 11.87 | | |
| $R$ | 6.89 | 0.13 | 53.0 |
| $T$ | 4.71 | 0.13 | 36.2 |
| $S$ | −0.84 | 0.13 | −6.5 |
| $R^2$ | 1.21 | 0.26 | 4.7 |
| $T^2$ | 0.21 | 0.26 | 0.8 |
| $S^2$ | 0.46 | 0.26 | 1.8 |
| $RT$ | 2.01 | 0.15 | 13.8 |
| $RS$ | −0.59 | 0.15 | −4.0 |
| $TS$ | −0.01 | 0.15 | −0.1 |

For the plan and fuel flow values in Table 6.1, Table 6.5 gives the coefficients, standard deviations and $t$ ratios, and Table 6.6 is a simplified form of anova table, which can be used to calculate $\hat{\sigma}$. We have not attached a $t$ ratio to the intercept, for a reason that will be given below.

## Fitted equation

Inspection of Table 6.5 shows that the equation constructed by multiple regression is identical to [6.1].

**Regression**

Spreadsheets have widely differing capabilities when it comes to regression. A good regression facility will allow the 'dependent' or $y$ variable to be regressed on several 'independent' or $x$ variables. The output, which can be stored in a convenient area of the worksheet, should consist of all the regression coefficients including the intercept, together with their standard deviations, and the residual sum of squares, or some quantity closely related to the residual sum of squares such as the root mean square. Equation [6.3] can easily be added as an extra feature to calculate the $t$ ratios. Residuals can be calculated by using the coefficients to construct a prediction equation for each experimental run and then calculating

$$\text{residual} = \text{observed } y \text{ value} - \text{predicted } y \text{ value}$$

*Table* 6.6 Analysis of variance for the data in Table 6.1

| Component | Degrees of freedom | Contribution to $SS_T$ |
|---|---|---|
| Regression | 9 $(= p)$ | 746.834 |
| Residual | 5 $(= n - 1 - p)$ | 0.850 |
| $SS_T$ | 14 $(= n - 1)$ | 747.684 |

## Anova table

In Table 6.6 the total sum of squares $SS_T$ has been split into two components, labelled 'regression' and 'residual' (sometimes called 'error'). The residual contribution is literally the sum of squares of the residuals from the fitted response surface, i.e. the sum of squares of the discrepancies between actual and predicted $y$ values for the 15 points of the design. The residual sum of squares can also be calculated by adding together a number of quantities which can be called 'single-degree-of-freedom sums of squares'. These quantities are found by squaring the values of a set of standardized orthogonal contrasts, as in equation [5.9]. The column headed 'Degrees of freedom' shows that five such contributions are needed to make up the residual sum of squares in this example.

## Estimation of σ

In general the numbers above the horizontal space in the 'degrees of freedom' column are $p$ and $(n - 1 - p)$, where $p$ is the number of terms in the fitted model other than the intercept. The number $(n - 1 - p)$ is known as the *residual degrees of freedom*. It shows that the sum of squares of the $n$ residuals is also the sum of squares of $(n - 1 - p)$ standardized orthogonal contrasts. If we *assume* that all systematic effects that are not included in the second order equation are negligible, the residuals are purely the result of random noise and it is to be expected that a suitable function of the residuals (some measure of their average size) will provide an estimate of σ. Specifically, we take

$$\hat{\sigma} = \sqrt{\left(\frac{\text{residual sum of squares}}{\text{residual degrees of freedom}}\right)} \qquad [6.4]$$

$$= \left(\frac{0.850}{5}\right) = 0.41$$

For another interpretation of the residual degrees of freedom, note that $(n - 1) - p$ is equal to

$$\begin{pmatrix}\text{maximum number of}\\ \text{orthogonal contrasts}\end{pmatrix} - \begin{pmatrix}\text{number of contrasts required to}\\ \text{provide coefficients in the model}\end{pmatrix}$$
$$= \text{maximum number of orthogonal checking contrasts}$$

As the reader may already have guessed, the residual sum of squares could in our example be calculated from the five standardized checking contrasts in Table 6.3, giving

$$(0.459)^2 + (-0.142)^2 + (-0.775)^2 + (-0.106)^2 + (0.090)^2 = 0.851$$

which differs from the value 0.850 given previously only because of round-off error.

The link between the residuals and the checking contrasts makes intuitive sense because, if there are no systematic effects on $y$ other than those included in the second-order equation, the residuals and the checking contrasts are all measures of random variation. With this link in mind we can compare our new $\hat{\sigma}$ value of 0.41 with the value 0.15 obtained from the complete 27-run experiment. The discrepancy between the two values suggests that our new estimate has been strongly influenced by higher-order effects, reflected in one or more of the checking contrasts but not detected in our analysis of Figs 6.3 and 6.4.

## Standard deviations

As we have pointed out in earlier chapters, the random noise that affects each individual response value is transmitted into any quantity calculated from those values, including the coefficients in the second-order equation. The standard deviation attached to each coefficient in the multiple regression output is calculated from the expression $k\hat{\sigma}$, where $\hat{\sigma}$ is the estimate given by equation [6.4] and $k$ indicates the extent to which random variation is attenuated in going from the individual values to the calculated coefficient. The number $k$ takes a different value for different types of term in the model, and in fact is the same $k$ we used to standardize the contrasts for normal plotting, in equation [5.8]. In this example, using the contrast matrix in Table 6.2 we find that $k$ is $\sqrt{(10/100)} = 0.3162$ for each of the linear terms, $\sqrt{(126/324)} = 0.6236$ for the quadratic terms, and $\sqrt{(8/100)} = 0.2828$ for the interaction terms. So we have the following values for the standard deviation:

$$0.3163 \times 0.41 = 0.13 \text{ for the linear terms}$$
$$0.6326 \times 0.41 = 0.26 \text{ for the quadratic terms}$$
$$0.2828 \times 0.41 = 0.12 \text{ for the interaction terms}$$

We can use this method to calculate the standard deviations of the coefficients in prediction equations even when the contrasts are not completely orthogonal — as in Table 6.2 — but most packages compute the standard deviations automatically. A general formula for $k$ is given in Appendix 6.3.

## *t* tests

The $t$ ratios can be used as a non-graphical method of dividing the measured effects into two sets, those which we treat as random and those which we treat as real. In Chapter 3, $F$ tests were used to carry out this type of analysis, and they can be used in our new setting too — the $F$ and $t$ tests will lead to identical conclusions, but $t$ tests are easier to implement on the basis of the usual output from a multiple regression program.

An effect is 'statistically significant' if its $t$ ratio lies in one of the 'tails' of a $t$ distribution, with degrees of freedom $(n - 1 - p)$. Figure 6.5 shows the $t$ distribution for five degrees of freedom, the value appropriate to our example. The lower and upper $2\frac{1}{2}\%$ points are often used as critical values. Under certain highly idealized conditions, which we mentioned in Chapter 3, there is then a 5% chance that random variation alone will produce a $t$ ratio that lies outside one of the critical values.

A table of $t$ test critical values is given in Appendix 6.2. As a rough rule of thumb, we can in most cases take the critical $t$ value to be 2, which means that a coefficient has to be bigger than twice its standard error before it is considered likely to represent a real effect. For five degrees of freedom the lower and upper $2\frac{1}{2}\%$ points are actually $\mp 2.57$. Using this criterion on the $t$ ratios in Table 6.5 leads us to the same set of six significant effects as in the Daniel plot, Figs 6.3 and 6.4. No $t$ test is carried out on the intercept because this number is defined relative to the scale used for the predictor variables,

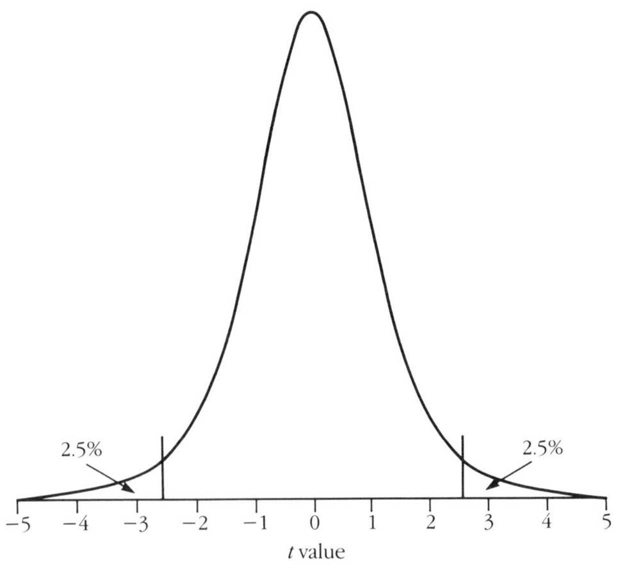


*Fig. 6.5* The $t$ distribution with five degrees of freedom

and is to some extent arbitrary. Equations without intercepts would not normally be considered unless they are suggested by existing scientific knowledge.

## Re-fitting

Whether we use a normal plot or $t$ tests, or a combination of both, there appear to be some terms that do not make an important contribution to predicting fuel flow. When the experiment is not fully orthogonal with respect to the second-order equation, these terms should not simply be deleted. When two columns of the $X$ matrix are correlated, *removing one changes the coefficient attached to the other*. The new coefficients can be found from suitably revised contrasts, but one of the advantages of using multiple regression is that it automatically makes the required adjustments. Although many of the terms in the equation will not be affected by re-fitting, the simplest procedure is to re-fit the whole equation.

Although Fig. 6.4 suggests that the quadratic term in $S$ could be omitted, we will include it on the basis of the knowledge we gained in Chapter 5. Note that in Table 6.5 the $t$ ratio for this term is approaching 2. The re-fitted equation is

$$y = 11.93 + 6.89R + 4.71T - 0.84S + 1.26R^2 + 0.51S^2 + 2.01RT - 0.59RS \qquad [6.5]$$

The residual sum of squares is now 0.96, with seven degrees of freedom, and equation [6.4] gives $\hat{\sigma} = 0.37$, still a lot higher than the value obtained in Chapter 5.

## The role of multiple regression

In this section we have presented multiple regression as a method for fitting a second-order equation, a convenient alternative to the direct calculation of contrasts. The information required to apply $t$ tests to the coefficients is also supplied, and the $t$ tests can be used as an alternative to a normal plot. However, the two approaches can be put together, because if used with proper care multiple regression can provide a quick way of calculating all the standardized contrasts that are needed for a normal plot, including the checking contrasts. We will illustrate the method on a different example in Section 6.3.

## Conclusion

As another check on the usefulness of our fitted equation, recall that the original engine map consisted of 584 points at various combinations of engine

*Table 6.7* Comparison of equation [6.5] with the results of a full engine map

| Coefficient | Equation [6.5] (from 15 points) | Full engine map (584 points) |
|---|---|---|
| Intercept | 11.9 | 12.3 |
| $R$ | 6.9 | 6.8 |
| $T$ | 4.7 | 4.7 |
| $S$ | −0.8 | −0.8 |
| $R^2$ | 1.3 | 1.8 |
| $T^2$ | 0.0 | 0.0 |
| $S^2$ | 0.5 | 0.2 |
| $RT$ | 2.0 | 2.0 |
| $RS$ | −0.6 | −0.5 |
| $ST$ | 0.0 | −0.1 |

speed, torque and spark. We can use multiple regression to fit a second-order equation to all these points. If we do so the coefficients of this larger regression can be compared to the coefficients obtained from the 15 point composite plan. The details are given in Table 6.7. The agreement between the two sets of coefficients is remarkably good.

Figure 6.6 shows some actual values of fuel flow from the 584-point map and predictions from the 15-point equation. Although there is some systematic lack of fit, the predictions from the 15-point equation would be

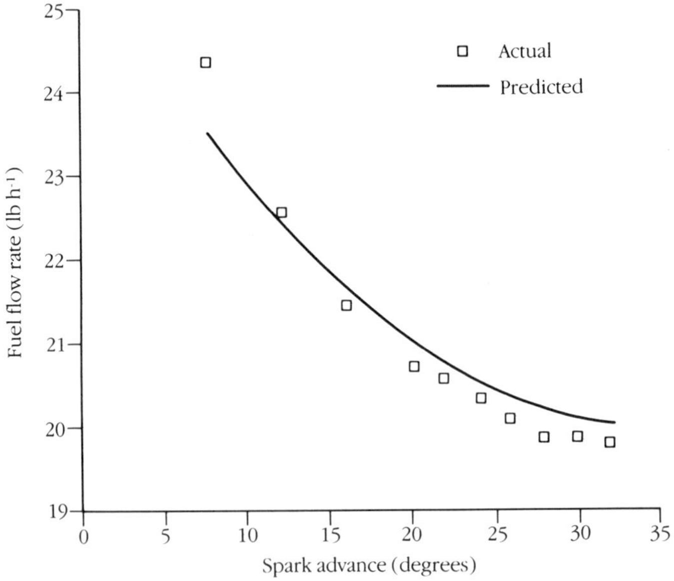


*Fig. 6.6* The fuel flow data in Table 6.1. Predictions (for $T = 33$ lb ft, $R = 5000$ rpm) using equation [6.1] from the 15-point plan, compared to actual values from the much larger data set on the same engine

perfectly adequate for many purposes, a powerful illustration of the benefits of experimental design.

## 6.3 AN EXAMPLE WITH FOUR FACTORS — TYRE TESTING

Steve Brenton of the Ford Motor Co. Ltd and Bradley Kemp ran an experiment to find prediction equations for two characteristics of tyres when they are in use on a vehicle. These characteristics were temperature and rolling resistance (often known as 'tyre loss'). Four factors were varied: axle load, tyre pressure, toe angle and speed. The equations were required for use in a computer model of vehicle performance. The levels used in the experiment were equally spaced (on a linear scale):

| | | Level | | |
|---|---|---|---|---|
| Factor | Label | (−) | (0) | (+) |
| Axle load (kg) | $L$ | 604 | 666 | 728 |
| Tyre pressure (psi) | $P$ | 26 | 45 | 64 |
| Toe angle (deg) | $A$ | −2 | 0 | +2 |
| Speed ($\text{km}\,\text{h}^{-1}$) | $S$ | 20 | 70 | 120 |

We will use just one response, the rolling resistance, to illustrate the analysis of this type of experiment.

The experimental plan was the 27-run Box–Behnken design for four factors, shown in Appendix 6.1, but the configurations were not run in standard order. The factor levels and the values of the rolling resistance, measured in Newtons, are given in Table 6.8, using the actual run order.

The experiment was run in this particular order because the load was a very difficult factor to change, involving the lifting of weight bottles filled with sand in and out of the boot of a car. The intention was to arrange the experiment so that this factor had to be changed as little as possible. The least number of changes required is two, which can be achieved by making six runs with the load at the (−) level, followed by 15 with the load at level (0) and finally six with the load at level (+). Unfortunately the experimenter made only four runs at $L-$ before changing to $L+$. He eventually added the other runs at the end of the experiment. This case study therefore highlights the need for considering practical difficulties in changing factor levels, and running the experiment in the order that best suits these circumstances.

We will centre the analysis on various normal plots constructed with the help of multiple regression. A complete Daniel plot, including checking contrasts, would have 26 points, but ours will have a maximum of 24, and we will explain the discrepancy below. It should be clear from Sections 6.1 and

*Table 6.8* An experiment on tyres

| Run | $L$ | $P$ | $A$ | $S$ | Rolling resistance |
|---|---|---|---|---|---|
| 1 | − | − | 0 | 0 | 86.98 |
| 2 | − | + | 0 | 0 | 97.20 |
| 3 | − | 0 | 0 | + | 105.75 |
| 4 | − | 0 | 0 | − | 84.70 |
| 5 | 0 | 0 | 0 | 0 | 124.50 |
| 6 | 0 | − | 0 | − | 126.48 |
| 7 | 0 | + | 0 | − | 114.30 |
| 8 | 0 | 0 | 0 | 0 | 118.90 |
| 9 | 0 | − | 0 | + | 134.70 |
| 10 | 0 | + | 0 | + | 146.80 |
| 11 | 0 | 0 | 0 | 0 | 122.58 |
| 12 | 0 | 0 | − | − | 103.27 |
| 13 | 0 | − | − | 0 | 107.58 |
| 14 | 0 | + | − | 0 | 109.30 |
| 15 | 0 | 0 | − | + | 110.60 |
| 16 | 0 | 0 | + | − | 120.40 |
| 17 | 0 | − | + | 0 | 143.70 |
| 18 | 0 | + | + | 0 | 132.70 |
| 19 | 0 | 0 | + | + | 143.61 |
| 20 | + | 0 | 0 | − | 113.99 |
| 21 | + | − | 0 | 0 | 121.10 |
| 22 | + | 0 | + | 0 | 119.13 |
| 23 | + | 0 | 0 | + | 126.40 |
| 24 | + | 0 | − | 0 | 121.30 |
| 25 | + | + | 0 | 0 | 119.13 |
| 26 | − | 0 | − | 0 | 89.35 |
| 27 | − | 0 | + | 0 | 75.90 |

6.2 that applying multiple regression to a suitable $X$ matrix is equivalent to calculating contrasts from the data. We shall show below that it is also possible to use the multiple regression output to standardize these contrasts. However, the reader who prefers to work directly with contrasts, as in Section 6.1, will find the relevant details in Appendix 6.1.

In the tyre example we apply multiple regression to an $X$ matrix with 24 columns. There is one column for each term in the second-order prediction equation, apart from the intercept. There are 14 such columns: $L$, $P$, $A$, $S$, $L^2$, $P^2$, $A^2$, $S^2$, $LP$, $LA$, $LS$, $PA$, $PS$ and $AS$. The columns for $L^2$, $P^2$, $LP$, etc., are generated by squaring or multiplying the relevant columns of the experimental plan.

The next eight columns in the $X$ matrix are listed in Table 6.9. The purpose of these is to produce checking contrasts relating to *third-order* effects. No divisors are necessary.

*Table 6.9* Checking contrasts for the tyre experiment

| Run | $CC_1$ | $CC_2$ | $CC_3$ | $CC_4$ | $CC_5$ | $CC_6$ | $CC_7$ | $CC_8$ |
|---|---|---|---|---|---|---|---|---|
| 1 | −1 | +1 | 0 | −2 | 0 | 0 | 0 | 0 |
| 2 | −1 | +1 | 0 | +2 | 0 | 0 | 0 | 0 |
| 3 | 0 | −2 | 0 | 0 | 0 | 0 | +1 | −1 |
| 4 | 0 | −2 | 0 | 0 | 0 | 0 | −1 | +1 |
| 5 | 0 | 0 | 0 | 0 | 0 | 0 | 0 | 0 |
| 6 | 0 | 0 | +1 | +1 | 0 | 0 | +1 | +1 |
| 7 | 0 | 0 | −1 | −1 | 0 | 0 | +1 | +1 |
| 8 | 0 | 0 | 0 | 0 | 0 | 0 | 0 | 0 |
| 9 | 0 | 0 | +1 | +1 | 0 | 0 | −1 | −1 |
| 10 | 0 | 0 | −1 | −1 | 0 | 0 | −1 | −1 |
| 11 | 0 | 0 | 0 | 0 | 0 | 0 | 0 | 0 |
| 12 | 0 | 0 | 0 | 0 | −1 | +1 | 0 | −2 |
| 13 | 0 | 0 | −1 | +1 | 0 | −2 | 0 | 0 |
| 14 | 0 | 0 | +1 | −1 | 0 | −2 | 0 | 0 |
| 15 | 0 | 0 | 0 | 0 | −1 | +1 | 0 | +2 |
| 16 | 0 | 0 | 0 | 0 | +1 | −1 | 0 | −2 |
| 17 | 0 | 0 | −1 | +1 | 0 | +2 | 0 | 0 |
| 18 | 0 | 0 | +1 | −1 | 0 | +2 | 0 | 0 |
| 19 | 0 | 0 | 0 | 0 | +1 | −1 | 0 | +2 |
| 20 | 0 | +2 | 0 | 0 | 0 | 0 | −1 | +1 |
| 21 | +1 | −1 | 0 | −2 | 0 | 0 | 0 | 0 |
| 22 | −1 | −1 | 0 | 0 | −1 | −1 | 0 | 0 |
| 23 | 0 | +2 | 0 | 0 | 0 | 0 | +1 | −1 |
| 24 | −1 | −1 | 0 | 0 | +1 | +1 | 0 | 0 |
| 25 | +1 | −1 | 0 | +2 | 0 | 0 | 0 | 0 |
| 26 | +1 | +1 | 0 | 0 | +1 | +1 | 0 | 0 |
| 27 | +1 | +1 | 0 | 0 | −1 | −1 | 0 | 0 |

The final two columns of $X$ are shown in Table 6.10. They define a pair of orthogonal contrasts in the three runs made at the centre point. In the tyre experiment these runs were genuine *replicates*, which means that they were made at the same configuration *and* that all possible sources of experimental error (including set-up errors) are reflected in their results. Any difference between their results is (ideally) a measure of random variation, and any contrasts between their results (suitably standardized) should plot 'on the line'. The more *replication contrasts* there are, the more likely it is that the normal plot will have a well defined line.

The multiple regression program will produce its usual output, including an equation containing 24 terms (which we call the *extended equation*), an estimate of $\sigma$ and (usually) a set of $t$ ratios. Standardized contrasts will not normally form part of the output, but this is not a problem because, for each term in the extended equation, the product ($t$ ratio) $\times$ $\hat{\sigma}$ can be interpreted as a standardized contrast:

$$t \text{ ratio} \times \hat{\sigma} = \frac{\text{contrast value}}{\text{standard deviation of contrast value}} \times \hat{\sigma}$$

$$= \frac{\text{contrast value}}{k\hat{\sigma}} \times \hat{\sigma}$$

$$= \frac{\text{contrast value}}{k}$$

which is exactly what we had in equation [5.8].

*Table 6.10* Two replication contrasts for the tyre experiment

| Run | $Rep_1$ | $Rep_2$ |
|---|---|---|
| 5 | +1 | +1 |
| 8 | −1 | +1 |
| 11 | 0 | −2 |

It is important to note that at this stage the coefficients in the extended equation and the number $\hat{\sigma}$ produced by the program are of interest *only* because they help us to calculate the standardized contrasts. In particular, $\hat{\sigma}$ should not be taken to be a valid estimate of $\sigma$, since we have not yet even begun to look for possible problems with the data. It is in any case based on only two degrees of freedom, and is inherently very variable. We have deliberately 'held back' those two degrees of freedom (i.e. put less than 26 columns into the $X$ matrix) to make the method work. If we do not leave at least one 'spare' degree of freedom the multiple regression package may either refuse to produce any output, or declare that $\hat{\sigma}$ is zero and the $t$ ratios indeterminate.

In the tyre example the two missing contrasts do not have a useful interpretation, but in other examples we may have a strong interest in every contrast, and therefore feel unhappy about sacrificing any one of them for the purpose of standardizing the others. In these circumstances it is possible to use equation [5.8] directly — see Appendix 6.3.

Table 6.11 gives the analysis of variance, $\hat{\sigma}$ and the standardized contrasts. The Daniel plot of the standardized contrasts is in Fig. 6.7(a). Because our interest is now primarily in fitting a second-order prediction equation, we have labelled the contrasts (other than the checking contrasts) according to the term in the equation to which they correspond. In this plot, the fifth and sixth largest contrasts (in absolute value) belong to $CC_5$ and $CC_6$, and both plot away from the line. Remove six points and re-plotting gives Fig. 6.7(b), and now it seems that the line does not point towards the origin. This is evidence for the existence of a single outlier. As we explained in Chapter 3, in these circumstances the full normal plot should have two 'lines', and this is indeed the case — see Fig. 6.8. The cause of the problem is identified below.

*Table 6.11* Tyre testing: multiple regression applied to 24 columns

| Component | Degrees of freedom | Contribution to $SS_T$ |
|---|---|---|
| Regression | 24 | 8401.38 |
| Residual | 2 | 47.93 |
| $SS_T$ | 26 | 8449.31 |

$$\hat{\sigma} = \sqrt{\left(\frac{47.93}{2}\right)} = 4.895$$

| Column in X matrix | Standardized contrast | Column in X matrix | Standardized contrast |
|---|---|---|---|
| $L$ | 52.3 | $CC_1$ | −6.8 |
| $P$ | −0.3 | $CC_2$ | −6.4 |
| $A$ | 27.1 | $CC_3$ | −3.3 |
| $S$ | 30.2 | $CC_4$ | 5.3 |
| $L^2$ | −41.9 | $CC_5$ | 23.2 |
| $P^2$ | 9.8 | $CC_6$ | 17.3 |
| $A^2$ | −8.4 | $CC_7$ | −2.6 |
| $S^2$ | 7.2 | $CC_8$ | −2.7 |
| $LP$ | −6.1 | $Rep_1$ | 2.6 |
| $LA$ | 5.6 | $Rep_2$ | −3.1 |
| $LS$ | −4.3 | | |
| $PA$ | −6.4 | | |
| $PS$ | 12.1 | | |
| $AS$ | 7.9 | | |

## Prediction equation

There are clear signs in Figs 6.7 and 6.8 that a second-order equation should not be used uncritically in this case, but for the moment we will ignore our concerns and proceed to calculate the equation, using multiple regression to fit only the second-order terms that plot 'off the line' in Fig. 6.7. There is a question mark over *PS*, but we will include it. The fitted equation is

$$y = 124.0 + 15.1L + 7.8A + 8.7S - 18.9L^2 + 6.1PS \qquad [6.6]$$

## Analysis of residuals

The residuals from the prediction equation [6.6] are plotted in time order, i.e. as a run chart, in Fig. 6.9. The importance of a run chart of residuals is that, if all systematic effects have been captured by the second-order equation, the

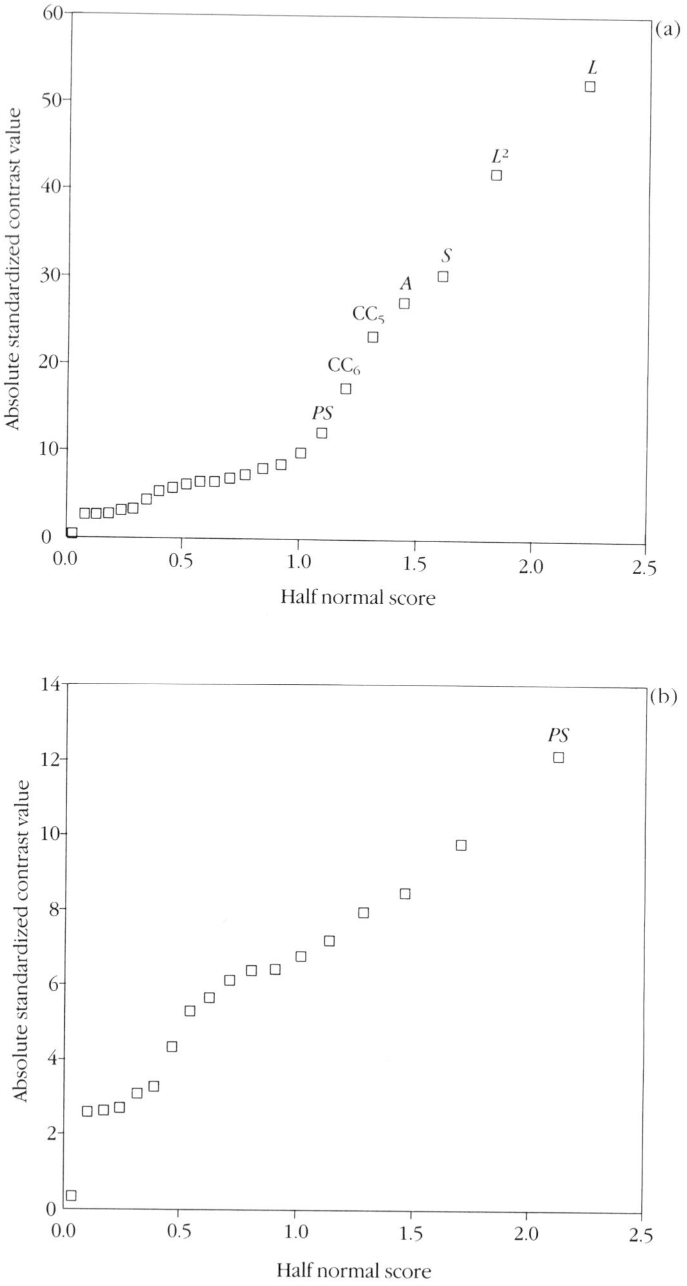


*Fig. 6.7* Tyre testing. (a) Daniel plot of 24 standardized contrasts; (b) re-plot with six contrasts removed

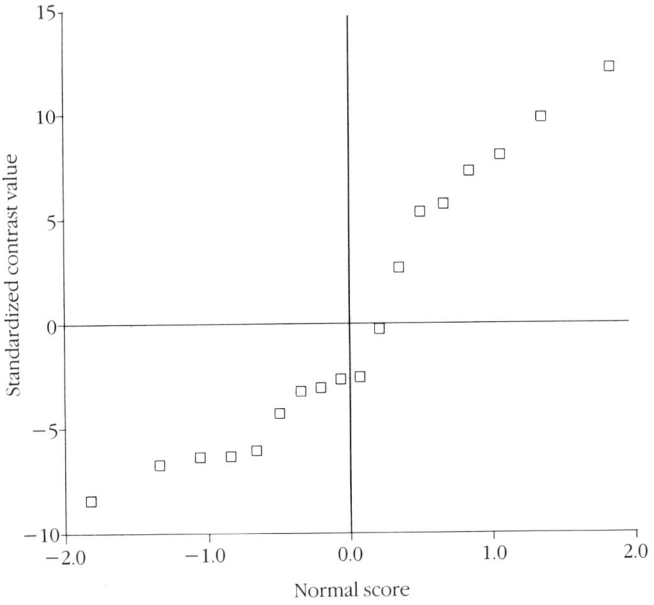


*Fig. 6.8* Tyre testing. Full normal plot of 18 standardized contrasts

residuals should plot as 'white noise', the output of a process in statistical control. (This statement is, strictly speaking, only true as an approximation, because of the built-in correlations between residuals that we noted in Chapter 5.) Statistical process control techniques can be applied to check whether it is sensible to treat the variation as random, and — if not — to help identify unwanted special causes of variation.

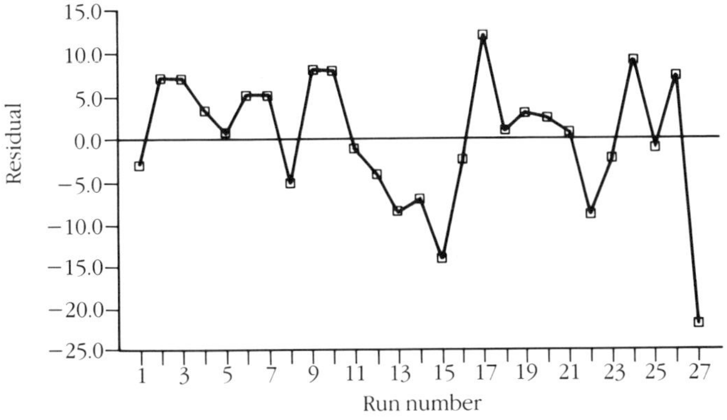


*Fig. 6.9* Tyre testing. Run chart of residuals, using equation [6.6] to predict rolling resistance

Even without the benefit of control limits it can be seen that there is a problem with the last run. The likely reason for this is, as we explained above, that the experimenter forgot to do two of the runs with load at the (−) level, and had to add them on at the end. He was running out of laboratory time at this point, and may have made an error in setting a factor level or recording the rolling resistance.

Close analysis of the $NO_x$ data given in Chapter 5 suggests that there is an outlier in that data set too. We leave it to the reader to discover which result is causing the trouble.

One way to assess what effect run 27 might have had on our analysis of the tyre data is to treat it as a missing value. An advantage of multiple regression is that, provided there are enough data, it is easy to delete individual values and repeat the analysis. In this case, if we retain the same terms as in equation [6.6] but delete the last result we get the following equation:

$$y = 124.0 + 12.7L + 10.3A + 8.7S - 16.4L^2 + 6.1PS \qquad [6.7]$$

The original decision to include a term in *PS* was a marginal one, and it would be very convenient to have an equation based only on main effects. Cuthbert Daniel has suggested that the importance of an individual term should be assessed by comparing full normal plots of residuals calculated with and without the term in question. The residuals from equation [6.7] are plotted in

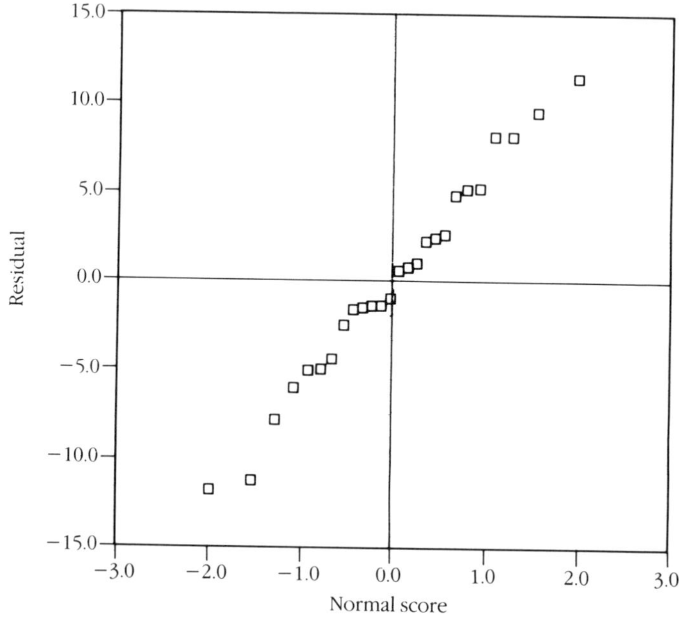


*Fig. 6.10* Tyre testing. Full normal plot of residuals, omitting run 27 and using equation [6.7] to predict rolling resistance

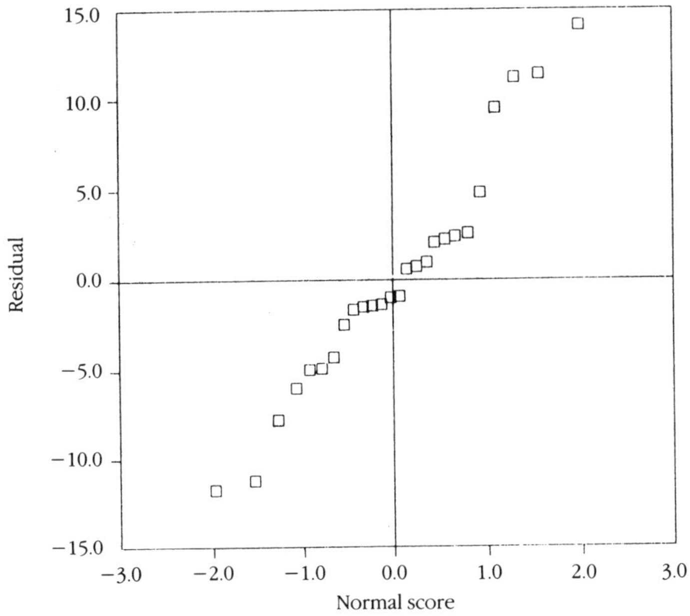


*Fig. 6.11* As Fig. 6.10, but with *PS* removed from the prediction equation

Fig. 6.10. Dropping *PS* leads to the residuals in Fig. 6.11. The latter is clearly a less satisfactory plot, suggesting that *PS* should be included.

(*Note on deleting the term in PS*: We warned earlier in this chapter that it is not always possible simply to delete a term from a fitted equation; re-fitting may be necessary. When a run is deleted from a balanced plan it may well create non-orthogonality between columns that were previously orthogonal, making re-fitting essential. It happens that in this particular case *PS can* simply be deleted from [6.7], despite the fact that run 27 has been ignored. We will not state any rules for deciding when re-fitting is required, because re-fitting is easy and can do no harm.)

In Section 6.2 we made a connection between the checking contrasts and the residuals from the fitted equation. One possible explanation for the prominence of the contrasts $CC_5$ and $CC_6$ in Fig. 6.7 is the influence of run 27. To check this we need a plot like Fig. 6.7(a), including checking contrasts, but without the influence of run 27. As we suggested in the note above, deleting runs destroys some of the orthogonality relationships and takes us further away from the ideal conditions for the use of normal plots. This effect can be reduced by replacing the suspect observation by a *predicted value* calculated from equation [6.7]. All the calculations that led to Fig. 6.7 can now be repeated on the modified data.

Substituting $L = -1$, $P = 0$, $A = 1$ and $S = 0$ into [6.7] gives a predicted value of about 105. Working with this value instead of 75.9 leads to the plot in Fig. 6.12. Four low-order effects are now much more prominent than in Fig. 6.7. As well as *PS*, $CC_5$ and $CC_6$ again appear to lie off the line,

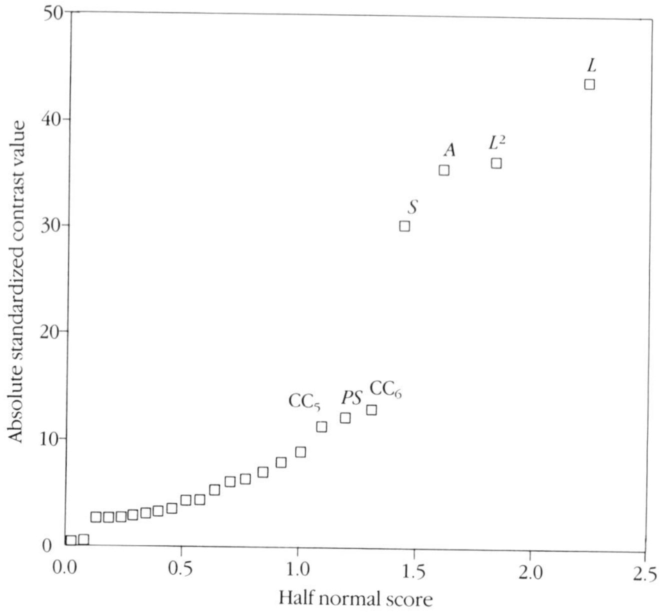


*Fig. 6.12* Tyre testing. Daniel plot of effects after replacing the result of run 27

but only just in this case. It appears that most, but not all, of the systematic lack of fit that we detected in Fig. 6.7 can be put down to a single outlier.

## Estimation of σ

We have suggested three methods of estimating σ. One might be called the orthodox anova method and is based on the sum of squares of residuals from the second-order equation — either the full equation or the re-fitted equation with some terms discarded. The re-fitted equation ([6.7] in our example) would generally be preferred. Another method is to fit a line by eye to the normal plot of standardized contrasts, after eliminating 'real' effects. The third (introduced in Chapter 3, and applied in Chapter 5, but not used so far in this chapter) is a combination of anova and normal plot, with $SS_\sigma$ obtained from the contrasts that the plot suggests are random.

When the data include an outlier any method of estimating σ is likely to give an inflated answer unless we find some way of discounting the outlier, which is why we did not try to get an estimate at an earlier stage of this analysis of the tyre experiment. Moreover, we feel that the two anova-based methods are probably safer than the graphical method when the deletion or replacement of outliers creates additional non-orthogonality. The first method is applied in Table 6.12(a). $SS_\sigma$ is taken to be the sum of squares of the residuals from equation [6.7], which was calculated ignoring the result of run 27.

Multiple regression provides a convenient framework for implementing the other anova-based method. For example, in Table 6.12(b) the residual sum of squares is derived from a multiple regression analysis with seven variables in the $X$ matrix, corresponding to the seven contrasts that appear to lie 'off the line' in Fig. 6.12: $L$, $A$, $S$, $L^2$, $PS$, $CC_5$ and $CC_6$. The point of this is *not* to find a prediction equation with a term for each of these seven variables — the fitted equation is of little interest because it represents a strange mixture of second- and third-order terms. But the residual sum of squares represents the part of $SS_T$ that is not influenced by effects which, on the basis of Fig. 6.12, we judge to be real. By using multiple regression we avoid the necessity of trying to add up the contributions to $SS_\sigma$ from individual contrasts; as we suggested in Section 6.1, when contrasts are not orthogonal it is impossible to measure their individual contributions in an unambiguous way.

In Table 6.12(b), as in Table 6.12(a), run 27 has been ignored. The difference between the two estimates reflects the influence of $CC_5$ and $CC_6$. Both these contrasts contribute to the residual sum of squares in Table 6.12(a) but not in Table 6.12(b), and Fig. 6.12 suggests that they are not just measuring random variation.

*Table 6.12* Tyre testing: use of analysis of variance to estimate σ

(a)

| Component | Degrees of freedom | Contribution to $SS_T$ |
|---|---|---|
| Regression | 5 | 5917.1 |
| Residual | 20 | 898.1 |
| $SS_T$ | 25 | 6815.2 |

$$\hat{\sigma} = \sqrt{\left(\frac{898.1}{20}\right)} = 6.7$$

(b)

| Component | Degrees of freedom | Contribution to $SS_T$ |
|---|---|---|
| Regression | 7 | 6292.3 |
| Residual | 18 | 522.9 |
| $SS_T$ | 25 | 6815.2 |

$$\hat{\sigma} = \sqrt{\left(\frac{522.9}{18}\right)} = 5.4$$

### Conclusion

The lesson of this example is that blindly fitting equations to data is likely to lead to misleading answers — we must always investigate how well the equation fits the data, and how well the equation makes sense physically. In [6.7], the consequence of the negative quadratic coefficient for load is that tyre loss is predicted to decrease with load after a certain point, which does not make sense physically. However, this drop-off is slight as Fig. 6.13 illustrates, so the fitted equation is still useful. It may make more sense to model the effect of load on tyre loss as exponential, since clearly there is curvature associated with this factor.

## 6.4 OTHER ASPECTS OF RESPONSE SURFACE METHODS

### Alternative fractional plans for four factors

The previous section dealt with a Box–Behnken plan for four factors. As an alternative, the three-level central composite plan for four factors consists of (i) a complete $2^4$ plan at the (−) and (+) levels, which we can think of as the corners of a hypercube in four dimensions, (ii) at least one, and usually two or

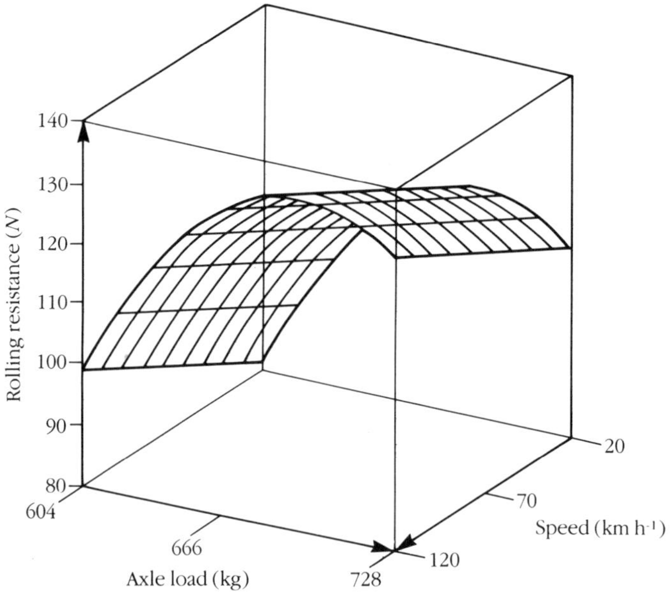


*Fig. 6.13* Predictions of rolling resistance as a function of load and speed

three, runs at the centre, and (iii) eight star or axial points, one pair for each factor. Table 6.13 shows the plan with one run at the centre. This plan has a smaller prediction variance than the Box–Behnken over most of the hypercube, but, as in the case of three factors, we may prefer the Box–Behnken on the grounds that it does not require more than two factors to be set at extreme values simultaneously.

For the experimenter who is using spreadsheets to analyse data it would be helpful if we could give full details of the contrasts that supply the coefficients in the second-order equation, based on the four-factor central composite design. Unfortunately the form of the *quadratic* contrasts alters according to the number of runs that are made at the centre point, and this also affects the formula for the intercept. The multiple regression approach automatically takes this into account.

If matrix manipulation facilities are available the multiple regression algorithm can be implemented along the lines of Appendix 6.3. As in Section 6.3, columns can be put into the $X$ matrix to produce checking contrasts and (if the centre point is replicated) replication contrasts. There are eight third-order checking contrasts. Four of them follow the pattern of $CC_1$ to $CC_3$ in Table 6.3, looking like a simple re-coding of one of the columns in the experimental plan except that the star points have extra weight (8 in this case) and their signs are reversed. The other four are given by multiplying the columns of the plan together in sets of three. Two higher-order checking contrasts are also available.

Another alternative is to allocate the factors to columns 1, 2, 5 and 9 of $L_{27}(3^{13})$. Although this plan is not fully orthogonal with respect to the second-order equation, the only correlations occur between pairs of linear by linear interaction contrasts, so from the point of view of making normal plots we are closer to the ideal situation than in the central composite and Box–Behnken plans. We have not explored the variance function in detail, but it appears to be quite competitive. The main reason for not positively recommending this design is that the checking contrasts have not been fully developed yet. Column 9 can be replaced by columns 10, 12 or 13.

## Five or more factors

For five factors the Box–Behnken plan has 46 runs, but a much smaller central composite plan exists: see Table 6.14. We have shown a plan with one run at the centre, but this would usually be replicated. The first 16 rows of this design make up the five-factor resolution V two-level plan given in Table 4.6; this is a half replicate of the full $2^5$ plan. For the calculation of contrasts see our discussion of the four-factor case above. There are in this case five third-order checking contrasts, which follow the pattern of $CC_1$–$CC_3$ in Table 6.3, except that the star points have weight 8.

For plans in six or more factors, see Box and Draper (1987).

*Table 6.13* Composite design for four factors

| Row | | | | |
|---|---|---|---|---|
| 1 | − | − | − | − |
| 2 | + | − | − | − |
| 3 | − | + | − | − |
| 4 | + | + | − | − |
| 5 | − | − | + | − |
| 6 | + | − | + | − |
| 7 | − | + | + | − |
| 8 | + | + | + | − |
| 9 | − | − | − | + |
| 10 | + | − | − | + |
| 11 | − | + | − | + |
| 12 | + | + | − | + |
| 13 | − | − | + | + |
| 14 | + | − | + | + |
| 15 | − | + | + | + |
| 16 | + | + | + | + |
| 17 | 0 | 0 | 0 | 0 |
| 18 | − | 0 | 0 | 0 |
| 19 | + | 0 | 0 | 0 |
| 20 | 0 | − | 0 | 0 |
| 21 | 0 | + | 0 | 0 |
| 22 | 0 | 0 | − | 0 |
| 23 | 0 | 0 | + | 0 |
| 24 | 0 | 0 | 0 | − |
| 25 | 0 | 0 | 0 | + |

## Smaller plans

The minimum number of configurations needed to fit a second-order equation is equal to the number of terms in the equation. The plans we have described in this chapter use more than the minimum number of configurations, and in some cases include replicate runs at the centre, in order to improve the precision with which the equation is estimated, and to allow the calculation of checking contrasts. In the case of four factors the plans we have recommended require 25–27 runs, and this seems rather a lot when compared with the minimum, which is 15. What we need is a suitably balanced plan with about 20 runs, but none seems to be available.

Roquemore's (1976) paper lists some plans for three, four and six factors which get close to the minimum number of runs while retaining certain types of symmetry and balance. See Draper (1985) for a discussion of the five-factor case.

*Table 6.14* Composite design for five factors

| Row | | | | | |
|---|---|---|---|---|---|
| 1 | − | − | − | − | + |
| 2 | + | − | − | − | − |
| 3 | − | + | − | − | − |
| 4 | + | + | − | − | + |
| 5 | − | − | + | − | − |
| 6 | + | − | + | − | + |
| 7 | − | + | + | − | + |
| 8 | + | + | + | − | − |
| 9 | − | − | − | + | − |
| 10 | + | − | − | + | + |
| 11 | − | + | − | + | + |
| 12 | + | + | − | + | − |
| 13 | − | − | + | + | + |
| 14 | + | − | + | + | − |
| 15 | − | + | + | + | − |
| 16 | + | + | + | + | + |
| 17 | 0 | 0 | 0 | 0 | 0 |
| 18 | − | 0 | 0 | 0 | 0 |
| 19 | + | 0 | 0 | 0 | 0 |
| 20 | 0 | − | 0 | 0 | 0 |
| 21 | 0 | + | 0 | 0 | 0 |
| 22 | 0 | 0 | − | 0 | 0 |
| 23 | 0 | 0 | + | 0 | 0 |
| 24 | 0 | 0 | 0 | − | 0 |
| 25 | 0 | 0 | 0 | + | 0 |
| 26 | 0 | 0 | 0 | 0 | − |
| 27 | 0 | 0 | 0 | 0 | + |

## Five-level plans

In many experiments with quantitative factors there is no great practical advantage in restricting the factors to three levels. In an engineering environment experimenters often have to use specially made, rather than off-the-shelf, parts and assemblies. In this situation it is hardly more difficult to arrange for a factor to have five levels than three.

Five-level factors have two main uses. Taking the two-factor case as an example, if the region of interest in factor space is approximately *circular* rather than square, there are advantages in arranging for all the experimental configurations but one to lie close to the edge of the circle — the exception is of course the centre point. Figure 6.14 shows a nine-run plan consisting of eight points on a circle plus a run at the centre. This is a composite plan, consisting of the four corners of a square, four star points and the origin. The coded levels are ($-1$, $-1/\sqrt{2}$, 0, $1/\sqrt{2}$, $+1$). For three and four factors the Box–Behnken plans provide a convenient set of points that are equidistant from the centre (in coded units), but, as we noted above, the five-factor Box–Behnken plan is very large. A suitable composite plan can be constructed but requires five-level factors.

The second reason for using five levels is rather more technical. It gives the experimenters more freedom to 'tune' the levels to achieve specific objectives. For example, J S Hunter (1985) strongly recommends that designs should be *rotatable*. Rotatability is a kind of symmetry, defined by the requirement that the variance function — which is a measure of the uncertainty attached to a predicted response — should depend only on the distance of the configuration from the centre, in coded units. For example, in three dimensions, all the configurations that lie on a sphere centred on the origin can be predicted with the same amount of uncertainty. The Box–Behnken plans are approximately rotatable (some are exactly so), but all the five-level composite plans can be tuned to make them rotatable.

Five-level plans can also be tuned to achieve 'blockability', i.e. to produce a plan that can be run in two or more orthogonal blocks. This type of plan facilitates sequential experimentation. To illustrate the idea we return to the three-factor design in Table 6.1. We might run the first nine configurations as a *two-level plus centre point* experiment. Depending on the results of the first stage (see Chapter 5), we might want to add the star points. If there is a substantial time interval between the two stages we should be concerned about a possible time effect. As they stand, the blocks formed by the first nine and last six runs in Table 6.1 are not orthogonal to the other effects, but this

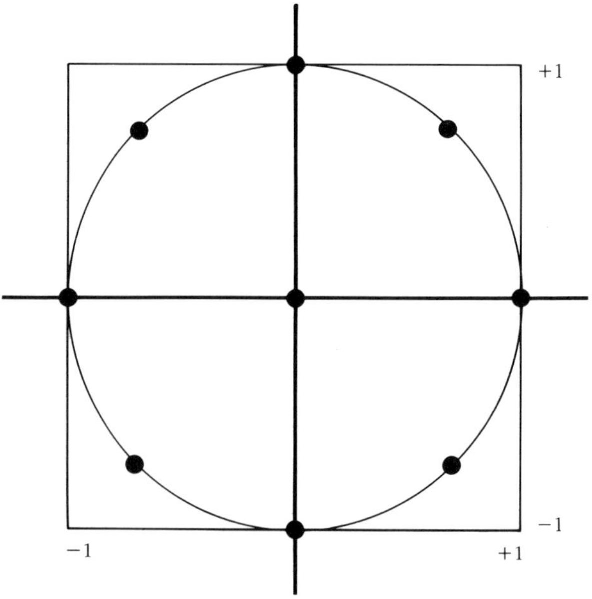


*Fig. 6.14* Five-level composite plan for two factors

can be remedied by moving the star points further out from the centre. If (−) and (+) in the plan correspond to −1 and +1 on the coded scale, the star points should be at a distance $\sqrt{(8/3)}$ from the origin. Each factor now has five levels: $(-\sqrt{(8/3)}, -1, 0, +1, +\sqrt{(8/3)})$. Clearly this coding is not based on the idea that −1 and +1 represent the extremes of the interesting or feasible range of each factor. In two-stage experiments of this kind it is convenient, though not essential, to continue to use −1, 0 and +1 to code the first-stage levels, adjusting the actual levels to allow for the potential second stage. For example, if the feasible range is from 50 to 60, the first-stage levels would be at $55 \pm \sqrt{(3/8)} \times 5$, i.e. 51.94 and 58.06.

Box and Draper (1987) explain these ideas in detail, and shown how to construct checking contrasts for five-level composite plans.

## Exploring the fitted response surface

Predicted response values calculated at selected points and two-dimensional contour plots can be used to give a limited view of the shape of a fitted response surface — a very limited view in the case of a five-factor equation. As animated graphics become generally available it will be possible to travel through the factor space and get a much better idea of the changes in response predicted by the equation. Mathematical techniques such as canonical analysis and ridge analysis are often helpful. For details see Box and Draper (1987).

## SUMMARY OF CHAPTER 6

Two types of fractional three-level plan, central composite and Box–Behnken, are useful for fitting a second-order prediction equation. From a geometric point of view these two types of plan are given by deleting different types of point from the full factorial. The central composite plans produce better predictions in the more extreme parts of the experimental region, but a Box–Behnken plan may be preferred because it does not require all the factors to be tested at extreme values simultaneously.

In these fractional plans the contrasts that provide the coefficients in the equation are no longer fully orthogonal. Third-order checking contrasts are available for both types of plan. A multiple regression program is a convenient way of fitting an equation without the direct calculation of contrasts. It also provides the information required to carry out $t$ tests, a more formal alternative to normal plots, and to estimate $\sigma$ from a residual sum of squares. When a quadratic term is deleted from the equation it is necessary to re-calculate the other quadratic terms. This process of re-fitting is easily accomplished by multiple regression.

Multiple regression can also be used to produce standardized contrasts (including checking contrasts) for making a normal plot. Replication contrasts help to define the line in the plot. Careful use of this plot in conjunction with analysis of variance provides a method of estimating σ that avoids inflation caused by higher-order effects.

A run chart of residuals can be treated by the methods of SPC. It will reveal individual 'bad' values, which can be deleted before re-fitting. Full normal plots of residuals can help us to decide whether specific terms should be included in the prediction equation.

Five-level designs are useful if the region of interest is (hyper-)spherical rather than rectangular. Five-level composite plans can be tuned to give an exactly rotatable design, or a design that can be run in orthogonal blocks, the first block being a two-level plan plus centre point, and the second containing the star points.

## APPENDIX 6.1 BOX–BEHNKEN DESIGNS

The Box–Behnken designs for three and four factors are shown in Tables A6.1 and A6.2, respectively. The coefficients for the linear contrasts are, as usual, given by replacing (−) by −1 and (+) by +1, and the linear by linear interaction contrasts by multiplying pairs of linear contrasts. For these contrasts the divisors are the numbers of ±1s in each column.

We have not given divisors for the checking contrasts. If you are working

*Table A6.1* Box–Behnken design for three factors

| Row | Plan | | | | Quadratic contrasts | | | Checking contrasts | | |
|---|---|---|---|---|---|---|---|---|---|---|
| 1 | − | − | 0 | | +3 | +3 | −3 | −1 | +1 | 0 |
| 2 | + | − | 0 | | +3 | +3 | −3 | +1 | +1 | 0 |
| 3 | − | + | 0 | | +3 | +3 | −3 | −1 | −1 | 0 |
| 4 | + | + | 0 | | +3 | +3 | −3 | +1 | −1 | 0 |
| 5 | − | 0 | − | | +3 | −3 | +3 | +1 | 0 | −1 |
| 6 | + | 0 | − | | +3 | −3 | +3 | −1 | 0 | −1 |
| 7 | − | 0 | + | | +3 | −3 | +3 | +1 | 0 | +1 |
| 8 | + | 0 | + | | +3 | −3 | +3 | −1 | 0 | +1 |
| 9 | 0 | − | − | | −3 | +3 | +3 | 0 | −1 | +1 |
| 10 | 0 | + | − | | −3 | +3 | +3 | 0 | +1 | +1 |
| 11 | 0 | − | + | | −3 | +3 | +3 | 0 | −1 | −1 |
| 12 | 0 | + | + | | −3 | +3 | +3 | 0 | +1 | −1 |
| 13 | 0 | 0 | 0 | | −4 | −4 | −4 | 0 | 0 | 0 |
| 14 | 0 | 0 | 0 | | −4 | −4 | −4 | 0 | 0 | 0 |
| 15 | 0 | 0 | 0 | | −4 | −4 | −4 | 0 | 0 | 0 |
| | | | | Divisor | 24 | 24 | 24 | | | |

*Table A6.2* Box–Behnken design for four factors

| Row | Plan | | | | Quadratic contrasts | | | | Checking contrasts | | | | | | | |
|---|---|---|---|---|---|---|---|---|---|---|---|---|---|---|---|---|
| 1 | − | − | 0 | 0 | +2 | +2 | −1 | −1 | −1 | +1 | 0 | −2 | 0 | 0 | 0 | 0 |
| 2 | + | − | 0 | 0 | +2 | +2 | −1 | −1 | +1 | −1 | 0 | −2 | 0 | 0 | 0 | 0 |
| 3 | − | + | 0 | 0 | +2 | +2 | −1 | −1 | −1 | +1 | 0 | +2 | 0 | 0 | 0 | 0 |
| 4 | + | + | 0 | 0 | +2 | +2 | −1 | −1 | +1 | −1 | 0 | +2 | 0 | 0 | 0 | 0 |
| 5 | 0 | 0 | − | − | −1 | −1 | +2 | +2 | 0 | 0 | 0 | 0 | −1 | +1 | 0 | −2 |
| 6 | 0 | 0 | + | − | −1 | −1 | +2 | +2 | 0 | 0 | 0 | 0 | +1 | −1 | 0 | −2 |
| 7 | 0 | 0 | − | + | −1 | −1 | +2 | +2 | 0 | 0 | 0 | 0 | −1 | +1 | 0 | +2 |
| 8 | 0 | 0 | + | + | −1 | −1 | +2 | +2 | 0 | 0 | 0 | 0 | +1 | −1 | 0 | +2 |
| 9 | 0 | 0 | 0 | 0 | −4 | −4 | −4 | −4 | 0 | 0 | 0 | 0 | 0 | 0 | 0 | 0 |
| 10 | − | 0 | 0 | − | +2 | −1 | −1 | +2 | 0 | −2 | 0 | 0 | 0 | 0 | −1 | +1 |
| 11 | + | 0 | 0 | − | +2 | −1 | −1 | +2 | 0 | +2 | 0 | 0 | 0 | 0 | −1 | +1 |
| 12 | − | 0 | 0 | + | +2 | −1 | −1 | +2 | 0 | −2 | 0 | 0 | 0 | 0 | +1 | −1 |
| 13 | + | 0 | 0 | + | +2 | −1 | −1 | +2 | 0 | +2 | 0 | 0 | 0 | 0 | +1 | −1 |
| 14 | 0 | − | − | 0 | −1 | +2 | +2 | −1 | 0 | 0 | −1 | +1 | 0 | −2 | 0 | 0 |
| 15 | 0 | + | − | 0 | −1 | +2 | +2 | −1 | 0 | 0 | +1 | −1 | 0 | −2 | 0 | 0 |
| 16 | 0 | − | + | 0 | −1 | +2 | +2 | −1 | 0 | 0 | −1 | +1 | 0 | +2 | 0 | 0 |
| 17 | 0 | + | + | 0 | −1 | +2 | +2 | −1 | 0 | 0 | +1 | −1 | 0 | +2 | 0 | 0 |
| 18 | 0 | 0 | 0 | 0 | −4 | −4 | −4 | −4 | 0 | 0 | 0 | 0 | 0 | 0 | 0 | 0 |
| 19 | 0 | − | 0 | − | −1 | +2 | −1 | +2 | 0 | 0 | +1 | +1 | 0 | 0 | +1 | +1 |
| 20 | 0 | + | 0 | − | −1 | +2 | −1 | +2 | 0 | 0 | −1 | −1 | 0 | 0 | +1 | +1 |
| 21 | 0 | − | 0 | + | −1 | +2 | −1 | +2 | 0 | 0 | +1 | +1 | 0 | 0 | −1 | −1 |
| 22 | 0 | + | 0 | + | −1 | +2 | −1 | +2 | 0 | 0 | −1 | −1 | 0 | 0 | −1 | −1 |
| 23 | − | 0 | − | 0 | +2 | −1 | +2 | −1 | +1 | +1 | 0 | 0 | +1 | +1 | 0 | 0 |
| 24 | + | 0 | − | 0 | +2 | −1 | +2 | −1 | −1 | −1 | 0 | 0 | +1 | +1 | 0 | 0 |
| 25 | − | 0 | + | 0 | +2 | −1 | +2 | −1 | +1 | +1 | 0 | 0 | −1 | −1 | 0 | 0 |
| 26 | + | 0 | + | 0 | +2 | −1 | +2 | −1 | −1 | −1 | 0 | 0 | −1 | −1 | 0 | 0 |
| 27 | 0 | 0 | 0 | 0 | −4 | −4 | −4 | −4 | 0 | 0 | 0 | 0 | 0 | 0 | 0 | 0 |
| | | | | Divisor | 24 | 24 | 24 | 24 | | | | | | | | |

*Table A6.3* Critical values for $t$ tests (upper $2\frac{1}{2}\%$ points)

| Residual degrees of freedom | Critical value |
|---|---|
| 5 | 2.57 |
| 6 | 2.45 |
| 7 | 2.36 |
| 8 | 2.31 |
| 9 | 2.26 |
| 10 | 2.23 |
| 11 | 2.20 |
| 12 | 2.18 |
| 13 | 2.16 |
| 14 | 2.14 |
| 15 | 2.13 |
| 16 | 2.12 |
| 17 | 2.11 |
| 18 | 2.10 |
| 19 | 2.09 |
| 20 | 2.09 |
| 21 | 2.08 |
| 22 | 2.07 |
| 23 | 2.07 |
| 24 | 2.06 |
| 25 | 2.06 |

directly with standardized contrasts, take the divisor to be 1. If you are working with a multiple regression program these columns can be included in the $X$ matrix as they stand.

The four-factor design can be divided into three blocks consisting of rows 1 to 9, 10 to 18 and 19 to 27. The two 'replication' contrasts in Table 6.10 will then measure differences *between blocks*. The two 'missing' contrasts that we used to obtain a value for $\hat{\sigma}$ in the tyre experiment will also measure block differences.

The intercept is calculated as the average response at the centre point.

## APPENDIX 6.2 CRITICAL VALUES FOR $t$ TESTS

The critical values for $t$ tests (upper $2\frac{1}{2}\%$ points) are listed in Table A6.3.

# APPENDIX 6.3 A DIRECT METHOD OF STANDARDIZING CONTRASTS

In multiple regression, the *regression coefficients* are given by the following formula:

$$\boldsymbol{b} = (\boldsymbol{X}'\boldsymbol{X})^{-1}\boldsymbol{X}'\boldsymbol{y}$$

In this formula $\boldsymbol{b}$ is a vector containing the regression coefficients, $\boldsymbol{y}$ is a vector of response values and $\boldsymbol{X}$ is a matrix (dimensions $n \times (p + 1)$), which can be represented as

$$\begin{bmatrix} 1 & \\ 1 & \\ \cdot & X \\ \cdot & \\ \cdot & \\ 1 & \end{bmatrix}$$

where $X$ is the matrix introduced in Section 6.2. In words, $X$ is augmented by a column of $n$ 1s. The first element of $\boldsymbol{b}$ will be the intercept in the prediction equation.

The regression coefficients must be standardized for inclusion in a normal plot, as in equation [5.8]. The value of $k$ for the $i$th contrast, $k_i$, is given by

$$k_i = \sqrt{d_i}$$

where $d_i$ is the $i$th diagonal element of $(\boldsymbol{X}'\boldsymbol{X})^{-1}$.

Some implementations of multiple regression produce $(\boldsymbol{X}'\boldsymbol{X})^{-1}$ as an optional component of the output.

CHAPTER 7

# Mixed-level factorial experiments

*When many factors must be screened we generally recommend that only two levels be used for each factor. Nevertheless, there are special circumstances in which factors with three levels, or a mixture of two and three levels, may sensibly be used. Because of the complicated confounding patterns typical of such plans, the logic behind these experiments usually has to be the one we attributed to Taguchi in Chapter 4. The data are analysed, and predictions are made, without taking interactions into account. If these predictions cannot be confirmed, further experimentation is demanded to make sense of the situation.*

*To save space, in this chapter we will sometimes write the coefficients that define a contrast as a row rather than as a column.*

## 7.1 SOME MORE ORTHOGONAL ARRAYS

Before we deal directly with the problem of running experiments with a mixture of two- and three-level factors we will introduce some orthogonal arrays that we have not yet discussed, but are nevertheless important for planning industrial experiments.

Table 7.1 is an orthogonal array that is due to Starks (1964). Because it has 16 runs, we have called Starks' array an $L_{16}$, but it is not directly related to the more familiar $L_{16}(2^{15})$ which we introduced in Chapter 3. It can be developed from $L_8(2^7)$, however, but we do not give details here — interested readers should refer to Starks' paper. Starks' array allows for the study of up to seven three-level factors. Note that the levels of each factor do not occur equally often — there are twice as many runs at level (0) as at either (+) or (−). The array can be called 'completely orthogonal' in spite of this, because it still has the property of balance, although the definition of balance has to be stretched somewhat. To see the pattern, note that for example the eight occurrences of (0) in any column are matched in any other column with (−), (0), and (+) with frequencies 2,4,2. These frequencies are in proportion to the overall frequencies (4,8,4) of levels (−), (0) and (+). This type of balance is therefore called *proportional frequencies* (for more details, see Dey (1985) p. 34). The condition of proportional frequencies allows the construction of orthogonal contrasts to measure main effects. The 15 orthogonal contrasts available from this plan include a linear and quadratic contrast for each factor, which is a total of 14. Runs 8 and 16 are at the centre point, with all factors at level (0), so that the missing fifteenth contrast (written as a row) is simply [0,0,0,0,0,0,0,−1,0,0,0,0,0,0,0,+1], which compares these two runs directly. This is a replication contrast (see Chapter 6), and provides a measure of experimental variation.

*Table 7.1* Starks' array $L_{16}(3^7)$

| Row | | | | | | | |
|---|---|---|---|---|---|---|---|
| 1 | + | 0 | 0 | − | 0 | − | − |
| 2 | − | + | 0 | 0 | − | 0 | − |
| 3 | − | − | + | 0 | 0 | − | 0 |
| 4 | 0 | − | − | + | 0 | 0 | − |
| 5 | − | 0 | − | − | + | 0 | 0 |
| 6 | 0 | − | 0 | − | − | + | 0 |
| 7 | 0 | 0 | − | 0 | − | − | + |
| 8 | 0 | 0 | 0 | 0 | 0 | 0 | 0 |
| 9 | − | 0 | 0 | + | 0 | + | + |
| 10 | + | − | 0 | 0 | + | 0 | + |
| 11 | + | + | − | 0 | 0 | + | 0 |
| 12 | 0 | + | + | − | 0 | 0 | + |
| 13 | + | 0 | + | + | − | 0 | 0 |
| 14 | 0 | + | 0 | + | + | − | 0 |
| 15 | 0 | 0 | + | 0 | + | + | − |
| 16 | 0 | 0 | 0 | 0 | 0 | 0 | 0 |

A word is in order about linear and quadratic contrasts for Starks' array, because of the unequal occurrence of runs at the three levels. The linear contrasts are given by the usual re-coding in [5.3], but the quadratic contrasts are obtained by writing a +1 wherever the plan has a (−) or a (+), and a −1 (*not* −2) wherever the plan has a (0). The reason for this can be seen by writing the quadratic contrast as

$$\text{quadratic contrast} = \tfrac{1}{2}(\bar{y}_- + \bar{y}_+) - \bar{y}_0 \qquad [7.1]$$

where $\bar{y}_-$, $\bar{y}_0$, and $\bar{y}_+$ are the average responses at each level (compare this with the quadratic contrast in Table 5.5). Because there are twice as many runs at level (0), each $y$ value ends up contributing the same 'weight' in the quadratic contrast.

In general, it is not possible to investigate interactions with Starks' array, because the confounding pattern is quite complicated. In particular, it is not possible to use Starks' array to estimate a second-order equation of the sort discussed in Chapters 5 and 6. It is best to use Starks' array for estimating main effects only, and to bear in mind that it is always resolution III.

Another three-level array for investigating up to seven factors, but this time in 18 runs, is given in Table 7.2, and is due to Plackett and Burman (1946). Compared to Starks' array in Table 7.1, this plan allows for the study of an extra two-level factor for just two extra runs.

*Table 7.2* Orthogonal array $L_{18}(2^1.3^7)$

| Row | | | | | | | | |
|---|---|---|---|---|---|---|---|---|
| 1 | − | − | − | − | − | − | − | − |
| 2 | − | − | 0 | 0 | 0 | 0 | 0 | 0 |
| 3 | − | − | + | + | + | + | + | + |
| 4 | − | 0 | − | − | 0 | 0 | + | + |
| 5 | − | 0 | 0 | 0 | + | + | − | − |
| 6 | − | 0 | + | + | − | − | 0 | 0 |
| 7 | − | + | − | 0 | − | + | 0 | + |
| 8 | − | + | 0 | + | 0 | − | + | − |
| 9 | − | + | + | − | + | 0 | − | 0 |
| 10 | + | − | − | + | + | 0 | 0 | − |
| 11 | + | − | 0 | − | − | + | + | 0 |
| 12 | + | − | + | 0 | 0 | − | − | + |
| 13 | + | 0 | − | 0 | + | − | + | 0 |
| 14 | + | 0 | 0 | + | − | 0 | − | + |
| 15 | + | 0 | + | − | 0 | + | 0 | − |
| 16 | + | + | − | + | 0 | + | − | 0 |
| 17 | + | + | 0 | − | + | − | 0 | + |
| 18 | + | + | + | 0 | − | 0 | + | − |

This is the first example in this book of a *mixture* of two- and three-level factors appearing in the same plan. Unlike Starks' array, there are no repeats of any of the runs in $L_{18}$. Because there are 18 runs in total, there are 17 orthogonal contrasts available: there are linear and quadratic contrasts for each three-level factor (14 in all), and a single main effect contrast for the two-level factor. The additional contrasts turn out to be two interaction contrasts between the two-level factor and the three-level factor immediately next to it in column 2 (if we call these factors $A$ and $B$, then these interactions might be written $A \times B_\ell$ and $A \times B_q$ for example).

The confounding pattern for the other interactions is somewhat similar to the confounding pattern for $L_{12}(2^{11})$. For example, with $B, C, \ldots, H$ denoting three-level factors allocated to columns 2, 3, . . ., 8, the linear by linear interaction contrast for factors $B$ and $C$ is a function of other contrasts, specifically $B_\ell \times C_\ell = -\frac{1}{4}D_\ell - \frac{1}{4}F_\ell - \frac{1}{12}H_\ell - \frac{1}{2}D_q + \frac{1}{6}E_q - \frac{1}{4}F_q$. In his work, Taguchi favours $L_{18}$ over other three-level arrays like $L_{27}$. Interestingly, Taguchi does not mention Starks' array in his writing.

A more ambitious plan that mixes two- and three-level factors together is $L_{36}(2^{11}.3^{12})$ — see Table 7.3. This array allows for up to 11 two-level factors and 12 three-level factors. There are 35 contrasts available from this plan, and these are used up by the main effects, one for each of the two-level factors (11) and two for each of the three-level factors (24). In this plan, all interactions bias the main effects. Because the array is so big, the confounding pattern is very complicated and is not worth writing down.

It is interesting to note that the two-level part of this plan is made up of three $L_{12}$ arrays (for example, rows 1, 4, 7, . . ., 34 is one of them), so that the confounding pattern for this part of the array is as discussed in Chapter 4. Taguchi often recommends $L_{36}$ for this reason.

Both $L_{18}$ and $L_{36}$ allow for two-level factors and three-level factors to exist in the same plan, but having just these two arrays is too restrictive to cover all situations where we may need to experiment with a mix of two- and three-level factors, and we require a more flexible approach. We deal with this point in the next three sections.

## 7.2 ASSIGNING A TWO-LEVEL FACTOR TO A THREE-LEVEL ARRAY

We begin by considering the method of *column collapsing*. This technique enables us to re-write an array by collapsing a $j$-level factor into a $(j-1)$-level factor, simply by coding *two* of the levels of the $j$-level factor into *one* of the levels of the $(j-1)$-level factor. The procedure is best illustrated directly by a simple example with $j = 3$:

| Three-level factor | | Two-level factor | |
|---|---|---|---|
| – | | – | |
| 0 | ⇒ | – | [7.2] |
| + | | + | |

or

| Three-level factor | | Two-level factor |
|---|---|---|
| – | | – |
| 0 | ⇒ | + |
| + | | + |

*Table 7.3* The $L_{36}(2^{11}.3^{12})$ orthogonal array

| Row | | | | | | | | | | | | | | | | | | | | | | | |
|---|---|---|---|---|---|---|---|---|---|---|---|---|---|---|---|---|---|---|---|---|---|---|---|
| 1 | − | − | − | − | − | − | − | − | − | − | − | − | − | − | − | − | − | − | − | − | − | − | − |
| 2 | − | − | − | − | − | − | − | − | − | − | − | 0 | 0 | 0 | 0 | 0 | 0 | 0 | 0 | 0 | 0 | 0 | 0 |
| 3 | − | − | − | − | − | − | − | − | − | − | − | + | + | + | + | + | + | + | + | + | + | + | + |
| 4 | − | − | − | − | − | + | + | + | + | + | + | − | − | − | − | 0 | 0 | 0 | 0 | + | + | + | + |
| 5 | − | − | − | − | − | + | + | + | + | + | + | 0 | 0 | 0 | 0 | + | + | + | + | − | − | − | − |
| 6 | − | − | − | − | − | + | + | + | + | + | + | + | + | + | + | − | − | − | − | 0 | 0 | 0 | 0 |
| 7 | − | − | + | + | + | − | − | − | + | + | + | − | − | 0 | + | − | 0 | + | + | − | 0 | 0 | + |
| 8 | − | − | + | + | + | − | − | − | + | + | + | 0 | 0 | + | − | 0 | + | − | − | 0 | + | + | − |
| 9 | − | − | + | + | + | − | − | − | + | + | + | + | + | − | 0 | + | − | 0 | 0 | + | − | − | 0 |
| 10 | − | + | − | + | + | − | + | + | − | − | + | − | − | + | 0 | − | + | 0 | + | 0 | − | + | 0 |
| 11 | − | + | − | + | + | − | + | + | − | − | + | 0 | 0 | − | + | 0 | − | + | − | + | 0 | − | + |
| 12 | − | + | − | + | + | − | + | + | − | − | + | + | + | 0 | − | + | 0 | − | 0 | − | + | 0 | − |
| 13 | − | + | + | − | + | + | − | + | − | + | − | − | 0 | + | − | + | 0 | − | + | + | 0 | − | 0 |
| 14 | − | + | + | − | + | + | − | + | − | + | − | 0 | + | − | 0 | − | + | 0 | − | − | + | 0 | + |
| 15 | − | + | + | − | + | + | − | + | − | + | − | + | − | 0 | + | 0 | − | + | 0 | 0 | − | + | − |
| 16 | − | + | + | + | − | + | + | − | + | − | − | − | 0 | + | 0 | − | − | + | 0 | + | + | 0 | − |
| 17 | − | + | + | + | − | + | + | − | + | − | − | 0 | + | − | + | 0 | 0 | − | + | − | − | + | 0 |

| | | | | | | | | | | | | | | | | | | | | | | | |
|---|---|---|---|---|---|---|---|---|---|---|---|---|---|---|---|---|---|---|---|---|---|---|---|
| 18 | − | + | + | + | − | + | + | − | + | − | − | + | − | 0 | − | + | + | 0 | − | 0 | 0 | − | + |
| 19 | + | − | + | + | − | − | + | + | − | + | − | − | 0 | − | + | + | + | − | 0 | 0 | − | 0 | + |
| 20 | + | − | + | + | − | − | + | + | − | + | − | 0 | + | 0 | − | − | − | 0 | + | + | 0 | + | − |
| 21 | + | − | + | + | − | − | + | + | − | + | − | + | − | + | 0 | 0 | 0 | + | − | − | + | − | 0 |
| 22 | + | − | + | − | + | + | + | − | − | − | + | − | 0 | 0 | + | + | − | 0 | − | − | + | + | 0 |
| 23 | + | − | + | − | + | + | + | − | − | − | + | 0 | + | + | − | − | 0 | + | 0 | 0 | − | − | + |
| 24 | + | − | + | − | + | + | + | − | − | − | + | + | − | − | 0 | 0 | + | − | + | + | 0 | 0 | − |
| 25 | + | − | − | + | + | + | − | + | + | − | − | − | + | 0 | − | 0 | + | + | − | + | − | 0 | 0 |
| 26 | + | − | − | + | + | + | − | + | + | − | − | 0 | − | + | 0 | + | − | − | 0 | − | 0 | + | + |
| 27 | + | − | − | + | + | + | − | + | + | − | − | + | 0 | − | + | − | 0 | 0 | + | 0 | + | − | − |
| 28 | + | + | + | − | − | − | − | + | + | − | + | − | + | 0 | 0 | 0 | − | − | + | 0 | + | − | + |
| 29 | + | + | + | − | − | − | − | + | + | − | + | 0 | − | + | + | + | 0 | 0 | − | + | − | 0 | − |
| 30 | + | + | + | − | − | − | − | + | + | − | + | + | 0 | − | − | − | + | + | 0 | − | 0 | + | 0 |
| 31 | + | + | − | + | − | + | − | − | − | + | + | − | + | + | + | 0 | + | 0 | 0 | − | 0 | − | − |
| 32 | + | + | − | + | − | + | − | − | − | + | + | 0 | − | − | − | + | − | + | + | 0 | + | 0 | 0 |
| 33 | + | + | − | + | − | + | − | − | − | + | + | + | 0 | 0 | 0 | − | 0 | − | − | + | − | + | + |
| 34 | + | + | − | − | + | − | + | − | + | + | − | − | + | − | 0 | + | 0 | + | − | 0 | 0 | + | − |
| 35 | + | + | − | − | + | − | + | − | + | + | − | 0 | − | 0 | + | − | + | − | 0 | + | + | − | 0 |
| 36 | + | + | − | − | + | − | + | − | + | + | − | + | 0 | + | − | 0 | − | 0 | + | − | − | 0 | + |

Here, we choose to re-code the (0) in the three-level array to either a (−) or a (+). It does not matter which re-coding is chosen but it is a good idea to arrange that in the re-coded column the level we know least about occurs the most.

Table 7.4 shows the plan given by applying the column collapsing scheme [7.2] on the first column of $L_9(3^4)$. To measure the effect of the two-level factor in this array, the appropriate contrast is [−1,−1,−1,−1,−1,−1,+2, +2,+2] and the divisor is 6. Another contrast is available in [−1,−1,−1,+1, +1,+1,0,0,0], where the −1 matches the (−) in the original array, and the +1 matches the original (0). If all interactions are negligible, this contrast measures only experimental error. Note that these contrasts resemble a pair of linear and quadratic contrasts for the original plan, but in the re-coded plan their interpretation is quite different.

*Table 7.4* Allocating a two-level factor to $L_9(3^4)$

| Original plan | | | | | Resulting plan | | | |
|---|---|---|---|---|---|---|---|---|
| $c_1$ | $c_2$ | $c_3$ | $c_4$ | | $c_1$ | $c_2$ | $c_3$ | $c_4$ |
| − | − | − | − | | − | − | − | − |
| − | 0 | 0 | 0 | | − | 0 | 0 | 0 |
| − | + | + | + | Apply | − | + | + | + |
| 0 | − | 0 | + | [7.2] | − | − | 0 | + |
| 0 | 0 | + | − | ⇒ to ⇒ | − | 0 | + | − |
| 0 | + | − | 0 | $c_1$ | − | + | − | 0 |
| + | − | + | 0 | | + | − | + | 0 |
| + | 0 | − | + | | + | 0 | − | + |
| + | + | 0 | − | | + | + | 0 | − |

Another two-level factor can be allocated to $L_9$ in exactly the same way by collapsing another column, say $c_2$. The $L_9$ array can in theory be used to allocate up to four two-level factors, one for each of the original columns, but in practice we would only allocate up to two two-level factors for reasons that we shall see in Section 7.3.

In much the same way, the three-level factors in $L_{18}(2^1.3^7)$ can be re-coded into two-level factors to give plans for $2^2.3^6$, $2^3.3^5$, $2^4.3^4$ etc. $L_{27}$ and $L_{36}$ can also be re-coded in this way, each new two-level factor replacing a three-level factor.

## Interactions

Interactions between the factors in the new array will be confounded with several other effects in a similar fashion to the interactions between the three-level factors in the original plan. Interaction contrasts can be generated as usual, by multiplying the relevant main effect contrasts. Interactions between two- and three-level factors involve only two types ($A \times B_\ell$ and $A \times B_q$, say, for a quantitative three-level factor $B$). For example, in Table 7.4 the interaction between the two-level factor and the linear effect of the three-level factor immediately next to it in the plan is measured by the contrast [+1,0,−1,+1,0, −1,−2,0,+2], but this is a mixture of contrasts available from the other two three-level factors.

## 7.3 ASSIGNING A THREE-LEVEL FACTOR TO A TWO-LEVEL ARRAY

The method of Section 7.2 applies when the basic plan is taken as a three-level one, and works best when the number of two-level factors is small compared to the number of three-level factors. This section deals with the reverse case, when the number of three-level factors is small compared to the number of two-level factors, and the basic plan is taken as a two-level array.

Three-level factors are assigned to two-level arrays by using the method of *column combining* to construct a four-level factor, then collapsing the four-level factor to a three-level factor by the method of Section 7.2. It is best to illustrate the method directly, and we use $L_8(2^7)$ to do so. Its multiplication table is reproduced for convenience as Table 7.5.

To assign a three-level factor to $L_8$, we choose a set of three columns such that, when any two are multiplied together, the result is the third column. Such a set, for example $c_1$, $c_2$ and $c_3$, is said to be *closed under multiplication*. For the purpose of re-coding we discard one of these columns ($c_3$ say) and concentrate on the other two, but all three must be left empty in the final plan.

We note first that there are four combinations of (+) and (−) that occur in $c_1$ and $c_2$, that is (+,+) in runs 4 and 8, (+,−) in runs 2 and 6, (−,+) in runs 3 and 7 and (−,−) in runs 1 and 5 (Table 7.6), and we can take these combinations as representing levels of a new four-level factor and stop at this

*Table 7.5* Column multiplication table for $L_8(2^7)$

| Column number | Column number 2 | 3 | 4 | 5 | 6 | 7 |
|---|---|---|---|---|---|---|
| 1 | 3 | 2 | 5 | 4 | 7 | 6 |
| 2 | | 1 | 6 | 7 | 4 | 5 |
| 3 | | | 7 | 6 | 5 | 4 |
| 4 | | | | 1 | 2 | 3 |
| 5 | | | | | 3 | 2 |
| 6 | | | | | | 1 |

point. Alternatively we can collapse the four-level factor into a three-level factor. This whole procedure is illustrated below:

| $c_1$ | $c_2$ | | Four-level factor | | Three-level factor |
|---|---|---|---|---|---|
| + | + | | ++ (high level) | | + (high level) |
| + | − | | + (mid-high level) | | 0 (mid-level) |
| − | + | ⇒ | − (mid-low level) | ⇒ | 0 (mid-level) |
| − | − | | −− (low level) | | − (low level) |

[7.3]

Other coding schemes could be used, for example:

| $c_1$ | $c_2$ | | Three-level factor |
|---|---|---|---|
| + | + | | 0 |
| + | − | | + |
| − | + | ⇒ | − |
| − | − | | − |

[7.4]

The coding scheme should be chosen to suit the application.

The basic $L_8(2^7)$ and the plan that results from using [7.3] are shown in Table 7.6. The modified plan is denoted $L_8(2^4.3^1)$.

Chapter 12 gives details of an experiment that used a generalization of the re-coding scheme illustrated by [7.3] to allocate a six-level factor to $L_{18}$. This was achieved by combining the two-level factor in the first column of Table 7.2 with the three-level factor in the second column. If this is done, there are six combinations of (−,+) in the first column with (−,0,+) in the second column, and each combination provides a level for the new factor.

## Linear and quadratic contrasts

Whether [7.3], [7.4] or an alternative coding is used, the levels of the three-level factor will not occur in equal proportions. To take account of this, use [7.1] to find the quadratic contrasts, and [7.5] to find the linear contrasts:

$$\text{linear contrast} = \tfrac{1}{2}(\bar{y}_+ - \bar{y}_-) \qquad [7.5]$$

For the new plan in Table 7.6 the contrasts are shown in Table 7.7. Note that the quadratic contrast is just $c_3$, the discarded column, in −1/+1 form! There are also four contrasts available for the two-level factors. This totals six. The missing contrast is [0,−1,+1,0,0,−1,+1,0], based on the four runs at the mid-level of the new three-level factor, which can be thought of as a checking contrast for interactions between the factors in $c_4$ to $c_7$.

*Table 7.6* Introducing a three-level factor into $L_8(2^7)$

| Row | $c_1$ | $c_2$ | $c_3$ | $c_4$ | $c_5$ | $c_6$ | $c_7$ | | Three-level factor | $c_4$ | $c_5$ | $c_6$ | $c_7$ |
|---|---|---|---|---|---|---|---|---|---|---|---|---|---|
| 1 | − | − | + | − | + | + | − | | − | − | + | + | − |
| 2 | + | − | − | − | − | + | + | | 0 | − | − | + | + |
| 3 | − | + | − | − | + | − | + | Apply | 0 | − | + | − | + |
| 4 | + | + | + | − | − | − | − | [7.3] | + | − | − | − | − |
| 5 | − | − | + | + | − | − | + | ⇒ to ⇒ | − | + | − | − | + |
| 6 | + | − | − | + | + | − | − | $c_1$, $c_2$, $c_3$ | 0 | + | + | − | − |
| 7 | − | + | − | + | − | + | − | | 0 | + | − | + | − |
| 8 | + | + | + | + | + | + | + | | + | + | + | + | + |

*Table 7.7* Main effect contrasts for the three-level factor in Table 7.6

| Three-level factor | Main effect contrasts Linear | Quadratic |
|---|---|---|
| − | −1 | +1 |
| 0 | 0 | −1 |
| 0 | 0 | −1 |
| + | +1 | +1 |
| − | −1 | +1 |
| 0 | 0 | −1 |
| 0 | 0 | −1 |
| + | +1 | +1 |
| Divisor | 4 | 4 |

## More than one three-level factor

To allocate another three-level factor to $L_8$ using the coding scheme [7.3] requires us to find another three columns that are closed under multiplication. Unfortunately, no such set of columns exists without involving one of $c_1$, $c_2$, or $c_3$, which we have already used. This means that we can only allocate one three-level factor to $L_8$. For two three-level factors we could use $L_9$, which has just one more run, and accommodate the two-level factors using the methods of Section 7.2.

Of the larger two-level arrays, we cannot modify $L_{12}$ at all because it does not have a column multiplication table. As a consequence, we cannot modify the two-level part of the $L_{36}$ array to take more three-level factors. Fortunately, $L_{16}(2^{15})$ is much more flexible and works in exactly the same way as $L_8$. We reproduce its multiplication table as Table 7.8.

To allocate three-level factors to $L_{16}$ we adopt the same re-coding method as for $L_8$. In the case of $L_{16}$ there are, from Table 7.8, five distinct groups of three columns that are closed under multiplication, these being $c_1$, $c_2$ and $c_3$; $c_4$, $c_8$ and $c_{12}$; $c_7$, $c_9$ and $c_{14}$; $c_5$, $c_{10}$ and $c_{15}$; and $c_6$, $c_{11}$ and $c_{13}$. Therefore we can allocate up to five three-level factors. For each three-level factor allocated, we lose three two-level factors, so we end up with plans such as $L_{16}(2^{12}.3^1)$, $L_{16}(2^9.3^2)$, $L_{16}(2^6.3^3)$, $L_{16}(2^3.3^4)$ and $L_{16}(3^5)$. Alternatives to the latter two plans can be derived using Starks' $L_{16}(3^7)$ in Section 7.1. The $L_{16}(2^3.3^4)$ is obtained by using the method of Section 7.2 on three columns, and the $L_{16}(3^5)$ just by leaving two of the columns empty.

In Appendix 7.1 we give a table of mixed-level plans that can be obtained by converting a basic two- or three-level array according to one of the schemes in Sections 7.2 and 7.3. This table is based on a larger version given in the book by Dey (1985) (it is his table 3.4), with some additions that Dey appears to have missed out with respect to $L_{18}$. For all the designs in

*Table 7.8* Column multiplication table for $L_{16}(2^{15})$

| Column number | Column number | | | | | | | | | | | | | |
|---|---|---|---|---|---|---|---|---|---|---|---|---|---|---|
| | 2 | 3 | 4 | 5 | 6 | 7 | 8 | 9 | 10 | 11 | 12 | 13 | 14 | 15 |
| 1 | 3 | 2 | 5 | 4 | 7 | 6 | 9 | 8 | 11 | 10 | 13 | 12 | 15 | 14 |
| 2 | | 1 | 6 | 7 | 4 | 5 | 10 | 11 | 8 | 9 | 14 | 15 | 12 | 13 |
| 3 | | | 7 | 6 | 5 | 4 | 11 | 10 | 9 | 8 | 15 | 14 | 13 | 12 |
| 4 | | | | 1 | 2 | 3 | 12 | 13 | 14 | 15 | 8 | 9 | 10 | 11 |
| 5 | | | | | 3 | 2 | 13 | 12 | 15 | 14 | 9 | 8 | 11 | 10 |
| 6 | | | | | | 1 | 14 | 15 | 12 | 13 | 10 | 11 | 8 | 9 |
| 7 | | | | | | | 15 | 14 | 13 | 12 | 11 | 10 | 9 | 8 |
| 8 | | | | | | | | 1 | 2 | 3 | 4 | 5 | 6 | 7 |
| 9 | | | | | | | | | 3 | 2 | 5 | 4 | 7 | 6 |
| 10 | | | | | | | | | | 1 | 6 | 7 | 4 | 5 |
| 11 | | | | | | | | | | | 7 | 6 | 5 | 4 |
| 12 | | | | | | | | | | | | 1 | 2 | 3 |
| 13 | | | | | | | | | | | | | 3 | 2 |
| 14 | | | | | | | | | | | | | | 1 |

Appendix 7.1 the main effects can be measured by the conventional orthogonal contrasts, provided it is remembered that, when levels do not occur in equal proportions, linear contrasts are obtained via [7.5] and quadratic contrasts via [7.1]. Such designs are known technically as orthogonal main effect plans.

## Interactions with a three-level factor

We return to the case of $L_8(2^7)$ and suppose for the moment that the new three-level factor ($T$ say) is quantitative. We consider its interaction with one of the two-level factors ($A$, allocated to $c_4$ say). Then two interaction contrasts are available, obtained as usual by multiplying the linear and quadratic contrasts by the two-level contrast. They are shown (without divisors) in Table 7.9.

If the three-level factor is qualitative, many possibilities arise. For example, imagine an experiment in which the performance of an engine in terms of torque is compared in the presence and absence of a turbo-charger. An added complication is that two versions of the turbo-charger are available. This generates a factor (we will call it $T$ again) at three 'levels' as follows:

- Turbo-charger present in version 1.
- Turbo-charger present in version 2.
- Turbo-charger absent.

We will call these levels (−), (+), (0), respectively. This is not intended to imply that 'Turbo-charger absent' lies some way *between* 'Turbo-charger present in version 1' and 'Turbo-charger present in version 2'. It is just a

*Table 7.9* Contrasts for the new array in Table 7.6

| $T_\ell$ | $T_q$ | $A$ | $T_\ell \times A$ | $T_q \times A$ |
|---|---|---|---|---|
| −1 | +1 | −1 | +1 | −1 |
| 0 | −1 | −1 | 0 | +1 |
| 0 | −1 | −1 | 0 | +1 |
| +1 | +1 | −1 | −1 | −1 |
| −1 | +1 | +1 | −1 | +1 |
| 0 | −1 | +1 | 0 | −1 |
| 0 | −1 | +1 | 0 | −1 |
| +1 | +1 | +1 | +1 | +1 |

convenient way to label the levels. Given this labelling, the re-coding scheme [7.3] is sensible because the number of engines with turbo-charger 1 is the same as with turbo-charger 2 and the numbers of engines with and without the turbo-charger are the same.

The main effect contrasts in Table 7.9 now have the nice interpretation of comparing the two versions ('linear' contrast), and comparing the average for turbo-charger present with the average for turbo-charger absent ('quadratic' contrast).

The two interaction contrasts in Table 7.9 answer, respectively, the following questions:

(i) How different is the $A$ effect for turbo-charger 1 and turbo-charger 2?
(ii) How different is the $A$ effect when a turbo-charger is present and absent?

Returning to the quantitative interpretation, the $T_\ell \times A$ contrast is not orthogonal to $c_5$ and $c_6$ and in fact is equal to half their sum, while $T_q \times A$ is identical to $c_7$, so to study these interactions we would have to leave the rest of the array empty! (We may wish to ignore the $T_q \times A$ interaction, since this is a third-order effect.) The position is not so serious in larger arrays, but measuring interactions takes up many of the available degrees of freedom.

If the reader is interested in studying interactions in mixed-level plans, Dey (1985) gives a table of resolution IV plans (his table 4.5). Orthogonal resolution V plans generally require a prohibitive number of runs. However, Margolin (1969) gives some plans for the case of one three-level factor. His designs are only partially orthogonal, which helps to keep the experiment to a manageable size. Margolin's designs can be written in the form shown in Table 7.10, where $A$, $B$, ... are two-level factors and $T$ is the three-level factor. $S_-$, $S_0$, and $S_+$ are *subdesigns*. Each of them specifies the levels of all the two-level factors in some of the runs in the experiment. $S_+$ is always given by switching the signs in $S_-$, i.e. by *reflection* or *fold-over*. The following (non-orthogonal) resolution V plans are available:

- $2^3.3^1$ in 16 runs: $S_- = L_4$; $S_0 = c_1$, $c_2$ and $c_4$ of $L_8$.
- $2^4.3^1$ in 24 runs: $S_- = S_0 = c_1$, $c_2$, $c_4$ and $c_7$ of $L_8$.

- $2^5.3^1$ in 32 runs: $S_- =$ any five columns of $L_8$; $S_0 = c_1, c_2, c_4, c_8$ and $c_{15}$ of $L_{16}$.
- $2^6.3^1$ in 48 runs: $S_- = S_0 = c_1, c_2, c_4, c_7, c_8$ and $c_{11}$ of $L_{16}$.

## 7.4 THE IDLE COLUMN METHOD

Taguchi has developed a method for assigning more three-level factors to a two-level array than is possible using the method of Section 7.3. This technique is called the *idle column method.* The drawback with the idle column method is that it does not produce orthogonal main effect plans in the sense defined in Section 7.3. We illustrate the method using the $L_8(2^7)$ array. Extension to $L_{16}$, $L_{32}$, etc., is straightforward. It cannot be used for $L_{12}$ or any plan that does not have a multiplication table.

Let $T$ and $S$ be three-level factors, with $A$, $B$, . . . reserved for two-level factors. The idle column method proceeds as follows. Choose any column of $L_8$ to be the idle column, for example $c_1$. The levels of $T$ are decided by re-coding a pair of columns whose product is $c_1$. From the column multiplication table (Table 7.5) two such columns are $c_2$ and $c_3$. The levels of factor $T$ are decided by the following re-coding scheme:

| $c_2$ | $c_3$ | $T$ |
|---|---|---|
| − | − | − |
| − | + | 0 |
| + | − | + |
| + | + | 0 |

[7.6]

At first sight, this scheme looks similar to those of Section 7.3, but the difference here is that the scheme [7.6] must be strictly adhered to. Apparently minor changes to the coding (such as using [7.3]) can have serious consequences for the resulting plan.

The levels of the other three-level factor $S$ are defined by applying [7.6] to *another* pair of columns whose product is $c_1$ (for example $c_4$ and $c_5$). We end up with the plan in Table 7.11 for two two-level factors and two three-level factors in eight runs. This may seem surprising since we said in Section 7.3 that we could not allocate more than one three-level factor to $L_8$, and the astute reader will naturally question the validity of this new plan. The price for allocating two three-level factors to $L_8$ is that the resulting design is not orthogonal with respect to the conventional main effect contrasts. Recalling that the quadratic contrasts will be of the form [7.1], we get the contrasts in Table 7.12.

The $T_q$ and $S_q$ contrasts are just (minus) $c_3$ and $c_5$ from the original $L_8$, but the $T_\ell$ and $S_\ell$ contrasts are not orthogonal. To cope with the non-orthogonality we could use the technique of multiple regression, as in Chapter

*Table 7.10* Margolin's resolution V designs

| A | B | C | etc. | T |
|---|---|---|---|---|
| | | | | − |
| | | | | · |
| | $S_-$ | | | · |
| | | | | · |
| | | | | − |
| | | | | 0 |
| | | | | · |
| | $S_0$ | | | · |
| | | | | · |
| | | | | 0 |
| | | | | + |
| | | | | · |
| | $S_+$ | | | · |
| | | | | · |
| | | | | + |

*Table 7.11* An idle column design based on $L_8(2^7)$

| T | S | A | B |
|---|---|---|---|
| 0 | 0 | + | − |
| − | − | + | + |
| + | 0 | − | + |
| 0 | − | − | − |
| 0 | + | − | + |
| − | 0 | − | − |
| + | + | + | − |
| 0 | 0 | + | + |

*Table 7.12* Conventional linear and quadratic contrasts for the plan in Table 7.11

| | $T_\ell$ | $T_q$ | $S_\ell$ | $S_q$ |
|---|---|---|---|---|
| | 0 | −1 | 0 | −1 |
| | −1 | +1 | −1 | +1 |
| | +1 | +1 | 0 | −1 |
| | 0 | −1 | −1 | +1 |
| | 0 | −1 | +1 | +1 |
| | −1 | +1 | 0 | −1 |
| | +1 | +1 | +1 | +1 |
| | 0 | −1 | 0 | −1 |
| Divisor | 4 | 4 | 4 | 4 |

6. It turns out, though, that a simpler approach is available, based on the surprising fact that each of the original columns of $L_8(2^7)$ (apart from the idle column itself) measures a main effect in the new plan. Specifically, $c_2$ measures the linear effect of $T$, $c_4$ the linear effect of $S$, and (as we have already shown in Table 7.12) $c_3$ and $c_5$ are (minus) the usual quadratic contrasts. There is a sense in which $c_2$ and $c_4$ are not the most efficient measures of the linear effects, but they are orthogonal, to each other and to all the other contrasts. Orthogonality is useful for many reasons, for example it helps to justify using a Daniel plot of the contrast values.

The idle column itself, $c_1$, can be used as a blocking contrast, provided that the block effect is of no interest. For more details on the idle column method see the paper by Grove and Davis (1991), which includes tables comparing idle column designs with those which can be obtained from standard arrays using the methods of Sections 7.2 and 7.3.

The idle column method can also be used when one factor has a large number of levels: see Taguchi (1987) for an example of re-coding $L_{16}(2^{15})$ to produce a $2^2.3^3.7^1$ plan.

## 7.5 NESTED FACTORS

There is another way of thinking about qualitative three-level factors. Returning to the hypothetical example of turbo-chargers, the factor $T$ can be thought of as a combination of two factors $T_1$ and $T_2$. Factor $T_1$ has two levels (turbo present, turbo absent). Factor $T_2$ also has two levels (version 1 and version 2), *but it only operates at one level of* $T_1$, and is said to be nested within that level of $T_1$.

In other experiments, two *different* factors ($T_2$ and $T_3$) may be nested within the two levels of $T_1$. In order to write down contrasts for this type of experiment we define four average $y$ values as follows:

$$
\begin{aligned}
\bar{y}_1&: T_1 \text{ at } (-),\ T_2 \text{ at } (-)\\
\bar{y}_2&: T_1 \text{ at } (-),\ T_2 \text{ at } (+)\\
\bar{y}_3&: T_1 \text{ at } (+),\ T_3 \text{ at } (-)\\
\bar{y}_4&: T_1 \text{ at } (+),\ T_3 \text{ at } (+)
\end{aligned}
$$

The main effect contrasts are defined in Table 7.13. Note that these coefficients could equally well be used to find three orthogonal main effect contrasts for a single four-level factor. In fact, any plan with a four-level factor can be converted to accommodate nested two-level factors.

*Table 7.13* Main effect contrasts for nested two-level factors

| | $T_1$ | $T_2$ | $T_3$ | |
|---|---|---|---|---|
| | −1 | −1 | 0 | $\bar{y}_1$ |
| | −1 | +1 | 0 | $\bar{y}_2$ |
| | +1 | 0 | +1 | $\bar{y}_3$ |
| | +1 | 0 | +1 | $\bar{y}_4$ |
| Divisor | 2 | 1 | 1 | |

## 7.6 LINEAR GRAPHS

Taguchi has invented what he calls *linear graphs* to describe the column multiplication structure of orthogonal arrays. Linear graphs are an arrangement of dots (nodes) with lines (links) joining the dots in various ways. Numbers are written next to nodes and links, which represent columns in the orthogonal array. The number on the *link* is the column that is the result of multiplying the columns on the two linked *nodes*.

We discuss here only the linear graphs for two-level arrays, since these are the most useful, and as an illustration we concentrate on $L_{16}(2^{15})$. There are many linear graphs for $L_{16}$, and each one provides a 'snapshot' of the column multiplication structure of the whole array. Figure 7.1 shows three basic types of linear graph for $L_{16}$. The different symbols used to represent the nodes are explained in Taguchi (1986).

Figures 7.1(a), (b) and (c) show linear graphs that are useful for allocating three-level factors to $L_{16}$ in the manner described in Section 7.3. For example, Fig. 7.1(a) gives us the following information:

- Multiplying column 1 by column 2 gives column 3.
- Multiplying column 4 by column 8 gives column 12.
- Multiplying column 5 by column 10 gives column 15.
- Multiplying column 7 by column 9 gives column 14.
- Multiplying column 6 by column 11 gives column 13.

Hence $c_1$, $c_2$ and $c_3$ provide a 'closed' set of columns to be re-coded into the three-level factor, as do $c_4$, $c_8$ and $c_{12}$; $c_7$, $c_9$ and $c_{14}$; $c_5$, $c_{10}$ and $c_{15}$; and $c_6$, $c_{11}$ and $c_{13}$. These are the sets that we picked out originally in Section 7.3 using the column multiplication table of $L_{16}(2^{15})$. However, the linear graphs in Figs 7.1(b) and (c) could be used just as well, resulting in different sets of columns. Whichever linear graph is used, a total of five three-level factors can be allocated to $L_{16}$ in this way.

The linear graphs illustrated in Figs 7.1(d), (e) and (f) are fundamentally different from the graphs in Figs 7.1(a), (b) and (c). For example, Fig. 7.1(d) gives the following information:

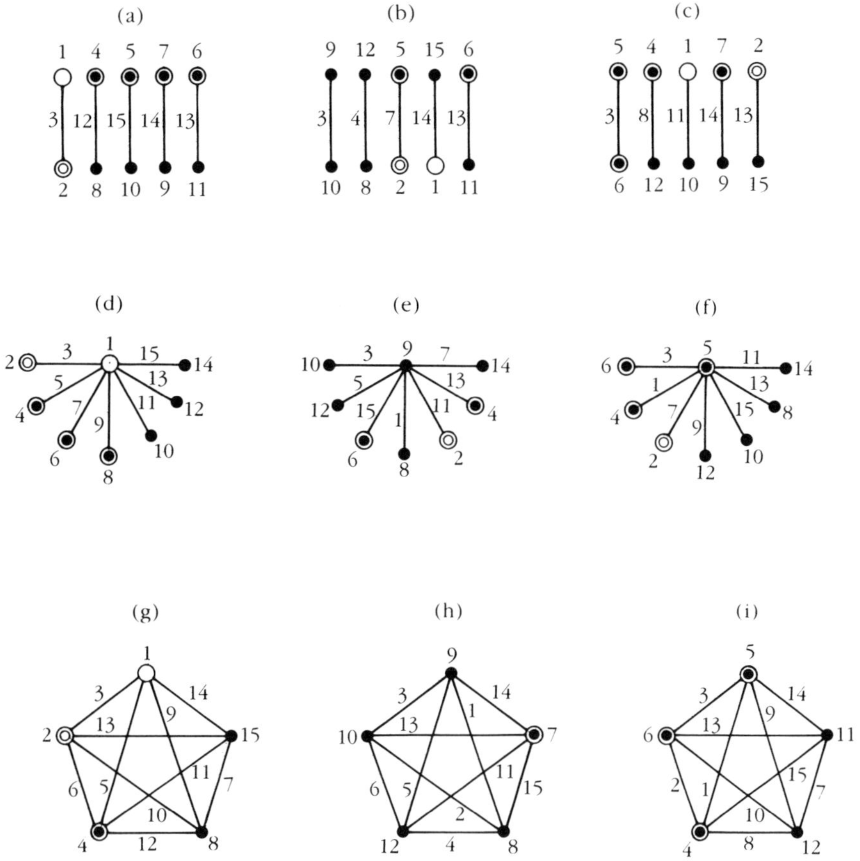


*Fig. 7.1* Three basic types of linear graph for $L_{16}(2^{15})$ (Taguchi, 1986)

- Multiplying column 1 by column 2 gives column 3.
- Multiplying column 1 by column 4 gives column 5.
- Multiplying column 1 by column 6 gives column 7.
- Multiplying column 1 by column 8 gives column 9.
- Multiplying column 1 by column 10 gives column 11.
- Multiplying column 1 by column 12 gives column 13.
- Multiplying column 1 by column 14 gives column 15.

Notice that column 1 is a node for every link. Linear graphs of this nature are useful when choosing an *idle column* as described in Section 7.4. With column 1 as the idle column, seven three-level factors can be accommodated by re-coding $c_2$ and $c_3$, $c_4$ and $c_5$, $c_6$ and $c_7$, $c_8$ and $c_9$, $c_{10}$ and $c_{11}$, $c_{12}$ and $c_{13}$, and $c_{14}$ and $c_{15}$. The linear graphs in Figs 7.1(e) and (f) could be used just as well.

### Using linear graphs to identify interactions

Because linear graphs illustrate the column multiplication structure of the orthogonal array, it is tempting to try to use them to identify interaction contrasts, since interaction contrasts are just given by multiplying main effect contrasts. However, because the linear graph is only a snapshot of the whole structure of the array, it is only possible to identify *some* interaction contrasts by using a linear graph. This gives us an incomplete picture of the confounding pattern. For example, if we used Fig. 7.1(a) we would rightly conclude that, for factor $A$ in column 5 and factor $B$ in column 10, the $A \times B$ interaction is measured in column 15. But if we allocate factor $C$ to column 8, the linear graph is no help in telling us where the $A \times C$ and $B \times C$ interactions occur (for the record they are in columns 13 and 2 respectively — see Table 7.8). This is the point that we made very briefly in Section 4.2.

An important and rare exception in the use of linear graphs to discover interaction contrasts occurs in Figs 7.1(g), (h) and (i). There are five nodes in each of these graphs. If factors are allocated to these columns, then, because each node is linked to every other node, every two-factor interaction is identified in a unique column, and so each linear graph represents a resolution V plan.

There are in fact other types of linear graph for $L_{16}(2^{15})$. For an example see the fuel tank case study in Chapter 10.

## SUMMARY OF CHAPTER 7

Starks' array accommodates seven three-level factors. It is balanced, but only in an extended sense that we have not introduced before, known as proportional frequencies. Starks' array has twice as many runs at level (0) as at (−) or (+), and care is necessary in constructing the quadratic contrasts.

$L_{18}$ and $L_{36}$ allow for two-level factors and three-level factors in the same plan, but for a flexible approach to mixed-level experiments we need to be able to modify a wide range of basic two- and three-level arrays.

Two-level factors can be introduced into a three-level array by the method of column collapsing. To introduce a three-level factor into a two-level array requires us to identify a set of three columns that is closed under multiplication. Although only two are used in the re-coding, all three columns are left empty in the final plan. This method actually produces a four-level factor, which can be collapsed into a three-level factor. Several coding schemes might be used. In the resulting three-level columns the levels will not occur in equal proportions, and this must be taken into account in forming the linear as well as the quadratic contrasts.

If the basic array is three-level, interactions between factors in the new array will be confounded with main effects in much the same way as interactions between three-level factors. If the basic array is two-level the confounding pattern is simpler, but measuring such interactions uses up many of the available degrees of freedom.

Margolin listed some non-orthogonal resolution V designs incorporating one three-level and several two-level factors.

Taguchi's idle column method also produces plans that are not fully orthogonal with respect to the usual contrasts, but it turns out that we can still find a simple set of orthogonal contrasts to measure all the linear and quadratic main effects. The main advantage of the idle column method is that it fits more three-level factors into a two-level array than other methods do.

We give a table of mixed-level plans. These are all of the type known as orthogonal main effect plans, which excludes those constructed by the idle column method.

A three-level qualitative factor can often be thought of as a pair of two-level factors, one of them 'nested' within a level of the other. Sometimes two different factors are nested within the two levels of a third factor. Main effect contrasts are easy to write down for this situation.

Taguchi's linear graphs are an arrangement of nodes and links that represent parts of the multiplication table of an orthogonal array. Some types of linear graph are useful for selecting the columns of a two-level array to accommodate three-level factors. In most cases it is unsafe to use a linear graph to work out the confounding pattern of a plan, but there are exceptions to this warning.

## APPENDIX 7.1 MIXED-LEVEL PLANS, AND HOW TO OBTAIN THEM

These are shown in Table A7.1.

*Table A7.1* Mixed-level plans, and how to obtain them.* To use this table, look down the rows until the desired number of three-level factors is found, and then choose the plan that accommodates the number of two-level factors required

| Number of three-level factors | Number of two-level factors | Number of runs | Basic array | Section in which conversion rule is given |
|---|---|---|---|---|
| 1 | 4 | 8 | $L_8(2^7)$ | 7.3 |
| 1 | 12 | 16 | $L_{16}(2^{15})$ | 7.3 |
| 1 | 20 | 24 | $L_{24}(2^{23})$ | 7.3 |
| 1 | 28 | 32 | $L_{32}(2^{31})$ | 7.3 |
| 2 | 2 | 9 | $L_9(3^4)$ | 7.2 |
| 2 | 9 | 16 | $L_{16}(2^{15})$ | 7.3 |
| 2 | 12 | 24 | See Appendix 7.2 | No conversion |
| 2 | 25 | 32 | $L_{32}(2^{31})$ | 7.3 |
| 3 | 1 | 9 | $L_9(3^4)$ | 7.2 |
| 3 | 6 | 16 | $L_{16}(2^{15})$ | 7.3 |
| 3 | 22 | 32 | $L_{32}(2^{31})$ | 7.3 |
| 4 | 3 | 16 | $L_{16}(2^{15})$ | 7.3 |
| | | or 16 | $L_{16}(3^7)$ | 7.2 |
| 4 | 4 | 18 | $L_{18}(2^1.3^7)$ | 7.2 |
| 4 | 9 | 27 | $L_{27}(3^{13})$ | 7.2 |
| 4 | 19 | 32 | $L_{32}(2^{31})$ | 7.3 |
| 5 | 2 | 16 | $L_{16}(3^7)$ | 7.2 |
| 5 | 3 | 18 | $L_{18}(2^1.3^7)$ | 7.2 |
| 5 | 8 | 27 | $L_{27}(3^{13})$ | 7.2 |
| 5 | 16 | 32 | $L_{32}(2^{31})$ | 7.3 |
| 6 | 1 | 16 | $L_{16}(3^7)$ | 7.2 |
| 6 | 2 | 18 | $L_{18}(2^1.3^7)$ | 7.2 |
| 6 | 7 | 27 | $L_{27}(3^{13})$ | 7.2 |
| 6 | 13 | 32 | $L_{32}(2^{31})$ | 7.3 |
| 7 | 1 | 18 | $L_{18}(2^1.3^7)$ | No conversion |
| 7 | 6 | 27 | $L_{27}(3^{13})$ | 7.2 |
| 7 | 10 | 32 | $L_{32}(2^{31})$ | 7.3 |
| 8 | 5 | 27 | $L_{27}(3^{13})$ | 7.2 |
| 8 | 7 | 32 | $L_{32}(2^{31})$ | 7.3 |
| 9 | 4 | 27 | $L_{27}(3^{13})$ | 7.2 |
| 10 | 3 | 27 | $L_{27}(3^{13})$ | 7.2 |
| 11 | 2 | 27 | $L_{27}(3^{13})$ | 7.2 |
| 12 | 1 | 27 | $L_{27}(3^{13})$ | 7.2 |
| 12 | 11 | 36 | $L_{36}(2^{11}.3^{12})$ | No conversion |

*This table is based on a larger version that appears in Dey (1985). The basic arrays can be found in the following places in this book: $L_8$ in Table 2.5; $L_{12}$ in Table 4.4; $L_{16}(2^{15})$ in Table 4.5; Starks' $L_{16}$ in Table 7.1; $L_{18}$ in Table 7.2; $L_{27}$ in Table 5.12; $L_{36}$ in Table 7.3. $L_{24}$ and $L_{32}$ are in Wheeler (1989)

## APPENDIX 7.2 SPECIAL ARRAY BASED ON $L_{12}(2^{11})$

This is given in Table A7.2.

*Table A7.2* Special array based on $L_{12}(2^{11})$. This array accommodates two three-level factors and 12 two-level factors

| Row | | | | | | | | | | | | | | |
|---|---|---|---|---|---|---|---|---|---|---|---|---|---|---|
| 1 | − | − | − | − | − | − | − | − | − | − | − | − | − | − |
| 2 | − | − | − | − | − | − | + | + | + | + | + | + | − | 0 |
| 3 | − | − | − | + | + | + | − | − | − | + | + | + | − | + |
| 4 | + | + | + | − | + | + | − | + | + | − | − | + | − | − |
| 5 | + | + | + | + | − | + | + | − | + | − | + | − | − | 0 |
| 6 | + | + | + | + | + | − | + | + | − | + | − | − | − | + |
| 7 | − | + | − | + | + | − | − | + | + | − | + | − | 0 | − |
| 8 | − | + | − | + | − | + | + | + | − | − | − | + | 0 | 0 |
| 9 | − | + | − | − | + | + | + | − | + | + | − | − | 0 | + |
| 10 | + | − | + | + | − | − | − | − | + | + | − | + | 0 | − |
| 11 | + | − | + | − | + | − | + | − | − | − | + | + | 0 | 0 |
| 12 | + | − | + | − | − | + | − | + | − | + | + | − | 0 | + |
| 13 | + | − | − | + | + | + | + | + | + | + | + | + | 0 | − |
| 14 | + | − | − | + | + | + | − | − | − | − | − | − | 0 | 0 |
| 15 | + | − | − | − | − | − | + | + | + | − | − | − | 0 | + |
| 16 | − | + | + | + | − | − | + | − | − | + | + | − | 0 | − |
| 17 | − | + | + | − | + | − | − | + | − | + | − | + | 0 | 0 |
| 18 | − | + | + | − | − | + | − | − | + | − | + | + | 0 | + |
| 19 | + | + | − | − | − | + | + | − | − | + | − | + | + | − |
| 20 | + | + | − | − | + | − | − | − | + | + | + | − | + | 0 |
| 21 | + | + | − | + | − | − | − | + | − | − | + | + | + | + |
| 22 | − | − | + | − | + | + | + | + | − | − | + | − | + | − |
| 23 | − | − | + | + | − | + | − | + | + | + | − | − | + | 0 |
| 24 | − | − | + | + | + | − | + | − | + | − | − | + | + | + |

CHAPTER 8

# Experiments to measure location and dispersion effects

*When several units of product are made during the same experimental run, measures of location and dispersion can be calculated for each run, and the factors that have important location or dispersion effects can be identified. These factors can be used to reduce the variation of the output and also to adjust or tune the process so that the distribution of the output is correctly centred.*

*In this chapter we use a case study to explain the details of location/dispersion analysis. We also introduce some of the signal-to-noise formulae popularized by Taguchi, and show how they are related to location/dispersion analysis.*

*Except where the base of the logarithm is explicitly stated, we use log to indicate $\log_{10}$ and ln to indicate the natural logarithm.*

## 8.1 MEASURING LOCATION AND DISPERSION EFFECTS

A typical experiment to measure location and dispersion effects would proceed as follows. For each setting of the factors, several (say $n$) units of product are made. From the $n$ values of $y$ we calculate a measure of location or average, and a measure of dispersion. The conventional measures are the arithmetic mean $\bar{y}$ and the standard deviation $s$, but whether these are sensible measures will depend on the behaviour of the process that produced the data. By 'process' we mean not just the manufacturing or assembly process that made the parts, but also the measurement, recording, copying, etc., that gave rise to the actual figures in front of us.

In the ideal situation we will have evidence, based on control charts, that this whole process is in statistical control, and can therefore be represented by

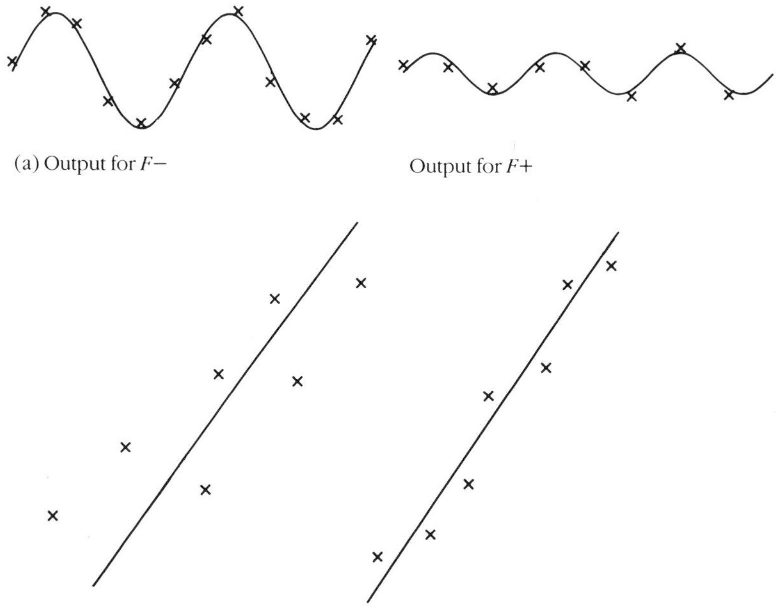

(a) Output for $F-$ Output for $F+$

(b) Output for $F-$ Output for $F+$

*Fig. 8.1* Hypothetical examples of 'unstable' variation. (a) A cyclic trend; (b) a linear trend

a distribution like those in Figs 1.10 and 1.11. Even then we cannot rule out the possibility of the occasional 'flier', 'wild' value or outlier, so it is essential to plot the data in a manner that will draw attention to outliers, before doing any calculation. Gross outliers have a disproportionate effect on $\bar{y}$ and an even more drastic effect on $s$, but as an alternative to deleting them we can use measures that are more *resistant* to the effect of outliers — for example the *median* (to measure location) and the *interquartile range* (for dispersion); see Ryan *et al.* (1985).

We have said that a state of statistical control is the ideal, but we realize that most engineers, if told that they can only experiment on stable processes, would be extremely disappointed. It is the out-of-control processes that they would most like to experiment on! This is a very difficult area in which to give general advice, because so-called *unstable* variation comes in so many different forms. For some of these, measures like the mean and standard deviation do retain some meaning. A hypothetical example is shown in Fig. 8.1(a).

The main type of variation is a regular cycle, and it would be legitimate to use the standard deviation $s$ to measure the improvement given by setting factor $F$ to $(+)$ rather than $(-)$. Standard deviation $s$ is defined as

$$s = \sqrt{\left(\frac{1}{n-1}\sum_{i=1}^{n}(y_i - \bar{y})^2\right)}$$

and $s$ is essentially the root-mean-square deviation from the mean, which is conventionally used to measure the spread of a periodic series.

In Fig. 8.1(a) the process does display a kind of stability, although it is not the kind of stability implied by the concept of statistical control — in the latter case no cycles or trends of any sort should be detectable. When there is a clear linear trend, such as in Fig. 8.1(b), the overall standard deviation would not be a useful way of measuring the difference in variability. There are lots of other possibilities, and we can only caution the reader to think carefully about these issues while planning the experiment and again before interpreting the results.

We have focused this discussion on variation within an experimental run, but the same sources will also contribute to variation between runs. A prime purpose of statistical techniques such as the Daniel plot is to decide how much of the variation between runs can reasonably be attributed to factor effects. As we showed in our discussion of randomization (Section 4.3), unstable 'background' variation between runs can lead to erroneous conclusions. But there is no hard-and-fast boundary between 'legitimate' and 'illegitimate' uses of experimentation and statistical analysis. The proof of the pudding lies, as always, in the success or failure of any *action* we take on the basis of our analysis.

Another important point to bear in mind when planning this type of experiment is that the variability we are primarily interested in measuring is *noise* in Taguchi's sense — sources of variation that would affect the product in normal production and use, and not created by the fact of running an experiment. If the factors include process variables, all $n$ units should be made before the process variables are re-set. Holding the configuration of a system constant while several units are produced is called *repetition*. It should not be confused with *replication*, which we discussed in Chapter 6.

## 8.2 CASE STUDY — TEE CLAMPS

To illustrate the ideas involved in location/dispersion analysis, we consider an experiment on a welding process that produces tee clamps for use in the transmission linkage of a car. Brian Clarke of the Ford Motor Co. Ltd ran this experiment in conjunction with Richard Bowen of W. Lander & Sons Ltd (now Lander Automotive Ltd). The tee clamp consists of two pieces of metal tube welded together, as illustrated in Fig. 8.2.

The weld must be strong enough to withstand the substantial torque required to fit the part to the vehicle. In addition, the height (shown on the drawing with a nominal of 37 mm) was fairly critical for a good fit. So the objective was two-fold: to achieve a height of 37 mm consistently and to maximize the strength of the weld. Both issues were tackled with one experiment.

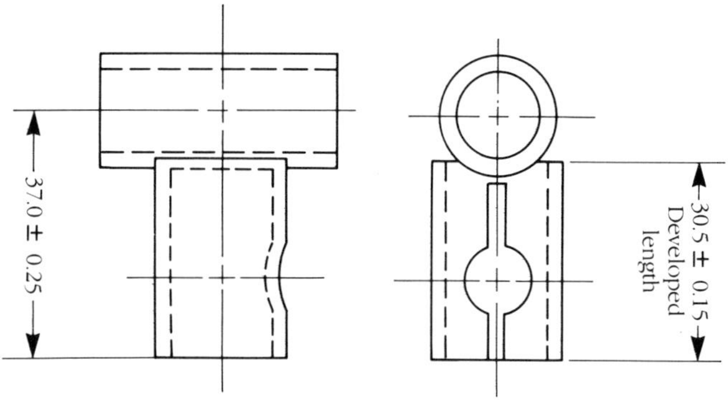


*Fig. 8.2* A tee clamp

After extensive discussion, including brainstorming sessions and the construction of a cause and effect diagram (Fig. 8.3), eight process factors were selected for investigation, each taking two levels:

| | | Level | |
|---|---|---|---|
| Factor | Label | (−) | (+) |
| Air pressure (psi) | *A* | 30 | 45* |
| Tube cleanliness | *T* | As received* | Cleaned |
| Pulse frequency during welding (cycles) | *P* | 0* | 10 |
| Squeeze time prior to welding (cycles) | *S* | 37* | 45 |
| Weld time (cycles) | *W* | 6* | 9 |
| Cool time between pulses (cycles) | *C* | 2* | 10 |
| Hold time after weld is complete (cycles) | *Ho* | 5 | 10* |
| Heat | *He* | 32 | 36* |

* Current process settings

A rough description of the factors is as follows. The air pressure dictates the force with which the two pieces of metal tubing are held together while they are being welded. The cleanliness of the tubing is self-explanatory. The welding equipment has the ability to 'pulse' the weld during the weld cycle, and factor $P$ reflects this ability. Level $(-)$ of factor $P$ is, however, chosen as zero cycles, so this means the weld is not pulsed. The squeeze time ($S$) is how long the two bits of metal are held in position prior to the welding operation, and the weld time ($W$) is the time that the weld is on *per pulse*. The cool time ($C$) is the time between weld pulses, and hold time ($Ho$) is the time that the two pieces of welded metal are held together after the weld is complete. For set-ups where the pulse frequency is zero, the hold time is effectively added to the cool time. Factors $P$, $S$, $W$, $C$ and $Ho$ are measured in cycles of the AC input (50 Hz frequency). Heat (amount of current) is measured in machine-dependent units, and changes the energy of the weld. Levels marked with an asterisk had previously been selected by trial and error over a period of about two months after the delivery of new welding equipment. We will comment on some of the factors individually in the subsequent discussion.

The eight factors were allocated to the first eight columns of an $L_{12}$ array, shown in Table 8.1. Comparison with the $L_{12}$ given in Chapter 4 will reveal that the signs have been switched in some of the columns, but this does not alter the important properties of the array. Each of the contrasts corresponding to the empty columns 9, 10 and 11 measures a complicated combination of interaction effects. Because of the complicated confounding pattern there is really no advantage in leaving columns empty in $L_{12}$. It is better to saturate the array and resolve any concerns about interaction with a follow-up experiment.

Twenty tee clamps were made at each process setting. The height of each was measured, then the weld strength was evaluated by measuring the torque required to break the weld by twisting. As a simple check on the behaviour of the data, dot plots were formed for each set of 20 results. Figure 8.4 shows the plots for height. Each set of data is reasonably well clustered (and plots of the results in time order do not reveal any obvious trends). We feel reasonably safe in using the mean and standard deviation as measures of location and dispersion, respectively. The plots for strength are similar, but more 'discrete' — some sets contain only two distinct values.

The plan and summary results of the experiment are in Table 8.1. The reason for calculating $-20\log(s)$ will be given below. The full set of data is given in Appendix 8.1.

Figure 8.5 is a plot of height against strength for the complete set of data (240 tee clamps), and clearly shows a tendency for high strength to be associated with low height.

Taking the heights first, we measure location and dispersion effects by calculating two distinct sets of 11 contrasts, using the columns of $L_{12}(2^{11})$. We first treat $\bar{y}$ as the response variable, to obtain the location contrasts. We then work with the column of values of $-20\log(s)$ to get the dispersion contrasts. Taking logs of standard deviations makes them behave more like normally distributed random variables with a constant spread, and that reduces the chance that techniques like normal plots and analysis of variance will give misleading results. From a statistical point of view the base of the logarithms is not important, and neither is the factor that multiplies the logarithm. We

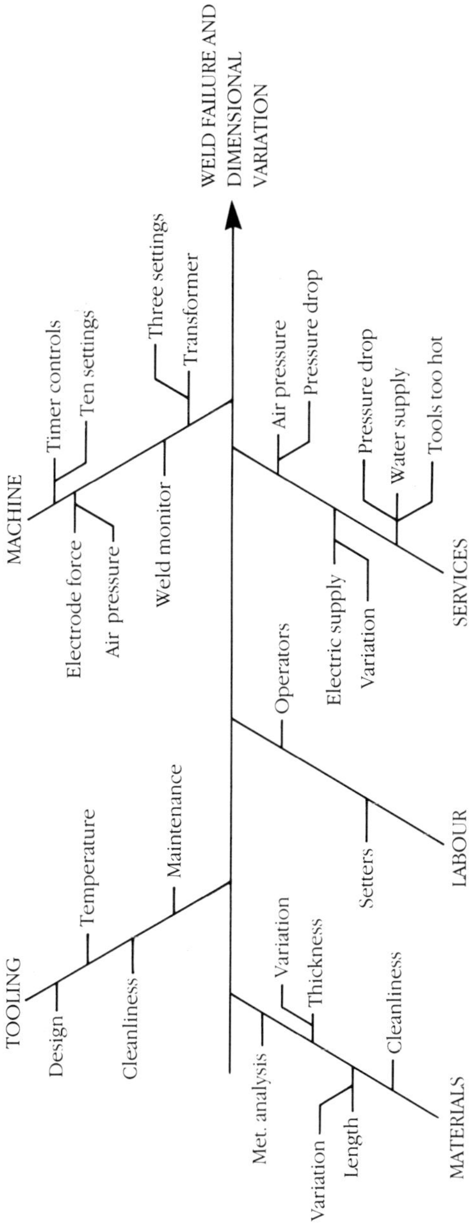


*Fig. 8.3* Tee clamp experiment. Cause and effect diagram

*Table 8.1* Plan and results of the tee clamp experiment

| | | | | | | | | | | | | Height (mm) | | | Weld strength (N m) | | |
|---|---|---|---|---|---|---|---|---|---|---|---|---|---|---|---|---|---|
| Run | $A$ | $T$ | $P$ | $S$ | $W$ | $C$ | $Ho$ | $He$ | $c_9$ | $c_{10}$ | $c_{11}$ | $\bar{y}$ | $s$ | $-20\log(s)$ | $\bar{y}$ | $s$ | $-20\log(s)$ |
| 1 | + | − | − | − | − | − | + | + | − | − | − | 36.93 | 0.068 | 23.30 | 136.5 | 5.9 | −15.37 |
| 2 | + | − | − | − | − | + | − | − | + | + | + | 37.21 | 0.039 | 28.09 | 133.5 | 4.9 | −13.79 |
| 3 | + | − | + | + | + | − | + | + | + | + | + | 36.42 | 0.068 | 23.36 | 152.0 | 4.1 | −12.26 |
| 4 | + | + | − | + | + | − | − | − | − | − | + | 36.68 | 0.040 | 28.03 | 148.0 | 4.1 | −12.26 |
| 5 | + | + | + | − | + | + | + | − | − | + | − | 36.70 | 0.044 | 27.13 | 149.5 | 3.9 | −11.91 |
| 6 | + | + | + | + | − | + | − | + | + | − | − | 37.00 | 0.043 | 27.25 | 135.5 | 5.1 | −14.16 |
| 7 | − | − | + | + | − | − | − | − | − | + | − | 37.29 | 0.119 | 18.52 | 116.5 | 9.3 | −19.40 |
| 8 | − | − | + | − | + | + | − | + | − | − | + | 36.34 | 0.116 | 18.70 | 135.0 | 10.0 | −20.00 |
| 9 | − | − | − | + | + | + | + | − | + | − | − | 36.84 | 0.105 | 19.57 | 130.5 | 3.9 | −11.91 |
| 10 | − | + | + | − | − | − | + | − | + | − | + | 37.11 | 0.119 | 18.51 | 100.5 | 10.5 | −20.42 |
| 11 | − | + | − | + | − | + | + | + | − | + | + | 36.80 | 0.130 | 17.74 | 115.5 | 10.0 | −19.99 |
| 12 | − | + | − | − | + | − | − | + | + | + | − | 36.36 | 0.125 | 18.05 | 134.5 | 7.6 | −17.61 |

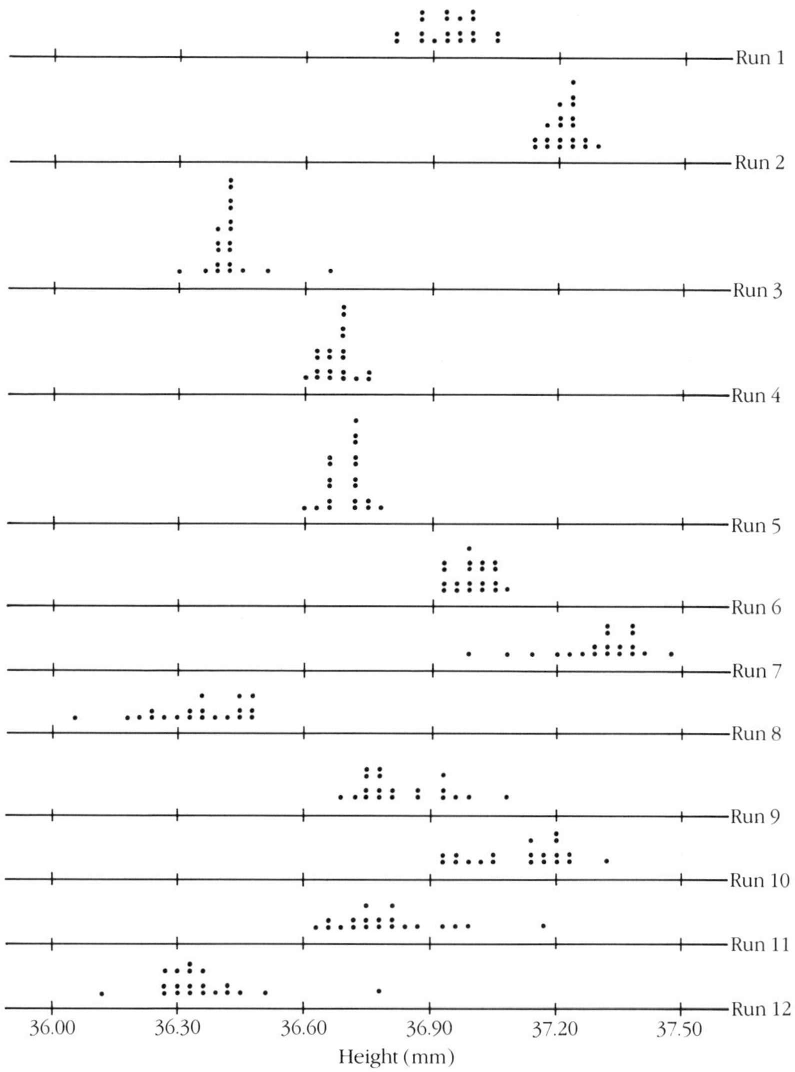


*Fig. 8.4* Tee clamp experiment. Dot plots of tee clamp heights, based on output from the MINITAB package

use the particular quantity $-20\log_{10}(s)$ because it is equal to $-10\log(s^2)$, which fits in well with Taguchi's ideas described in Section 8.4. In order to minimize dispersion we need to maximize $-20\log_{10}(s)$.

If we ignore interactions, the first eight contrasts provide the estimated main effects of the eight factors on tee clamp height. Repeating the method on the strength data, we obtain four sets of effects in all, as shown in Table 8.2. Table 8.3 gives the corresponding results for the three empty columns in the array.

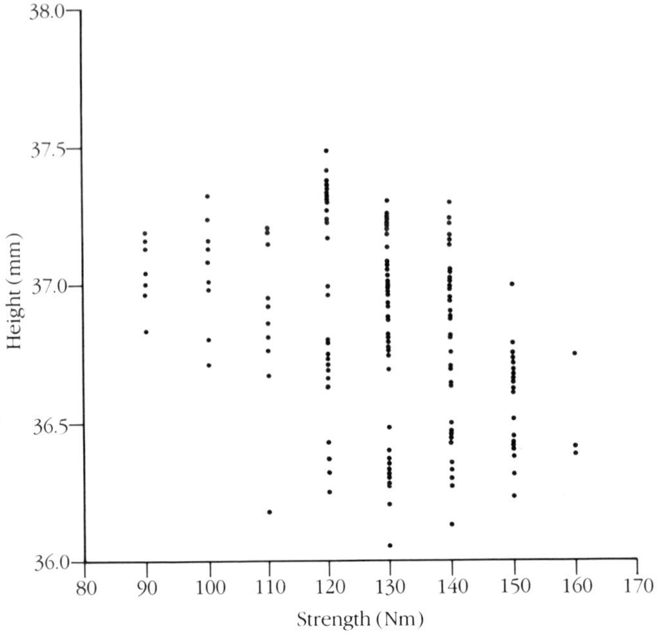


*Fig. 8.5* Tee clamp experiment. Plot of height versus strength

*Table 8.2* Tee clamp experiment: estimated effects on height and strength

| | | *A* | *T* | *P* | *S* | *W* | *C* | *Ho* | *He* |
|---|---|---|---|---|---|---|---|---|---|
| Height | Location | 0.03 | −0.07 | 0.01 | 0.06 | −0.50 | 0.02 | −0.01 | −0.33 |
| | Dispersion | 7.7 | 0.9 | −0.2 | 0.1 | 0.2 | 1.4 | −1.5 | −1.9 |
| Strength | Location | 20.4 | −3.4 | −1.6 | 1.4 | 18.6 | 1.9 | −3.1 | 5.1 |
| | Dispersion | 4.9 | −0.6 | −1.2 | 1.5 | 2.9 | 0.9 | 0.9 | −1.6 |

*Table 8.3* Tee clamp experiment: contrast values for the empty columns in $L_{12}$

| | | $c_9$ | $c_{10}$ | $c_{11}$ |
|---|---|---|---|---|
| Height | Location | 0.03 | −0.02 | −0.09 |
| | Dispersion | 0.2 | −0.4 | 0.1 |
| Strength | Location | −2.4 | 2.6 | −3.1 |
| | Dispersion | 1.5 | −0.1 | −1.4 |

## Effects on height

Figure 8.6 is a Daniel plot of the 11 dispersion contrasts for height, including the three contrasts for the empty columns. Factor *A* appears to have a large impact on the variation in height of the tee clamps, with the remaining contrasts falling fairly close to a straight line. In order to keep this presentation within reasonable bounds we will treat all the other contrasts as random noise, but it could be argued that there are four or five real effects in Fig. 8.6. However, *A* is dominant and should be considered first. Other factors can be re-investigated if the *A* effect cannot be confirmed. The *A* contrast is positive (+7.7), implying that the dispersion is smaller when *A* is at the (+) level. To help interpretation, note that an effect of −2.0 on $-20\log(s)$ corresponds to an effect of 0.1 on $\log(s)$, which in turn implies that $s$ is multiplied by $10^{0.1}$, or 1.26.

A Daniel plot of the location contrasts is given in Fig. 8.7. It appears that the factors *W* and *He* have an important influence on the average height of the tee clamps, but do not affect the dispersion (provided we adopt the simpler interpretation of Fig. 8.6). If height were the only consideration, we could use *W* and *He* to adjust the average height to 37 mm, while maintaining air pressure at the (+) level to minimize variability. The 'heat' control affects the rate at which energy is used in the welding process, and the 'weld' control adjusts the time for which the heat is applied.

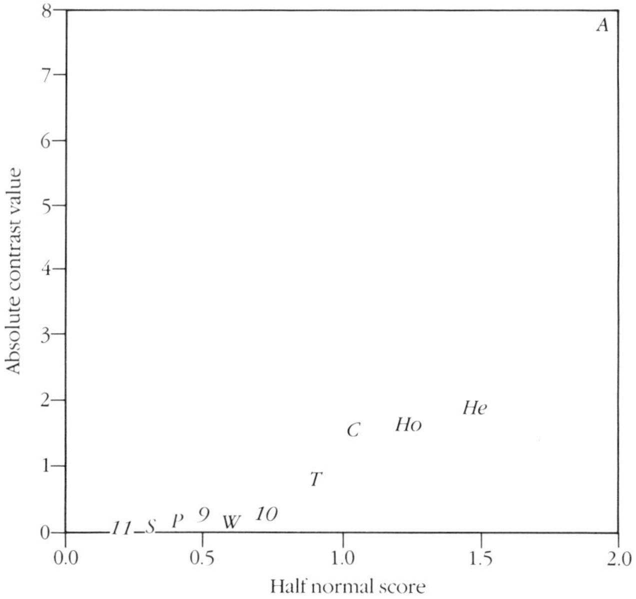


*Fig. 8.6* Tee clamp heights. Daniel plot of the dispersion contrasts

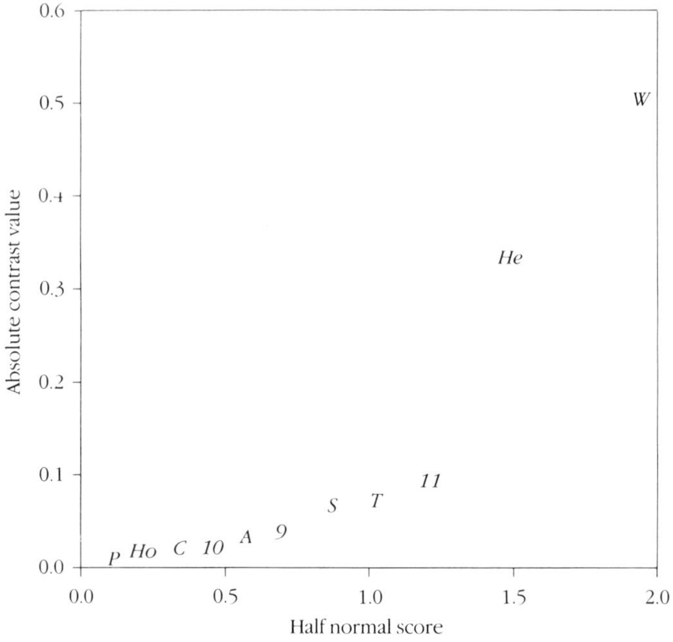


*Fig. 8.7* Tee clamp heights. Daniel plot of the location contrasts

Table 8.4 gives predicted values of the average tee clamp height for the four combinations of values of *W* and *He*, obtained from the prediction formula [2.8]. These four combinations were each run three times during the experiment, and the table shows that the actual values were very close to the predictions. Comparison of actual and predicted values is a form of *residual* analysis (Chapter 6) — it has the potential to reveal problems with the data such as individual 'bad' values, but it should not be seen as a substitute for proper confirmation runs using hitherto untested configurations. Table 8.4 suggests that the combination *W*−, *He*+ will give a mean height close to 37 mm. A further experiment in just these two factors could be used to check these predictions and at the same time to look for possible interaction between weld and heat.

*Table 8.4* Predicted values of tee clamp height

| | *W* | *He* | Prediction | Actual results |
|---|---|---|---|---|
| | − | − | 37.2 | 37.2, 37.3, 37.1 |
| Overall mean = 36.81 | − | + | 36.9 | 36.9, 37.0, 36.8 |
| | + | − | 36.7 | 36.7, 36.7, 36.8 |
| | + | + | 36.4 | 36.4, 36.3, 36.4 |
| Estimated effect | −0.50 | −0.33 | | |

It is also possible to predict *dispersion* by applying the same method to $-20\log(s)$. If only *one* main effect is involved, the process of prediction is greatly simplified: the prediction is just *the average observed response value* at the required factor level. For example, if we take $-20\log(s)$ as the response and assume that $A$ is the only factor with a real effect (see Fig. 8.6), the prediction for $A+$ is the average value of $-20\log(s)$ in the first six runs of Table 8.1, and we have

$$\text{predicted value of } -20\log(s) = 26.15$$

Solving this equation for $s$ gives

$$\text{predicted value of } s = 0.05\,\text{mm}$$

Since 0.05 is more or less the average $s$ value in the first six runs, this indicates that working directly with $s$ rather than $-20\log(s)$ would do no harm in this particular example, but the latter is a safer general method.

### Effects on weld strength

We now turn our attention to weld strength. The location and dispersion contrasts are plotted in Figs 8.8 and 8.9. Figure 8.8 suggests two real location effects ($A$ and $W$), and possibly a third ($He$). The effects are all positive. Figure 8.9 is difficult to interpret, but $A$ is again prominent. $A$ has a positive effect on $-20\log(s)$, which means a negative effect on dispersion, suggesting that $A+$ gives a higher average weld strength and lower variability of both height and strength, an unusually favourable situation.

Factors $W$ and $He$ present more of a problem. If it is true that both have a positive effect on strength, then the configuration that is predicted to maximize strength, $W+$ and $He+$, is one for which average height is well below target. One way round the problem would be to use a longer tube, but the tubes were purchased to a commercial standard and this was seen as a high-cost solution. In practice, some sort of trade-off between height and strength would be necessary. Table 8.5 shows some predicted values of strength for $A$ at the $(+)$ level. These predictions should be seen in the light of the fact that the torque employed to fit the tee clamp to the vehicle was estimated to be around 100 N m.

## 8.3 A FOLLOW-UP EXPERIMENT

The original experiment was followed up by a single confirmation run, and then by an eight-run study based on Taguchi's version of $L_8(2^7)$. Factors were allocated to all the columns except $c_6$. New levels were used for most of the factors, based on the results of the first experiment:

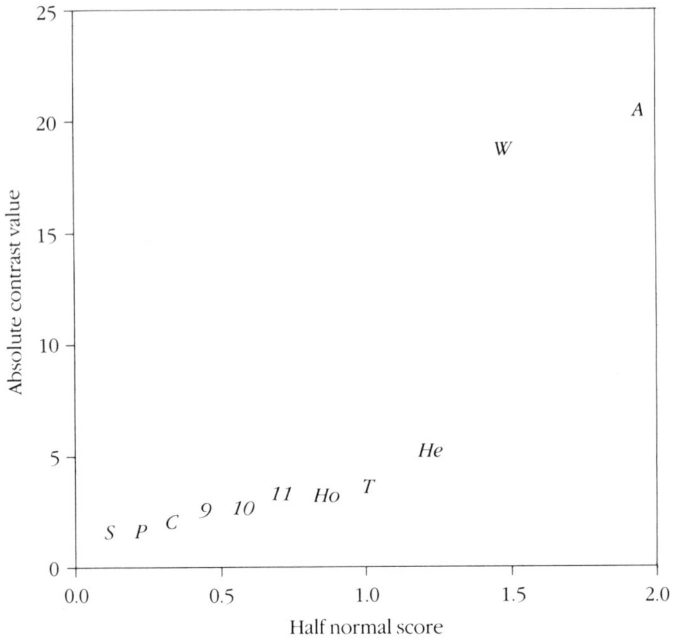


*Fig. 8.8* Tee clamp strengths. Daniel plot of the location contrasts

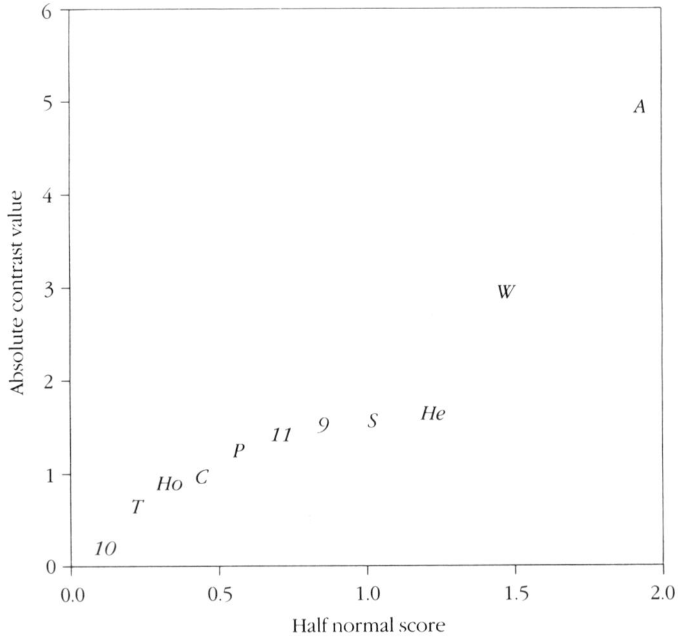


*Fig. 8.9* Tee clamp strengths. Daniel plot of the dispersion contrasts

| Factor | Label | (−) | (+) |
|---|---|---|---|
| Air pressure | *A* | 45 | 50 |
| Tube cleanliness | *T* | As received* | Cleaned |
| Squeeze time | *S* | 45 | 60 |
| Weld | *W* | 7 | 8 |
| Hold | *Ho* | 7 | 15 |
| Heat | *He* | 35 | 40 |

As before, 20 tee clamps were welded in each run. The results for *weld strength* indicated that the effects of air pressure on both the average and the variability are not maintained for pressures higher than 45 psi. They also suggested a rather larger effect of heat on mean strength than in the first experiment. The results for *height* are shown in Table 8.6. The plan in Table 8.6 is resolution III, with a complicated confounding pattern, which we have not indicated in the table. The contrast corresponding to the unallocated sixth column measures, among other things, the $W \times He$ interaction.

Looking first at the location effects, if we *assume* that the second and fourth contrasts are measuring only main effects, and that $W$ and $He$ have roughly linear effects over the ranges studied, we arrive at the following estimates:

$$\text{effect of } W = -0.16\,\text{mm per machine unit}$$

$$\text{effect of } He = \frac{-0.36}{5} = -0.07\,\text{mm per machine unit}$$

The comparable figures derived from the first experiment are

$$\text{effect of } W = \frac{-0.50}{3} = -0.17\,\text{mm per machine unit}$$

$$\text{effect of } He = \frac{-0.33}{4} = -0.08\,\text{mm per machine unit}$$

The fact that such similar estimates are obtained from two experiments with very different confounding patterns suggests that in both cases we are

*Table 8.5* Predicted values of tee clamp strength

| | *A* | *W* | *He* | Prediction |
|---|---|---|---|---|
| | + | − | − | 131 |
| Overall mean = 132.2 | + | − | + | 136 |
| | + | + | − | 149 |
| | + | + | + | 154 |
| Estimated effect | 20.4 | 18.6 | 5.1 | |

*Table 8.6* Follow-up to the tee clamp experiment: experimental plan, height data and contrast values for height

| Run | $A$ | $W$ | $T$ | $He$ | $S$ | $c_6$ | $Ho$ | $\bar{y}$ | $s$ | $-20\log(s)$ |
|---|---|---|---|---|---|---|---|---|---|---|
| 1 | − | − | − | − | − | − | − | 37.03 | 0.042 | 27.5 |
| 2 | − | − | − | + | + | + | + | 36.68 | 0.055 | 25.2 |
| 3 | − | + | + | − | − | + | + | 36.80 | 0.050 | 26.0 |
| 4 | − | + | + | + | + | − | − | 36.45 | 0.049 | 26.2 |
| 5 | + | − | + | − | + | − | + | 36.95 | 0.041 | 27.7 |
| 6 | + | − | + | + | − | + | − | 36.61 | 0.049 | 26.2 |
| 7 | + | + | − | − | + | + | − | 36.90 | 0.063 | 24.0 |
| 8 | + | + | − | + | − | − | + | 36.50 | 0.072 | 22.9 |
| Location | 0.00 | −0.16 | −0.08 | −0.36 | 0.01 | 0.02 | −0.02 | | | |
| Dispersion | −1.0 | −1.9 | 1.6 | −1.2 | 0.1 | −0.7 | −0.5 | | | |

primarily measuring main effects. Furthermore, the $c_6$ contrast in Table 8.6 suggests that any interaction between *W* and *He* is small.

The second experiment therefore plays a useful role in clarifying the results of the first, despite the fact that it does not meet the recommendation we made in Chapter 4 for a follow-up experiment with a resolution number of at least IV.

In Table 8.6 the average level of factor *W* (in machine units) was 7.5, as in the original experiment, but the average level of *He* was 37.5, an increase of 3.5. If we treat all the effects except *W* and *He* as noise, and continue to assume that these effects are linear, we can predict the overall average for the second experiment from the overall average of the first (36.81 mm) and the estimated *He* effect (−0.33 mm per machine unit). We get

$$\text{predicted overall average} = 36.81 - \left(3.5 \times \frac{0.33}{4}\right) = 36.52$$

The actual value was 36.74, and a detailed analysis made on the same assumptions reveals that all the *y* values in the second experiment are 0.2 to 0.3 mm higher than predicted. Moreover, the results for strength are also higher than predicted. This is intriguing, because the obvious candidate for a 'special cause' that might shift the mean is the voltage of the electricity supply. An increase in voltage would result in an increased energy supply to the process for any given 'heat' setting on the machine. But since heat is believed to have opposite effects on height and strength, this could not be the explanation for an upward shift in both responses.

We now briefly examine the dispersion contrasts shown in the bottom line of Table 8.6. These were obtained, as before, by analysing $-20\log(s)$. The large positive effect of *A* has disappeared. This is disappointing, because it suggests that there is no potential for reducing variation further by working at a higher air pressure. The largest contrast value corresponds to $c_2$. Bearing in mind that *W* did not show a dispersion effect in the first experiment, and that in the follow-up its levels were much closer together, this effect might be attributed to an interaction. Finally, of the four factors that Fig. 8.6 suggested *might* affect height dispersion, *C* was not included in the follow-up but *T*, *Ho* and *He* show similar effects to before. There may be potential for further reduction in dispersion but these hints were not followed up any further.

## Conclusions

After another follow-up study involving *He* and *W*, a weld setting of 7 and a heat setting of 35 (with an air pressure of 45 psi) were recommended as an acceptable compromise, with a predicted strength of around 145 N m and a predicted height close to 37 mm. However, the variability in height was a continuing concern. Perhaps owing to an inconsistent supply voltage, the variability was sometimes a lot higher than would be predicted on the basis of the original and follow-up experiments. It was doubtful whether the process was capable of holding the tolerance ($37 \pm 0.25$), and constant voltage units were recommended for the welding machines.

In the terminology of Section 1.4, purchasing constant voltage units is a way of removing the cause of the effect (on height variation), and setting air pressure to a level that minimizes dispersion is a way of reducing the effect of the cause. As we have explained, in this case study the latter strategy was only partially successful because even with $A$ at the higher level the variation was still unacceptably large. In general, though, this type of experiment gives us two types of leverage in our efforts to reduce variation:

- When a factor has a *location* effect it is likely that variation of this factor around its nominal value is a cause of variation in the quality characteristic (in the tee clamp example, there was probably variation in the amount of energy used in each weld, despite the fixed nominal heat and weld settings on the machine). Such factors are candidates for tighter control, by statistical and other methods.
- When a factor has a *dispersion* effect it can be set to the level that minimizes variability without the necessity of trying to understand the *root causes* of that variability.

## 8.4 RESPONSE TRANSFORMATION AND SIGNAL-TO-NOISE RATIOS

Response transformation means deciding to measure the response on a different scale, or — as it is sometimes put — in a different *metric*. Some response transformations are very familiar, for example conversion from Fahrenheit to Celsius or from inches to centimetres. These are *linear* transformations, but there are many non-linear transformations that have a potentially useful role in the analysis of experimental data. The most commonly used non-linear transformation is to take natural logarithms of the data. In effect we have a new response variable $Y = \ln(y)$, for which we can calculate means, standard deviations and location and dispersion contrasts. Because the transformation is non-linear, summary measures are not transformed in a simple way. For example $\bar{Y}$ is not equal to $\ln(\bar{y})$.

For illustration, Table 8.7 shows the 20 tee clamp heights corresponding to the first run in Table 8.1, before and after conversion to the log scale.

A transformation may help to create *separability* of the location and dispersion effects. For the tee clamp heights we found two factors ($W$ and $He$) with large effects on location but little or no effect on dispersion, so the effects were already separable, and we were able to suggest a strategy for adjusting the mean height while keeping dispersion as small as possible. A factor that affects location but not dispersion is called an *adjustment* or *tuning* factor. If no adjustment factor emerges from a first analysis it is worth trying a

*Table 8.7* Conversion of tee clamp heights to natural logarithms

| Height (mm) | ln(height) |
|---|---|
| 36.99 | 3.61065 |
| 36.87 | 3.60740 |
| 36.93 | 3.60902 |
| 36.95 | 3.60957 |
| 36.95 | 3.60957 |
| 36.93 | 3.60902 |
| 36.97 | 3.61011 |
| 36.93 | 3.60902 |
| 36.99 | 3.61065 |
| 36.99 | 3.61065 |
| 36.88 | 3.60767 |
| 36.81 | 3.60577 |
| 36.87 | 3.60740 |
| 37.05 | 3.61227 |
| 36.93 | 3.60902 |
| 37.05 | 3.61227 |
| 36.90 | 3.60821 |
| 36.80 | 3.60550 |
| 36.88 | 3.60767 |
| 36.98 | 3.61038 |

data transformation. As well as revealing adjustment factors, the transformation may uncover dispersion effects that were masked by the link between location and dispersion on the original scale.

The log transformation can be expected to be effective when increases in the mean produce *proportionate* increases in dispersion. One way of checking for a link between location and dispersion is to plot $\bar{y}$ against $s$ on logarithmic scales. A visible linear pattern with a slope of about 1 indicates that a logarithmic transformation would be useful. For the tee clamp heights the 'log-log plot' is in Fig. 8.10. The numbers of the runs are used as plotting symbols. No link is apparent, and it turns out that an analysis on the log scale leads to virtually the same conclusions as before.

For the strength data (Fig. 8.11), there is an obvious link between $\bar{y}$ and $s$ but:

- it is an *inverse* relationship — the runs with higher $\bar{y}$ have (on the whole) smaller values of $s$ — and so the log transformation would be completely inappropriate;
- it is a beneficial relationship, because we can have high average strength combined with low variability.

Inverse relationships between location and dispersion are rare in practice. In general, two points are worth bearing in mind:

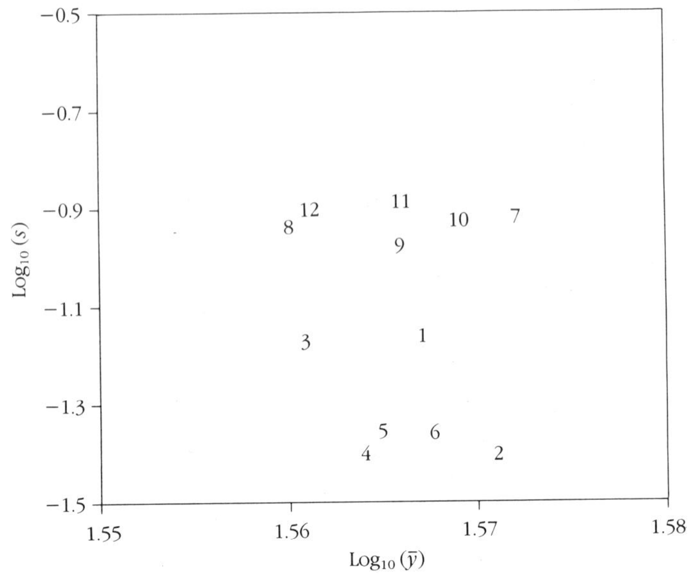


*Fig. 8.10* Tee clamp heights. Plot of $\log_{10}(s)$ against $\log_{10}(\bar{y})$. The plotting symbols are the run numbers

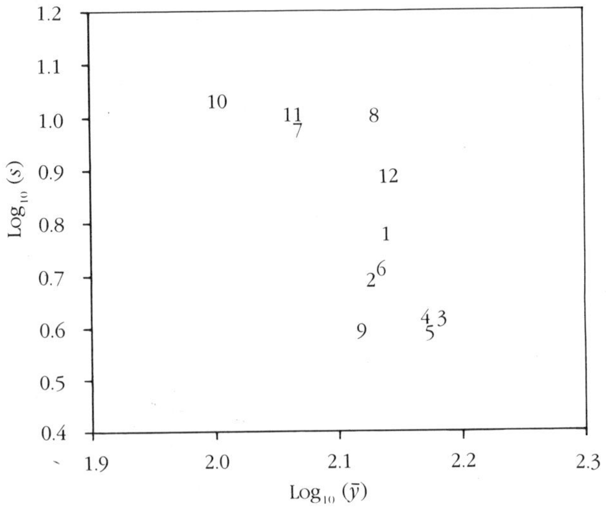


*Fig. 8.11* Tee clamp strengths. Plot of $\log_{10}(s)$ against $\log_{10}(\bar{y})$

(i) A transformation *may* be helpful despite the lack of an apparent pattern in a log–log plot.

(ii) We should nevertheless be cautious about transforming the data because, if separability has already been achieved, transformation may destroy it.

For further discussion of response transformations and the role of the log–log plot see Chapter 11.

It seems that Taguchi frequently encountered the problem of a lack of separability in his practical work, and on the basis of his experience he suggested a method of analysis based on what he calls *signal-to-noise ratios* (S/N ratios). Each S/N ratio is a function of the $n$ response values derived from one run of the experiment. Different types of quality characteristic require different functions, as follows.

When *nominal is best* (i.e. the quality characteristic has a target value), as in the case of the tee clamp heights, use

$$10\log_{10}(\bar{y}/s) \qquad [8.1]$$

(Note that Taguchi actually uses the formula $10\log_{10}\{(S_m - V_e)/nV_e\}$, where $S_m = n(\bar{y})^2$ and $V_e = s^2$, but since this can be re-written as $10\log_{10}\{(\bar{y}/s)^2 - n^{-1}\}$, the difference is not usually important and we prefer the simpler version.)

For *larger-the-better* characteristics like weld strength use

$$-10\log_{10}\left(\sum_{i=1}^{n} y_i^{-2}/n\right) \qquad [8.2]$$

For *smaller-the-better* characteristics use

$$-10\log_{10}\left(\sum_{i=1}^{n} y_i^{2}/n\right) \qquad [8.3]$$

Whichever definition we use, our aim should be to maximize the S/N ratio.

The term 'signal-to-noise ratio' is in common use in some branches of engineering. Formula [8.1] can be justified by the argument that $s$ measures noise and is the useless part of the data, while $\bar{y}$ represents the useful part or signal. Taking $10\log_{10}$ enables Taguchi to attach decibel units to his S/N measures, and to interpret data in the language of communications engineering. The use of familiar language may help people to feel more comfortable when trying to get to grips with an unfamiliar area of knowledge. On the other hand, [8.2] and [8.3] are *not* ratios of quantities that can be identified as 'signal' and 'noise', so the terminology is potentially confusing. We doubt whether the analogy with communications engineering helps people to draw sensible conclusions from experimental data, except when they are working in a framework that makes this terminology a natural one: see the discussion of energy in Chapter 11 and the example in Chapter 12.

Leaving aside the question of terminology, there is a reason for regarding these three formulae as different versions of a single idea: they can all be linked in one way or another to the assumption that the loss function is exactly quadratic. We do not think it is worth setting out the mathematical arguments in detail because, as we suggested in Chapter 1, in practice we are very unlikely to be able to assess whether the loss function is even approximately quadratic.

Taguchi has used a further argument in favour of his S/N ratios, to the effect that they are likely to behave additively in circumstances when a simpler measure like $\bar{y}$ or $s$ does not. In other words, if we use $\bar{y}$ or $s$ as the response we may find interactions, but if an S/N ratio is used instead we will not. We return to this argument in Chapter 11, but we can say at this stage that there seem to be no compelling theoretical reasons for expecting additivity from a S/N ratio. The justification for using them remains pragmatic: in most applications they do the job required of them, but we may well be able to find alternative methods that work just as well and have other advantages such as simplicity.

In the remainder of this chapter we illustrate the use of formulae [8.1] and [8.2], and make comparisons with alternative methods. An example of a smaller-the-better quality characteristic will be found in Chapter 9.

## Characteristics for which nominal is best

We return to the tee clamp heights first given in Table 8.1 to illustrate the use of formula [8.1]. As in our first analysis of the height data, we summarize the heights of each group of 20 clamps by two numbers, but in our new analysis those numbers are $\bar{y}$ and $10\log(\bar{y}/s)^2$. The results are in Table 8.8. In this new framework a tuning factor is one which affects location without changing the S/N ratio. If a tuning factor exists we can use a two-stage strategy:

(i) Maximize the S/N ratio.
(ii) Use the tuning factor to bring the mean on to target.

As before, we calculate two sets of contrasts. For the contrasts based on $\bar{y}$

*Table 8.8* S/N analysis of the tee clamp heights

| Run | $\bar{y}$ | $10\log(\bar{y}/s)^2$ |
|---|---|---|
| 1 | 36.93 | 54.7 |
| 2 | 37.21 | 59.5 |
| 3 | 36.42 | 54.6 |
| 4 | 36.68 | 59.3 |
| 5 | 36.70 | 58.4 |
| 6 | 37.00 | 58.6 |
| 7 | 37.29 | 49.9 |
| 8 | 36.34 | 49.9 |
| 9 | 36.84 | 50.9 |
| 10 | 37.11 | 49.9 |
| 11 | 36.80 | 49.1 |
| 12 | 36.36 | 49.3 |

the Daniel plot was shown in Fig. 8.7. The plot for the S/N ratio is in Fig. 8.12, and strongly resembles Fig. 8.6. The two-stage strategy therefore leads to the same suggestions as before:

(i) Set $A$ at the (+) level.
(ii) Use $W$ and $He$ to adjust the mean height to 37 mm.

As we shall explain in Chapter 11, there is a close connection between Taguchi's method and the logarithmic transformation. In the tee clamp example, if $Y = \ln(y)$ and $s_Y$ represents the standard deviation of the 20 values of $Y$ for one run, the dispersion contrasts for $Y$ would be based on 12 values of $-20\log(s_Y)$. To three significant figures *these values are identical to the S/N values shown in Table 8.8.*

The transformation method has an extra element of flexibility, because if we cannot find an adjustment factor on the logarithmic scale we can simply try another transformation. The close connection between the S/N formula and the logarithmic transformation implies that, if that particular transformation is inappropriate, so is the S/N formula. It will not simplify the analysis, and may make it more complicated. For this reason it is best to start with separate analyses of location and dispersion, and not treat the S/N formula [8.1] as a standard method for tackling all location/dispersion problems.

## Larger-the-better characteristics

We will apply formula [8.2] to the tee clamp weld strengths from the first experiment. For each experimental run the 20 weld strengths are summarized

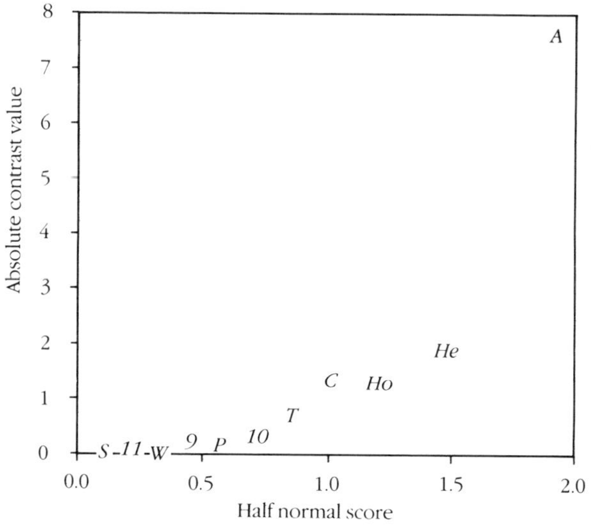


*Fig. 8.12* Tee clamp heights. Daniel plot of effects on Taguchi's S/N ratio

by the value of

$$-10\log_{10}\left(\sum_{i=1}^{20} y_i^{-2}/20\right) \qquad [8.4]$$

The results are in the second column of Table 8.9. Table 8.9 also shows the values of $\bar{y}$, first given in Table 8.1. The reason for giving both sets of values lies in Fig. 8.13, in which they are plotted against each other: the correlation is almost perfect, and the S/N analysis will lead to the same conclusion as in Section 8.1, that factors *W* and *He* should both be at their high levels if strength is to be maximized.

In other examples the S/N ratio and $\bar{y}$ will not be so closely correlated,

*Table 8.9* Taguchi's larger-the-better S/N ratio applied to the weld strengths

| Run | $-10\log\left(\sum_{i=1}^{20} y_i^{-2}/20\right)$ | $\bar{y}$ |
|---|---|---|
| 1 | 42.7 | 136.5 |
| 2 | 42.5 | 133.5 |
| 3 | 43.6 | 152.0 |
| 4 | 43.4 | 148.0 |
| 5 | 43.5 | 149.5 |
| 6 | 42.6 | 135.5 |
| 7 | 41.2 | 116.5 |
| 8 | 42.5 | 135.0 |
| 9 | 42.3 | 130.5 |
| 10 | 39.9 | 100.5 |
| 11 | 41.1 | 115.5 |
| 12 | 42.5 | 134.5 |

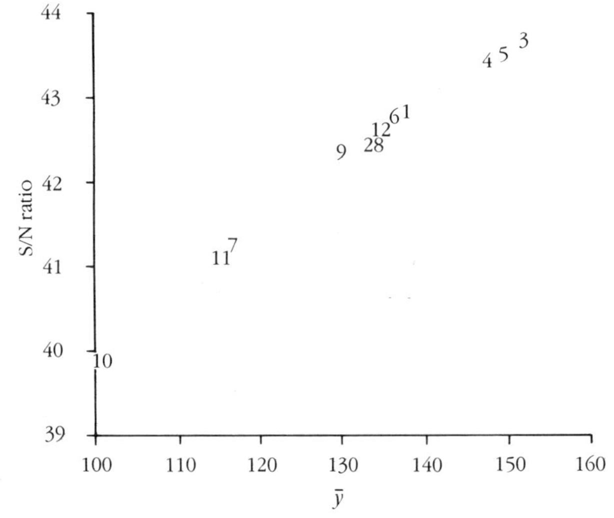


*Fig. 8.13* Tee clamp strengths. Plot of Taguchi's larger-the-better S/N ratio against $\bar{y}$

but we prefer not to use the S/N ratio because it cannot be given a clear interpretation as either a measure of location or a measure of dispersion. We recommend the calculation of two sets of contrasts based on $\bar{y}$ and $\log(s)$ or $-20\log(s)$. Note that in the case of the weld strengths a single set of S/N contrasts would not have revealed the important fact that factor $A$ has a positive effect on weld strength and a negative effect on dispersion.

**Transformations**

Spreadsheets are an ideal environment in which to try out different transformations of the data, including signal-to-noise ratios. With a worksheet already set up to calculate all the desired contrasts, replacing the data with a transformed set of data will automatically re-calculate a new set of contrast values, and update all the graphs such as normal plots. It is a good idea to keep a set of the original data somewhere in the worksheet, and perform transformations directly from this set of data.

## SUMMARY OF CHAPTER 8

Repetition data are generated by holding all factors constant while several units of product are made. Each run is summarized by a measure of location and a measure of dispersion. The conventional measures are the arithmetic mean $\bar{y}$ and the standard deviation $s$, but whether these are sensible measures will depend on the behaviour of the process that produced the data. Ideally, this process should be in statistical control, but it is impracticable to insist on this as a precondition for carrying out an experiment. In any case, it is essential to plot the data before calculating summary measures. $\text{Log}(s)$ is usually a better measure of dispersion than $s$ for this purpose.

In measuring dispersion the aim should be to reflect sources of variation that would be present in everyday production and use, and not created by the experiment itself. Location and dispersion contrasts are calculated and plotted separately.

This type of experiment opens up two possible paths to reduced variation: factors with location effects are candidates for tighter control, and factors with dispersion effects should be set at levels that reduce dispersion.

Factors with location effects can also be used to adjust or tune the process to target. It is helpful if the factor effects are separable, which enables adjustment to take place without affecting variability. A transformation may help to create separability, and unmask dispersion effects that were missed in the original analysis.

A useful diagnostic technique is a scatter plot of $\bar{y}$ against $s$ on logarithmic scales. A visible linear pattern with a slope of about 1 indicates that a log transformation is worth trying.

Taguchi's signal-to-noise formulae provide an alternative method of dealing with repetition data. There are different formulae for different types of quality characteristic. They can all be related to different forms of quadratic loss function, but this is mainly of mathematical interest. The 'nominal is best' formula will often give very similar results to an analysis of dispersion on the log scale. For larger-the-better characteristics the S/N formula will not usually be as informative as location/dispersion analysis.

## APPENDIX 8.1 DATA FROM THE TEE CLAMP EXPERIMENT

These values are shown in Table A8.1.

*Table A8.1* Data from the tee clamp experiment

(a) Heights (mm)

| Run | | | | | | | | | | |
|---|---|---|---|---|---|---|---|---|---|---|
| 1 | 36.99 | 36.87 | 36.93 | 36.95 | 36.95 | 36.93 | 36.97 | 36.93 | 36.99 | 36.99 |
| | 36.88 | 36.81 | 36.87 | 37.05 | 36.93 | 37.05 | 36.90 | 36.80 | 36.88 | 36.98 |
| 2 | 37.18 | 37.24 | 37.26 | 37.22 | 37.24 | 37.21 | 37.16 | 37.20 | 37.21 | 37.21 |
| | 37.22 | 37.14 | 37.29 | 37.23 | 37.22 | 37.21 | 37.25 | 37.18 | 37.24 | 37.13 |
| 3 | 36.66 | 36.41 | 36.45 | 36.41 | 36.40 | 36.41 | 36.43 | 36.41 | 36.41 | 36.38 |
| | 36.41 | 36.40 | 36.31 | 36.38 | 36.37 | 36.42 | 36.42 | 36.51 | 36.43 | 36.38 |
| 4 | 36.60 | 36.68 | 36.67 | 36.67 | 36.62 | 36.69 | 36.67 | 36.68 | 36.74 | 36.70 |
| | 36.75 | 36.64 | 36.70 | 36.73 | 36.62 | 36.69 | 36.68 | 36.69 | 36.67 | 36.63 |
| 5 | 36.66 | 36.72 | 36.72 | 36.60 | 36.71 | 36.66 | 36.73 | 36.73 | 36.74 | 36.72 |
| | 36.66 | 36.71 | 36.65 | 36.67 | 36.64 | 36.75 | 36.78 | 36.67 | 36.71 | 36.72 |
| 6 | 36.95 | 37.07 | 36.99 | 37.03 | 36.94 | 36.94 | 37.01 | 37.01 | 36.99 | 36.99 |
| | 37.05 | 37.00 | 37.05 | 37.04 | 36.94 | 37.02 | 36.96 | 36.98 | 37.05 | 36.93 |
| 7 | 37.08 | 37.37 | 37.20 | 36.98 | 37.33 | 37.37 | 37.13 | 37.30 | 37.35 | 37.41 |
| | 37.38 | 37.31 | 37.35 | 37.27 | 37.23 | 37.37 | 37.30 | 37.33 | 37.32 | 37.48 |
| 8 | 36.05 | 36.35 | 36.20 | 36.32 | 36.48 | 36.25 | 36.46 | 36.40 | 36.35 | 36.28 |
| | 36.18 | 36.33 | 36.30 | 36.23 | 36.47 | 36.44 | 36.42 | 36.37 | 36.47 | 36.45 |
| 9 | 36.93 | 37.00 | 36.92 | 36.81 | 36.74 | 36.88 | 36.77 | 36.73 | 36.77 | 36.69 |
| | 37.08 | 36.79 | 36.76 | 36.93 | 36.75 | 36.88 | 36.77 | 36.76 | 36.82 | 36.97 |
| 10 | 37.16 | 37.19 | 37.04 | 37.24 | 37.15 | 37.32 | 37.21 | 37.15 | 37.19 | 36.96 |
| | 37.00 | 37.21 | 37.04 | 37.16 | 36.92 | 37.24 | 36.95 | 37.13 | 36.93 | 37.01 |
| 11 | 36.71 | 36.96 | 36.63 | 36.80 | 37.17 | 36.76 | 36.69 | 36.99 | 36.66 | 36.67 |
| | 36.75 | 36.81 | 36.80 | 36.77 | 36.71 | 36.79 | 36.74 | 36.92 | 36.86 | 36.83 |
| 12 | 36.33 | 36.31 | 36.43 | 36.37 | 36.27 | 36.33 | 36.37 | 36.33 | 36.26 | 36.32 |
| | 36.27 | 36.77 | 36.50 | 36.44 | 36.35 | 36.29 | 36.41 | 36.13 | 36.30 | 36.40 |

(b) Weld strengths (N m)

| Run | | | | | | | | | | |
|---|---|---|---|---|---|---|---|---|---|---|
| 1 | 150 | 130 | 140 | 140 | 140 | 130 | 130 | 130 | 130 | 130 |
| | 130 | 140 | 140 | 140 | 140 | 140 | 140 | 140 | 130 | 140 |
| 2 | 130 | 140 | 130 | 140 | 130 | 130 | 140 | 130 | 130 | 130 |
| | 130 | 140 | 140 | 130 | 130 | 130 | 130 | 140 | 140 | 130 |
| 3 | 150 | 150 | 150 | 160 | 150 | 150 | 150 | 160 | 160 | 160 |
| | 150 | 150 | 150 | 150 | 150 | 150 | 150 | 150 | 150 | 150 |
| 4 | 150 | 150 | 150 | 150 | 150 | 150 | 150 | 150 | 150 | 140 |
| | 150 | 150 | 140 | 150 | 150 | 140 | 150 | 150 | 150 | 140 |
| 5 | 150 | 150 | 150 | 150 | 150 | 150 | 150 | 150 | 160 | 150 |
| | 150 | 150 | 150 | 150 | 140 | 140 | 150 | 150 | 150 | 150 |
| 6 | 140 | 130 | 140 | 130 | 140 | 140 | 140 | 130 | 130 | 130 |
| | 140 | 130 | 140 | 140 | 140 | 140 | 130 | 130 | 130 | 140 |
| 7 | 100 | 120 | 110 | 100 | 120 | 120 | 90 | 120 | 120 | 120 |
| | 120 | 120 | 120 | 120 | 120 | 120 | 130 | 120 | 120 | 120 |
| 8 | 130 | 140 | 130 | 120 | 130 | 120 | 140 | 130 | 140 | 130 |
| | 110 | 140 | 140 | 150 | 140 | 140 | 140 | 150 | 140 | 140 |
| 9 | 130 | 130 | 130 | 130 | 130 | 130 | 130 | 120 | 130 | 130 |
| | 130 | 130 | 130 | 130 | 140 | 140 | 130 | 130 | 130 | 130 |
| 10 | 100 | 110 | 90 | 120 | 110 | 100 | 110 | 110 | 90 | 90 |
| | 90 | 110 | 90 | 90 | 110 | 100 | 110 | 100 | 80 | 100 |
| 11 | 100 | 120 | 120 | 120 | 120 | 110 | 120 | 120 | 120 | 110 |
| | 120 | 110 | 100 | 130 | 120 | 120 | 120 | 130 | 110 | 90 |
| 12 | 140 | 130 | 120 | 120 | 130 | 130 | 130 | 140 | 140 | 140 |
| | 140 | 130 | 140 | 140 | 130 | 140 | 150 | 140 | 130 | 130 |

CHAPTER 9

# Parameter design and transmitted variation

*In Chapter 1 we introduced Taguchi's use of the term 'robustness'. A robust product or process displays low functional variability despite the influence of noise. Parameter design is the process of maximizing robustness by a careful choice of key design parameters. In this chapter we discuss some of the methods by which designed experiments can be used to support parameter design, illustrating them with two examples.*

## 9.1 METHODS OF PARAMETER DESIGN

The tee clamp case study in Chapter 8 can be thought of as a kind of parameter design experiment because one of its aims was to reduce the variation in the height of the clamps. This might be called a passive parameter design experiment because no attempt was made to *manipulate* the factors that cause variation in height; instead, variation was allowed to arise naturally, simply by running the process. In fact the experimenters were aware that variation in the input voltage to the welding equipment was likely to have an effect on output, but they were unable to make deliberate changes to its level during the experiment.

Sometimes, however, deliberate manipulation of such a *noise factor* is feasible. There will then be two types of experimental factor:

- *control* factors, which remain under the engineers' control in the real world of production and use, and not just in the experiment;
- *noise* factors, whose levels can be chosen (at least approximately) in the experiment but not in the real world.

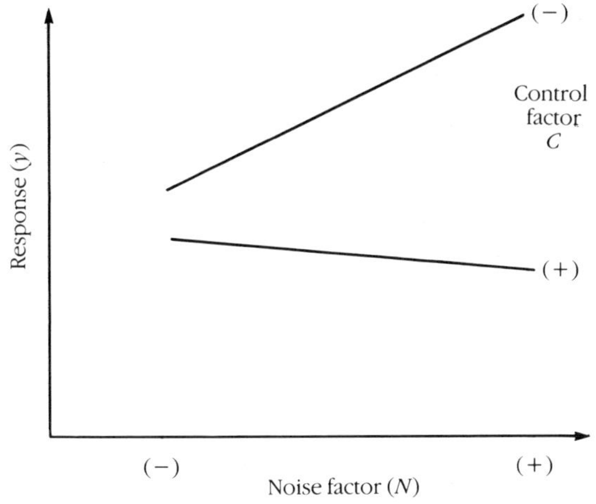


*Fig. 9.1* Interaction between a control factor $C$ and a noise factor $N$

Although we have portrayed interactions as a problem for experimenters, this is the one context in which they are helpful, indeed essential. To say that by setting control factor $C$ (say) at level (+) we *reduce the effect of noise factor* $N$ is actually to say that $C$ and $N$ interact. Figure 9.1 illustrates the point. Exploiting this type of interaction to reduce variation is very like exploiting a factor with a dispersion effect, but with more knowledge of why the improvement occurs.

Taguchi has suggested a way of laying out an experiment with control and noise factors using *inner* and *outer* arrays. A hypothetical example is represented by the layout in Table 9.1. The inner array is written in the usual way, with its rows representing eight different design (or process) configurations, generated by three control factors $A$, $B$ and $C$. The outer array is turned through 90°, so that its *columns* represent different noise combinations. In this case we imagine that there are two two-level noise factors $M$ and $N$, giving four noise combinations in all. Each configuration in the inner array is run under each combination of noise conditions, generating 32 results, which are shown symbolically by asterisks.

This type of layout demands a large number of runs, and a careful reading of Taguchi's work suggests that he only intended it to be used when each result costs very little to obtain, as in certain kinds of experiment with electrical circuits or computer-based simulation models. Misunderstanding of this point has led to some unnecessarily large experiments in recent years. Of late, Taguchi has been careful to point out that the number of runs can be greatly reduced by employing the idea of *compounded* noise. For example, it is often possible to identify a *best* and a *worst* noise combination, or more generally two extreme combinations, from the point of view of product performance. These can then be treated as the levels $N-$ and $N+$ of a single two-level factor $N$.

*Table 9.1* A hypothetical parameter design experiment with inner and outer arrays

| Inner array | | | Outer array | | | | |
|---|---|---|---|---|---|---|---|
| | | | − | + | − | + | *M* |
| *A* | *B* | *C* | − | − | + | + | *N* |
| − | − | − | * | * | * | * | |
| + | − | − | * | * | * | * | |
| − | + | − | * | * | * | * | |
| + | + | − | * | * | * | * | |
| − | − | + | * | * | * | * | |
| + | − | + | * | * | * | * | |
| − | + | + | * | * | * | * | |
| + | + | + | * | * | * | * | |

However many noise conditions are tested, Taguchi advocates using the same methods of analysis as for repetition data gathered by allowing a process to run without intervention. If, for example, the quality characteristic is smaller-the-better, the signal-to-noise ratio [8.3] should be calculated for each row of the inner array. The effects of the control factors on [8.3] are then calculated and plotted.

## 9.2 SEAT BELT EXAMPLE

We will use this example to illustrate the application of the S/N formula [8.3] to a case with compounded noise, and follow this up with a special form of location/dispersion analysis. The results we are mainly concerned with are shown in Table 9.2.

The data come from a computer simulation of the effectiveness of rear seat belts, and the experiment was run at TRW Repa GmbH under the guidance of Paul Fleming. One of the most important requirements is that the restraint system should prevent *submarining,* in which the lap portion of the belt rides upwards until it acts on the abdomen rather than on the pelvic bones, with the potential for causing serious abdominal injury. However, the experimenters realized that merely observing whether or not submarining takes place is a very inefficient procedure. Instead, they measured certain characteristics that were known to be associated with the tendency to submarine, including *back angle at peak*, the angle that the passenger's back makes with the vertical at the moment of maximum restraint. Back angle is a smaller-the-better characteristic.

The number 0.3500 in the ninth row is an artificial value that we have inserted to replace a reading that looks very extreme in the light of the rest of

*Table 9.2* Data from the seat belt example: back angle at peak (in radians)

| | Inner array | | | | | | | | Outer array (compounded noise) | |
|---|---|---|---|---|---|---|---|---|---|---|
| Row | *F* | *C* | *B* | *H* | *A* | *E* | *G* | *D* | *N*− | *N*+ |
| 1 | − | − | − | − | − | − | − | − | 0.3408 | 0.3044 |
| 2 | + | − | − | + | − | + | + | − | 0.3403 | 0.2915 |
| 3 | − | + | − | + | − | + | − | + | 0.2780 | 0.3067 |
| 4 | + | + | − | − | − | − | + | + | 0.4608 | 0.3984 |
| 5 | − | − | + | + | − | − | + | + | 0.5274 | 0.4556 |
| 6 | + | − | + | − | − | + | − | + | 0.3682 | 0.3627 |
| 7 | − | + | + | − | − | + | + | − | 0.2913 | 0.2385 |
| 8 | + | + | + | + | − | − | − | − | 0.2961 | 0.2647 |
| 9 | − | − | − | − | + | + | + | + | 0.3453 | 0.3500* |
| 10 | + | − | − | + | + | − | − | + | 0.4450 | 0.4398 |
| 11 | − | + | − | + | + | − | + | − | 0.3674 | 0.3384 |
| 12 | + | + | − | − | + | + | − | − | 0.3517 | 0.3538 |
| 13 | − | − | + | + | + | + | − | − | 0.3886 | 0.4024 |
| 14 | + | − | + | − | + | − | + | − | 0.3758 | 0.3580 |
| 15 | − | + | + | − | + | − | − | + | 0.2757 | 0.3206 |
| 16 | + | + | + | + | + | + | + | + | 0.4504 | 0.4076 |

*See text

the data. (The original value was 0.49; the reader who wants more insight into the thinking behind this decision should try plotting the data in various ways, for example a scatter plot of the results for $N-$ against the results for $N+$.) The reason for this odd reading may be that this type of simulation model is calibrated against 'reality' (in the form of sled tests on dummies, for example) at only a small number of points in the factor space. The particular combination of factor levels in run 9 may have been a long way from any of the calibration points.

Eight potentially important control factors were identified and allocated to columns of $L_{16}(2^{15})$, to produce the inner array shown in Table 9.2. This is essentially the eight-factor resolution IV plan given in Table 4.6, but with different factor labels. The control factors were as follows:

| | |
|---|---|
| (*A*) | Belt webbing stiffness |
| (*B*) | Belt webbing friction |
| (*C*) | Upper anchorage stiffness |
| (*D*) | Tongue friction characteristic |
| (*E*) | Buckle cable stiffness |
| (*F*) | Lower anchorage position |
| (*G*) | Lap belt force limiting device |
| (*H*) | Front seatback bolster |

In each case the (−) level corresponded to the currently favoured design and the (+) level to a possible modification or a feature that had been used in previous restraint systems.

The experimenters identified three noise factors: severity of collision, shape of rear seat and type of seat fabric. They tested three noise combinations: an industry standard (dictated by legal requirements) and two which were judged to be least and most favourable. It turned out that the first two of these noise conditions gave similar results, so little is lost by working with just the latter two, which we shall refer to as $N-$ (believed to be least favourable) and $N+$ (believed to be most favourable).

Note that in five cases $N-$ actually gave a lower result than $N+$. This has implications for the strategy of relying on compounded noise, implications that we will explore in Chapter 11. In this application it might have been better to use a proper outer array, i.e. an orthogonal array in the three original noise factors. This would have provided estimates of all the two-way interactions between the control factors and the original noise factors.

Before proceeding to analyse the back angle data, it is necessary to comment on the use of statistical methods such as normal plots on computer-generated data. The results of a simulation are of course exactly reproducible, in the sense that a specific configuration of factor levels will always give the same result. There is nothing comparable to piece-to-piece variation, experimental error, or other forms of variation that are modelled as random and supply the orthodox justification for statistical methods.

The usual reason for experimenting with a simulation model is to find a fairly simple equation that can be used to predict the output to an acceptable degree of accuracy and hence avoid the need for repeatedly running the simulation with slightly different inputs. If a simple equation fits the data well, the residuals (discrepancies between true and predicted outputs) may well behave like random noise to the extent that knowledge of the residual at one point in the factor space gives no information about the residual at some other point, provided the points are not very close. It therefore still makes sense to try to divide the observed effects into two groups, those which will be treated as the result of noise and those which would be expected to persist if the experiment were run with a different set of factor configurations (and to persist in real life, if the simulation model is a good representation of reality).

## Signal-to-noise analysis

The experimenters used Taguchi's recommended analysis for a smaller-the-better characteristic, based on [8.3]. When there are only two noise conditions [8.3] reduces to

$$SN = -10\log_{10}\left(\frac{y_-^2 + y_+^2}{2}\right)$$

where $y_-$ and $y_+$ are the results for $N-$ and $N+$ respectively. Table 9.3

*Table 9.3* Analysis of the back angle data

| Row | *SN* | $\frac{1}{2}(y_- + y_+)$ | $\frac{1}{2}(y_- - y_+)$ |
|---|---|---|---|
| 1 | 9.6449 | 0.3226 | 0.0182 |
| 2 | 9.7102 | 0.3159 | 0.0244 |
| 3 | 10.1447 | 0.2923 | −0.0143 |
| 4 | 7.1875 | 0.4296 | 0.0312 |
| 5 | 7.1371 | 0.4915 | 0.0359 |
| 6 | 8.4893 | 0.3654 | 0.0027 |
| 7 | 11.0739 | 0.2649 | 0.0264 |
| 8 | 10.7022 | 0.2804 | 0.0157 |
| 9 | 8.0503 | 0.3476 | −0.0023 |
| 10 | 6.8759 | 0.4424 | 0.0026 |
| 11 | 8.8132 | 0.3529 | 0.0145 |
| 12 | 8.8896 | 0.3527 | −0.0010 |
| 13 | 7.8975 | 0.3955 | −0.0069 |
| 14 | 8.4225 | 0.3669 | 0.0089 |
| 15 | 9.9004 | 0.2981 | −0.0224 |
| 16 | 7.1826 | 0.4290 | 0.0214 |

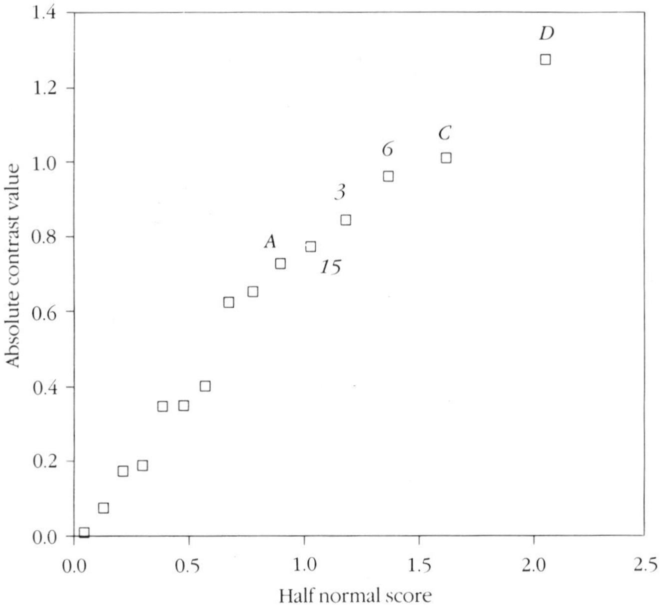


*Fig. 9.2* Seat belt experiment. Daniel plot of contrasts for *SN*. Italic numbers correspond to the empty columns of $L_{16}(2^{15})$. These contrasts measure sums of two-way interactions

shows the value of *SN* for each configuration of the control factors, and Fig. 9.2 contains the corresponding Daniel plot.

No effects stand out clearly on the plot. Interactions are of the same order as main effects. It is conceivable that there are no important effects at all. Nevertheless, the experimenters selected the 'best' combination from a response table (this turned out to be $A-, B+, C+, D-, E+, F-, G-, H-$), predicted the 'best' and 'worst' results, and ran these configurations, with the following results:

| | 'Best' | 'Worst' |
|---|---|---|
| Predicted | 0.28 | 0.47 |
| Actual | 0.28 | 0.53 |

The fact that one system is so much better than the other implies that the experiment was a success, but the gap between the actual and predicted results for the 'worst' configuration suggests the presence of interactions. If these had been investigated, it might have been possible to achieve an even better understanding of the restraint system.

## An alternative analysis

One disadvantage of basing the analysis on *SN* is that it is hard to relate the calculated effects to the particular system under study. On the decibel (dB) scale the effect of factor *D* was about $-1.3$, but in order to develop any kind of feel for the data it is necessary to go back to the original scale on which back angle is measured (radians). On that scale it turns out that the average effect of *D*, taking both noise conditions into account, is about $-0.05$ (roughly 3°).

Another reason for looking for an alternative to *SN* is to try to incorporate the insight summarized in Fig. 9.1, that increased robustness depends on the existence of interactions between control and noise factors. The back angle data can be used to measure these interactions individually, and we will mention this approach at the end of the section. Our main analysis is something of a compromise — it is numerically equivalent to the direct measurement of interactions, but it is presented in a form that we hope will clarify its relationship to Taguchi's formula [8.3].

If we followed the method developed in Chapter 8 we would carry out a location/dispersion analysis based on the mean and standard deviation of each pair $(y_-, y_+)$. When there are only two noise conditions there are advantages to working instead with the mean and half the difference of each pair: $\frac{1}{2}(y_- + y_+)$ and $\frac{1}{2}(y_- - y_+)$. The difference $(y_- - y_+)$ measures the effect of noise. It can be thought of as a dispersion effect or — better still in the present context — as a robustness effect. Taking *half* the effect simplifies the analysis later on.

*Table 9.4* Effects on $\frac{1}{2}(y_- + y_+)$ and $\frac{1}{2}(y_- - y_+)$ for each column in $L_{16}(2^{15})$

| | Effects on $\frac{1}{2}(y_- + y_+)$ | Effects on $\frac{1}{2}(y_- - y_+)$ |
|---|---|---|
| $F$ | 0.027 | 0.007 |
| $C$ | −0.043 | −0.002 |
| $c_3$ | 0.044 | 0.009 |
| $B$ | 0.004 | 0.001 |
| $c_5$ | −0.029 | −0.003 |
| $c_6$ | −0.043 | 0.002 |
| $H$ | 0.031 | 0.004 |
| $A$ | 0.028 | −0.016 |
| $c_9$ | 0.022 | 0.005 |
| $c_{10}$ | 0.014 | 0.004 |
| $E$ | −0.028 | −0.007 |
| $c_{12}$ | −0.006 | −0.004 |
| $G$ | 0.031 | 0.021 |
| $D$ | 0.056 | −0.006 |
| $c_{15}$ | 0.032 | 0.008 |

The sum of squares $y_-^2 + y_+^2$, which lies at the heart of *SN*, can be expressed as

$$\tfrac{1}{2}(y_- + y_+)^2 + \tfrac{1}{2}(y_- - y_+)^2$$

so that *SN* essentially *confounds* location and robustness effects.

The values of $\frac{1}{2}(y_- + y_+)$ and $\frac{1}{2}(y_- - y_+)$ are shown in Table 9.3 and the contrasts based on these values are in Table 9.4. Columns that do not have letter labels measure sums of two-way interactions.

Although we have suggested that it is better to look at location and robustness effects separately rather than combine them in a measure such as *SN*, in this particular case the two sets of contrasts can be formed into a single normal plot with 30 points. The advantage of this is that plots with a larger number of points are usually easier to interpret.

Generally, it is not legitimate to combine different sets of contrasts into one plot. However, this is a special case because all the location and robustness contrasts can be written as orthogonal contrasts in the 32 data values. Furthermore, we do not have to standardize the contrasts before we plot them, because all these contrasts end up being patterns of −1s and +1s, as in the early chapters of this book.

The combined Daniel plot is shown in Fig. 9.3. There are in fact 31 points in this plot — the source of the thirty-first contrast will be revealed below.

Of the location contrasts, all the main effects except $B$ and six of the seven interaction contrasts stand away from the line. Each of the interaction contrasts measures a sum of four effects, so on the basis of these results we can only say that as far as location effects are concerned a lot of the

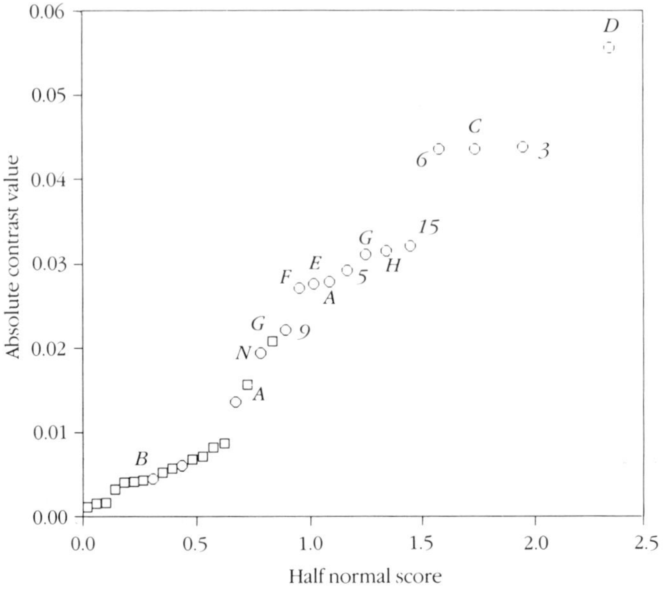


*Fig. 9.3* Seat belt experiment. Combined Daniel plot of location and robustness contrasts: circles indicate a location contrast; squares indicate a robustness contrast

interactions are important, without knowing which.

The robustness effects show a completely different picture. Only two of the main effects ($A$ and $G$), and none of the interaction contrasts, stand away from the line. It appears that $A$ and $G$ could be used to reduce the effect of noise. Table 9.5 shows some predicted values of $\frac{1}{2}(y_- - y_+)$. The ideal difference is zero (no noise effect). It turns out that the combination $A-$, $G-$ selected by the experimenters on the basis of the S/N ratio is a good one from the point of view of maximizing robustness. However, it appears that a certain amount of luck was involved in this selection, since the S/N ratio confounds location and robustness effects.

*Table 9.5* Predicted values of $\frac{1}{2}(y_- - y_+)$

| | $A$ | $G$ | Prediction |
|---|---|---|---|
| | $-1$ | $-1$ | $0.0097 + \frac{1}{2}(0.0157 - 0.0207) = 0.007$ |
| | $+1$ | $-1$ | $-0.009$ |
| | $-1$ | $+1$ | $0.028$ |
| | $+1$ | $+1$ | $0.012$ |
| Estimated main effects | $-0.0157$ | $0.0207$ | |

## Direct measurement of interactions

We justified the single normal plot in Fig. 9.3 by reference to the fact (which we did not prove) that the contrasts shown in the plot can be interpreted as a set of 31 orthogonal contrasts in the 32 back angle values. An alternative approach is to lay the data out as in Table 9.6. Instead of having inner and outer arrays, we now have a single plan matrix with 32 rows, specifying 32 configurations of nine factors, and a value of back angle for each configuration. The plan can be thought of as nine columns selected from the $L_{32}(2^{31})$ orthogonal array.

*Table 9.6* Alternative layout of the back angle data

| Run | *F* | *C* | *B* | *H* | *A* | *E* | *G* | *D* | *N* | Back angle |
|---|---|---|---|---|---|---|---|---|---|---|
| 1 | − | − | − | − | − | − | − | − | − | 0.3408 |
| 2 | + | − | − | + | − | + | + | − | − | 0.3403 |
| 3 | − | + | − | + | − | + | − | + | − | 0.2780 |
| 4 | + | + | − | − | − | − | + | + | − | 0.4608 |
| 5 | − | − | + | + | − | − | + | + | − | 0.5274 |
| 6 | + | − | + | − | − | + | − | + | − | 0.3682 |
| 7 | − | + | + | − | − | + | + | − | − | 0.2913 |
| 8 | + | + | + | + | − | − | − | − | − | 0.2961 |
| 9 | − | − | − | − | + | + | + | + | − | 0.3453 |
| 10 | + | − | − | + | + | − | − | + | − | 0.4450 |
| 11 | − | + | − | + | + | − | + | − | − | 0.3674 |
| 12 | + | + | − | − | + | + | − | − | − | 0.3517 |
| 13 | − | − | + | + | + | + | − | − | − | 0.3886 |
| 14 | + | − | + | − | + | − | + | − | − | 0.3758 |
| 15 | − | + | + | − | + | − | − | + | − | 0.2757 |
| 16 | + | + | + | + | + | + | + | + | − | 0.4504 |
| 17 | − | − | − | − | − | − | − | − | + | 0.3044 |
| 18 | + | − | − | + | − | + | + | − | + | 0.2915 |
| 19 | − | + | − | + | − | + | − | + | + | 0.3067 |
| 20 | + | + | − | − | − | − | + | + | + | 0.3984 |
| 21 | − | − | + | + | − | − | + | + | + | 0.4556 |
| 22 | + | − | + | − | − | + | − | + | + | 0.3627 |
| 23 | − | + | + | − | − | + | + | − | + | 0.2385 |
| 24 | + | + | + | + | − | − | − | − | + | 0.2647 |
| 25 | − | − | − | − | + | + | + | + | + | 0.3500 |
| 26 | + | − | − | + | + | − | − | + | + | 0.4398 |
| 27 | − | + | − | + | + | − | + | − | + | 0.3384 |
| 28 | + | + | − | − | + | + | − | − | + | 0.3538 |
| 29 | − | − | + | + | + | + | − | − | + | 0.4024 |
| 30 | + | − | + | − | + | − | + | − | + | 0.3580 |
| 31 | − | + | + | − | + | − | − | + | + | 0.3206 |
| 32 | + | + | + | + | + | + | + | + | + | 0.4076 |

If the complete $L_{32}(2^{31})$ array is used as the contrast matrix, the set of 31 orthogonal contrasts comprises:

(i) 15 contrasts that are identical to the location contrasts in Fig. 9.3;
(ii) 15 contrasts that are identical to the robustness contrasts in Fig. 9.3;
(iii) a single contrast that measures the main effect of $N$.

We omit the details, but in the light of Fig. 9.1 it is clear that what we previously called the *robustness* effect of $A$ will now show up as $A \times N$ *interaction*. And what we previously regarded as a robustness interaction (between $A$ and $B$ say, in their effect on $\frac{1}{2}(y_- - y_+)$) becomes three-way ($A \times B \times N$) interaction. With this new interpretation in mind it can be seen that none of the three-way interaction contrasts lie off the line in Fig. 9.3.

### Separate normal plots for $\frac{1}{2}(y_- + y_+)$ and $\frac{1}{2}(y_- - y_+)$

If we had not combined the location and robustness contrasts into a single normal plot we would have obtained the separate plots shown in Fig. 9.4. The location plot is uninformative (it closely resembles Fig. 9.2, the plot based on $SN$) but the robustness plot picks out the two contrasts that were identified from Fig. 9.3.

### A remark on sources of variation

In Fig. 9.3 there are only two location contrasts among the 15 that we have interpreted as essentially random, and two robustness contrasts among the remainder. If the plot had not been based on computer-generated data, it might well have been argued that this is an example of the *split plot* phenomenon described in Section 4.4; in other words that variation among the location contrasts is inherently larger than among the robustness contrasts. This in turn would suggest that experimental error between the rows in Table 9.2 is greater than between the columns.

## 9.3 SYSTEMS WITH TRANSMITTED VARIATION

Figure 9.5 represents a system with several components. The variables $z_1$, $z_2$, $z_3$, etc., are important characteristics of the components and $y$ is any output of the system. Here we will refer to $z_1$, $z_2$, etc., as input variables, but they are also control factors in Taguchi's sense, because we can choose their nominals.

Variation of the input variables causes variation in $y$, in other words variation is *transmitted* from input to output. The word 'variation' can refer either to changes that occur in one system over a period of time, or to

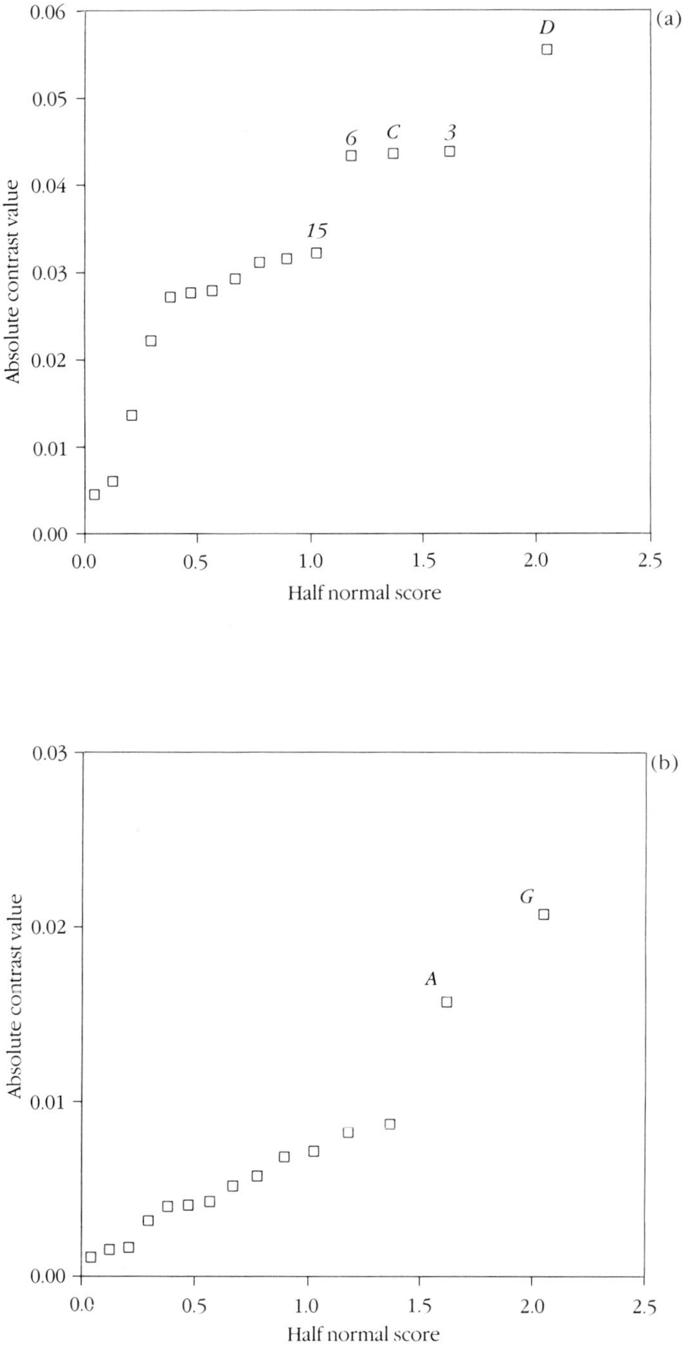


*Fig. 9.4* Seat belt experiment. (a) Location effects; (b) dispersion effects

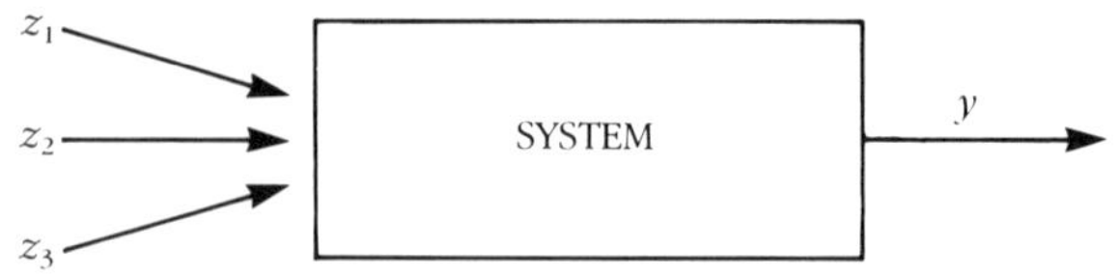


*Fig. 9.5* A system. The variables $z_1$, $z_2$, etc., are characteristics of system components — we treat these as system inputs

differences between mass-produced (and supposedly identical) copies of the same system. It is the second kind of variation with which we are concerned in this chapter.

Some engineering examples (both products and processes) of this idea of transmitted variation are as follows:

| System (product) | Input ($z$) | Output ($y$) |
|---|---|---|
| Throttle position sensor | Bore size<br>Plate angle | Voltage<br>Voltage |
| Engine ignition | Flywheel tooth geometry<br>Injector location | Spark angle<br>Air/fuel ratio |
| Electrical circuit | Component resistor | Voltage |
| Passenger air bag | Vent size | Rate of air expulsion |
| Speedometer | Hairspring strength | Rate of change of needle angle |

| System (process) | Input ($z$) | Output ($y$) |
|---|---|---|
| Stitch seam welding | Electric current | Weld width |
| Injection moulding | Material temperature | Surface finish |
| Extrusion | Screw speed | Final dimension |

It could be argued that Fig. 9.5 is generic to the parameter design of a product or process, or at least to any situation in which individual sources of noise can be identified. The special features of our discussion in this section derive from the fact that piece-to-piece variation between supposedly identical components can often be modelled as random. In contrast, it is not usually sensible to use a random model of an external source of noise such as variation between the types of car seat with which a safety belt system must be used.

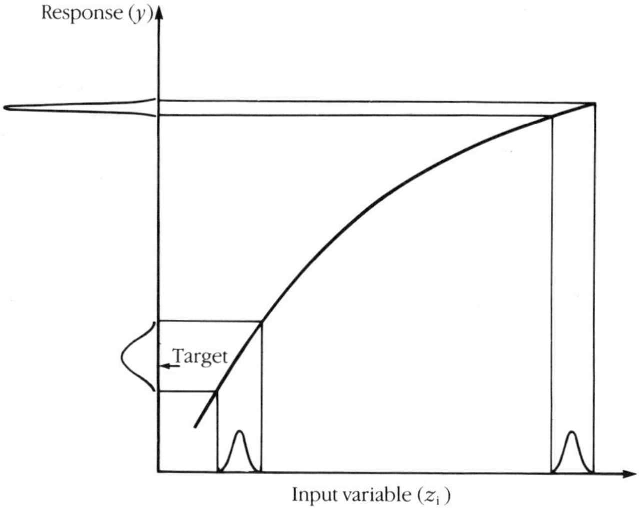


*Fig. 9.6* Variation is transmitted from the input variable $z_1$ to the system output $y$

We make several simplifying assumptions: that the different $z$ variables vary independently, and that this variation can be represented by a symmetrical distribution with a known dispersion, centred on a known nominal value. For example, Fig. 9.6 shows two possible distributions for $z_i$, a typical input variable. The rising curve shows a hypothetical relationship between $y$ and $z_i$, assuming that the remaining input variables are held constant. When the $z_i$ distribution is located in a region where the curve has a steep gradient, the resulting distribution for $y$ is more dispersed than if the $z_i$ distribution falls in a region where the gradient is small.

In effect, our aim is to exploit the non-linear nature of the relationship between $y$ and the $z$ variables to reduce the amount of transmitted variation, thereby making the system more robust against the effect of variation in the input variables. We say 'in effect' because no explicit attempt is made to discover or model the shape of the curve.

In general we will need to use a two-stage strategy similar to those outlined in Chapter 8, reducing the variation in $y$ and then looking for an adjustment factor to bring the system back on target. For example, in the situation represented by Fig. 9.6 it is clear that dispersion in $y$ could be minimized by pushing the nominal for $z_i$ as far to the right as possible, but the resulting average $y$ value is well above the target. An adjustment factor would be used to move the $y$ distribution down until it is centred at or near the target, without affecting its dispersion. Note that the strategy is to reduce variability first and *then adjust to target*, rather than the other way round. There is a profound difference between the two strategies, which has many implications for the way in which systems are engineered. We will expand on some of these ideas in Chapter 11.

In this chapter we will leave the question of adjustment to one side, and concentrate on choosing nominal values for the input variables so as to minimize output variability, which we will measure by $\sigma_y^2$, the variance of $y$. Two types of information are required to implement this form of parameter design.

First, we need to be able to calculate or estimate the value of $\sigma_y^2$ associated with a specific configuration of nominal values for the input variables. We denote the variance of $z_i$ by $\sigma_i^2$. The following method is based on the assumption that curvature in the input–output function is small over the effective range of variation of $z_i$ (nominal $\pm$ $3\sigma_i$ say). We first calculate $\Delta_i$ as follows:

$$\Delta_i = \begin{pmatrix} y \text{ value when } z_i \text{ is set at nominal } + \sigma_i \\ \text{(all other input variables set at nominal)} \end{pmatrix} - \begin{pmatrix} y \text{ value with all input} \\ \text{variables set at nominal} \end{pmatrix} \quad [9.1]$$

Then an estimate of $\sigma_y^2$ is given by

$$s_y^2 = \sum_i \Delta_i^2 \quad [9.2]$$

$\Delta_i/\sigma_i$ is an estimate of the gradient of the curve in Fig. 9.6 when all input variables are at nominal. The method amounts to treating the input variables as noise factors in an outer array defined by varying one factor at a time, as shown in Table 9.7. Bearing in mind our earlier criticisms of this approach, the reader might expect us to recommend an orthogonal array instead. This point will be taken up in Section 9.4.

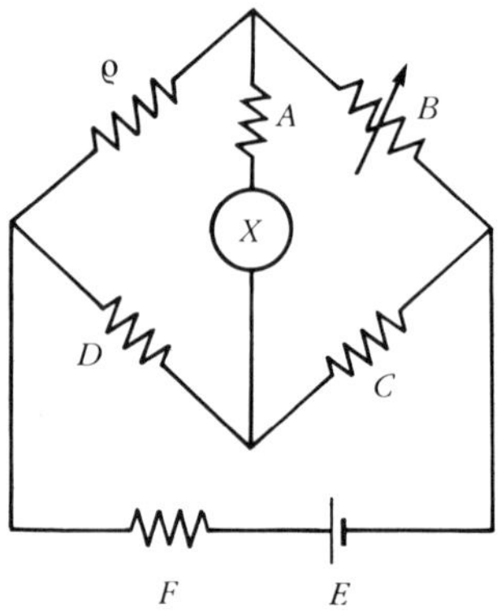


*Fig. 9.7* The Wheatstone bridge circuit

*Table 9.7* Outer array for calculating $\Delta_i$ for each input variable

| Input variable | | | |
|---|---|---|---|
| $z_1$ | $z_2$ | $z_3$ | etc. |
| Nominal | Nominal | Nominal | |
| Nominal + $\sigma_1$ | Nominal | Nominal | |
| Nominal | Nominal + $\sigma_2$ | Nominal | |
| Nominal | Nominal | Nominal + $\sigma_3$ | |
| etc. | etc. | etc. | |

Table 9.7 describes a finite-difference method in which the step length for $z_i$ is $\sigma_i$. In general, if the step length for $z_i$ is given by $\alpha\sigma_i$, we use

$$s_y^2 = \sum_i (\Delta_i^2/\alpha^2)$$

Next we must systematically study the effect that changes to the nominals have on $\sigma_y^2$. Specifically, we conduct a planned experiment in which $\sigma_y^2$ (or, strictly speaking, $s_y^2$) is the response variable, and the nominals of the input variables are treated as control factors to be allocated to an inner array.

As we have described the method, each input variable plays a dual role, as control factor and also as noise factor. In some examples there may be components for which it is impracticable to change the nominals. These components are not included in the list of control factors but they continue to act as noise factors. Some systems are intended to be self-adjusting and special variables are included to enable the adjustment to take place; again, while these are not control factors, they do contribute noise. An example of this type of factor occurs in the example below.

## 9.4 THE WHEATSTONE BRIDGE

Many people in Britain and the USA first encountered Taguchi's ideas in Taguchi and Wu (1979). That book contains an extended discussion of the application of parameter design to a Wheatstone bridge circuit intended to be assembled from cheap components and to be suitable for mass production. The example generated a lot of interest because the concepts that Taguchi and Wu introduced were novel and of obvious importance. Box and Fung (1986) offered a variety of ideas for reducing the amount of calculation required to implement Taguchi's approach and for making it more effective. The method we have outlined in Section 9.3 and our application of it (below) to the Wheatstone bridge are based on ideas in Box and Fung's article. We used a spreadsheet to do all the calculations and analysis of the Wheatstone bridge both in this chapter and in Chapter 11.

The basic Wheatstone bridge circuit was designed by S H Christie in 1833, although it is named after Sir Charles Wheatstone who called attention to Christie's work in 1843. Figure 9.7 shows the circuit: $\varrho$ is an unknown resistance; $X$ is an ammeter reading; $A$, $C$, $D$ and $F$ are fixed resistances whose nominal values are known; and $B$ is a variable resistor. If $\varrho C = BD$ no current will flow through the ammeter and the bridge is said to be balanced. In practice $B$ is adjusted until $X$ *appears* to be zero, and $\varrho$ is estimated as $BD/C$. What sources of error may affect this estimate? We note first that, even if the bridge is truly balanced, the reading $B$ is subject to error, and the actual resistances $C$ and $D$ will deviate somewhat from their nominal values. Moreover, in reality there will be a small current flowing even when $X$ appears to the user to be zero. In this unbalanced state the true circuit equation is a complicated one derived from Kirchhoff's laws and involving $A$, $E$, $F$ and $X$ as well as $\varrho$, $B$, $C$ and $D$. Mathematical details will be found in Box and Fung's article and in Section 4.3 of Fewkes and Yarwood (1959), but the key point is that, *provided* the deviations of $C$ and $D$ from nominal and the errors in reading $B$ and $X$ can all be regarded as sources of random variation, the estimate of $\varrho$ can be treated as an output variable $y$ from a system governed by the equation

$$y = \frac{BD}{C} - \frac{X}{C^2E}\{A(C+D) + D(B+C)\}\{B(C+D) + F(B+C)\} \qquad [9.3]$$

and $\sigma_y^2$ can be estimated by applying equations [9.1] and [9.2] to the noise factors $B$, $C$, $D$ and $X$. Because $B$ is used to balance the bridge, the distribution induced by variation in the noise factors is centred very close to $\varrho$, the true value, for any set of nominals, so the system is self-adjusting.

## Estimation of $\sigma_y^2$ for given nominals

In this example the application of equation [9.1] has some special features. First, because $B$ is a variable resistor it cannot be said to have a nominal value in the usual sense. A mathematical argument, which we omit, is required to show that, for the purpose of calculating $s_y^2$, $B$ can in fact be treated exactly like $C$ and $D$, with a nominal equal to the value that would balance the bridge if $C$ and $D$ were at *their* nominals, i.e.

$$\text{'nominal' } B = \frac{\varrho \times \text{nominal } C}{\text{nominal } D} \qquad [9.4]$$

Because it is involved in equation [9.4], the unknown resistance $\varrho$ has an influence on $s_y^2$. In the calculations that follow we take $\varrho$ to be $2\Omega$.

The nominal value for $X$ is zero. Putting $X = 0$ in [9.3] and substituting for $B$ from [9.4], we get the sensible result that, when all input variables are at nominal, $y = \varrho$. Also, when $X$ is zero equation [9.3] gives the same result irrespective of the values of $A$, $E$ and $F$. For these variables [9.1] would give $\Delta_i = 0$, showing that the effects of small changes in these variables are negligible at the level of approximation that we have adopted. That is the reason for omitting $A$, $E$ and $F$ from the list of effective noise factors.

In their discussion of the Wheatstone bridge, Taguchi and Wu (1979) assumed that $B$, $C$ and $D$ have a known *coefficient of variation*. In other words, rather than assume that each of these variables has a fixed standard deviation, they took the standard deviations to be a known *multiple* of the nominal values:

$$\text{standard deviation } (\sigma_i, \text{ in } \Omega) = \sqrt{(6)} \times 10^{-3} \times \text{nominal} \qquad [9.5]$$

It is sometimes preferable to think of systems in which the standard deviations are constant, and in this example taking the factors to have constant standard deviations *on a logarithmic scale* is virtually equivalent to assuming a constant coefficient of variation for each factor. The main disadvantage of having the factors on a log scale is that equation [9.3] looks a good deal more complicated. Box and Fung (1986) did work with the factors on the log scale but it makes no difference in the end, and on balance we decided to work with the original units.

Following Taguchi and Wu, $X$ was taken to have a fixed standard deviation of $\sqrt{(8/3)} \times 10^{-4} = 0.0001633$ amps.

Table 9.8 shows the calculation of each $\Delta_i$ for the following configuration of nominals: $A = 500$, $C = 50$, $D = 2$ (so $B = 50$), $E = 6$, $F = 2$ and $X = 0$. Using equation [9.2]

$$\begin{aligned} s_y^2 &= (0.004899)^2 + (0.004887)^2 + (0.004899)^2 + (0.7986)^2 \\ &= 0.638 \end{aligned} \qquad [9.6]$$

*Table 9.8* The Wheatstone bridge: example of calculating $\Delta_i$ for each noise factor

| Input variable | Nominal value | Standard deviation ($\sigma_i$) | $y$ value at nominal + $\sigma_i$ (from [9.3]) | $\Delta_i$ (from [9.1]) |
|---|---|---|---|---|
| $A$ (Ω) | 500 | – | – | – |
| $B$ (Ω) | 50 | 0.122475 | 2.004899 | 0.004899 |
| $C$ (Ω) | 50 | 0.122475 | 1.995113 | −0.004887 |
| $D$ (Ω) | 2 | 0.0048 | 2.004899 | 0.004899 |
| $E$ (V) | 6 | – | – | – |
| $F$ (Ω) | 2 | – | – | – |
| $X$ (A) | 0 | 0.0001633 | 2.7986 | 0.7986 |

## Which nominals give the lowest value of $s_y^2$?

Taguchi and Wu (1979) explored a wide range of nominal values, as follows:

$$20\,\Omega \leq A \leq 500\,\Omega$$

$$2\,\Omega \le C \le 50\,\Omega$$
$$2\,\Omega \le D \le 50\,\Omega$$
$$1.2\,\mathrm{V} \le E \le 30\,\mathrm{V}$$
$$2\,\Omega \le F \le 50\,\Omega$$

As we pointed out above, $B$ does not have a nominal value in the usual sense, and cannot be used to optimize the circuit. Nor can $X$, which has a fixed nominal of zero. We therefore have a five-dimensional region of possible configurations. If all the assumptions we have made are correct, $s_y^2$ can easily be calculated for any configuration. Given suitable software it would be straightforward, using a search technique, to locate the configuration with the smallest $s_y^2$.

In practice it is useful not just to know the optimal setting for each nominal, but to explore the way each of them affects $s_y^2$. Even with powerful graphical software the exploration of a five-dimensional region is a formidable task. One way of proceeding is to use the ideas in Chapter 6: we calculate $s_y^2$ for a set of configurations which span the region of interest and allow a second-order prediction equation to be calculated. This equation need not predict the actual $s_y^2$ values very precisely in order to be useful, as we will show below.

We used the five-factor central composite plan given in Table 6.14. Only one run is required at the centre because this is a simulation experiment in which replication has no meaning. The plan and results are in Table 9.9. All the factors have equally spaced levels on a logarithmic scale. Note the extreme variation in $s_y^2$, far too extreme for a second-order equation to describe, even approximately. The very large values of $s_y^2$ occur at corners of the experimental region, and as we suggested in Chapter 6, there are alternative experimental plans that do not set more than two factors at the ends of their ranges simultaneously. In any case, there is an obvious case for taking logs before proceeding any further. Taguchi's analysis was based on the signal-to-noise formula

$$SN = -10\log_{10}(s_y^2/\varrho^2) \qquad [9.7]$$

where $\varrho$, the true value of the unknown resistance, is 2. In this case the 'signal' part of $SN$ is a constant and serves no analytical purpose. On the other hand $s_y^2/\varrho^2$ is sometimes a useful measure of circuit performance, particularly if different values of $\varrho$ are considered. Note that in order to minimize $s_y^2$ we need to maximize $SN$.

The values of $SN$ are in the last column of Table 9.9. Using multiple regression (explained in Section 6.2) to fit a second-order equation, we obtained the coefficients shown in Table 9.10. This equation is, as usual, expressed in terms of the *coded* factor range $-1$ to $+1$. The coded levels refer to the log scale. They can be de-coded using equations such as

$$A \text{ (in } \Omega) = 100 \times 5^{(\text{coded } A)}$$

*Table 9.9* The Wheatstone bridge: computer experiment to investigate changes in $s_y^2$

| Run | *A* | *C* | *D* | *E* | *F* | $s_y^2$ | *SN* |
|---|---|---|---|---|---|---|---|
| 1 | 20 | 2 | 2 | 1.2 | 50 | 0.39 | 10.13 |
| 2 | 500 | 2 | 2 | 1.2 | 2 | 1.19 | 5.25 |
| 3 | 20 | 50 | 2 | 1.2 | 2 | 0.04 | 20.48 |
| 4 | 500 | 50 | 2 | 1.2 | 50 | 117.48 | −14.68 |
| 5 | 20 | 2 | 50 | 1.2 | 2 | 0.10 | 15.81 |
| 6 | 500 | 2 | 50 | 1.2 | 50 | 9226.43 | −33.63 |
| 7 | 20 | 50 | 50 | 1.2 | 50 | 0.49 | 9.10 |
| 8 | 500 | 50 | 50 | 1.2 | 2 | 0.76 | 7.23 |
| 9 | 20 | 2 | 2 | 30.0 | 2 | 0.00* | 47.23 |
| 10 | 500 | 2 | 2 | 30.0 | 50 | 0.32 | 10.93 |
| 11 | 20 | 50 | 2 | 30.0 | 50 | 0.00* | 39.09 |
| 12 | 500 | 50 | 2 | 30.0 | 2 | 0.03 | 21.94 |
| 13 | 20 | 2 | 50 | 30.0 | 50 | 0.03 | 21.48 |
| 14 | 500 | 2 | 50 | 30.0 | 2 | 0.09 | 16.60 |
| 15 | 20 | 50 | 50 | 30.0 | 2 | 0.00* | 46.92 |
| 16 | 500 | 50 | 50 | 30.0 | 50 | 0.10 | 15.90 |
| 17 | 100 | 10 | 10 | 6.0 | 10 | 0.01 | 26.68 |
| 18 | 20 | 10 | 10 | 6.0 | 10 | 0.00* | 38.35 |
| 19 | 500 | 10 | 10 | 6.0 | 10 | 0.19 | 13.14 |
| 20 | 100 | 2 | 10 | 6.0 | 10 | 0.06 | 18.42 |
| 21 | 100 | 50 | 10 | 6.0 | 10 | 0.01 | 27.27 |
| 22 | 100 | 10 | 2 | 6.0 | 10 | 0.01 | 25.33 |
| 23 | 100 | 10 | 50 | 6.0 | 10 | 0.05 | 18.89 |
| 24 | 100 | 10 | 10 | 1.2 | 10 | 0.21 | 12.73 |
| 25 | 100 | 10 | 10 | 30.0 | 10 | 0.00* | 39.86 |
| 26 | 100 | 10 | 10 | 6.0 | 2 | 0.00* | 34.45 |
| 27 | 100 | 10 | 10 | 6.0 | 50 | 0.14 | 14.67 |

*Actually <0.005

i.e.

$$\log(A) = 2 + \text{coded } A \times \log(5)$$

but for the purpose of interpreting Table 9.10 it is simpler to continue thinking about the factors on logarithmic scales. Because the factor levels in Table 9.9 are equally spaced on log scales, the constants in Table 9.10 can be given their usual interpretation as measures of the linear and quadratic main effects of the factors, and of their linear by linear interactions.

The terms that involve *A* are dominated by the linear effect, and the same is true, though to a lesser extent, for *E* and *F*. It appears that *SN* is roughly linear in *A*, *E* and *F*, suggesting that the optimal values of these factors will lie at one of their extremes: the (−) level in the case of *A* and *F* (because their linear terms are negative) and the (+) level of *E*. For *C* and *D* the position is completely different, and we note in particular the relatively large linear by

*Table 9.10* The Wheatstone bridge: coefficients in prediction equation for *SN*

| Term | Coefficient | Term | Coefficient |
|---|---|---|---|
| Intercept | 26.6 | $AC$ | 0.6 |
| $A$ | −11.4 | $AD$ | 0.4 |
| $C$ | 3.4 | $AE$ | 0.1 |
| $D$ | −2.6 | $AF$ | −1.4 |
| $E$ | 12.6 | $CD$ | 4.1 |
| $F$ | −7.9 | $CE$ | 0.2 |
| $A^2$ | −0.9 | $CF$ | 1.8 |
| $C^2$ | −3.8 | $DE$ | 0.3 |
| $D^2$ | −4.5 | $DF$ | −1.5 |
| $E^2$ | −0.3 | $EF$ | 2.0 |
| $F^2$ | −2.1 | | |

linear interaction. This suggests that it is worth exploring the two-dimensional 'subspace' given by fixing $A$, $E$ and $F$ at their optimal levels and allowing $C$ and $D$ to vary. Figure 9.8 is a contour plot of *SN* in this subspace; this plot is based on a picture in the book by Box *et al.* (1990, p. 175). In generating this plot Box *et al.* used direct differentiation of $y$ in [9.3] rather than the finite-difference method in [9.1] and [9.2], but the two approaches give almost identical results.

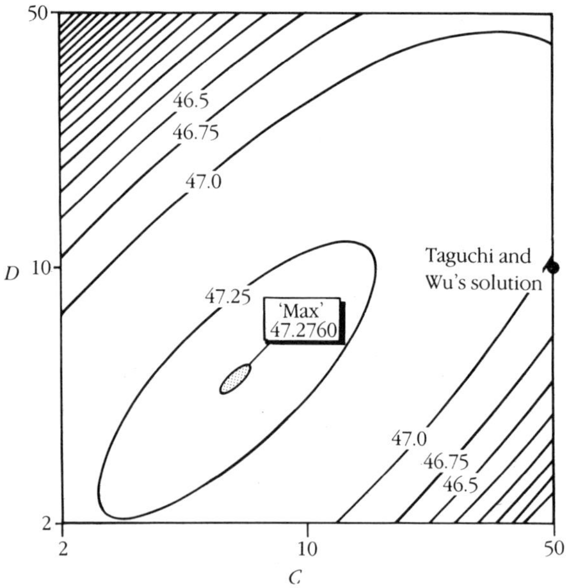


*Fig. 9.8* The Wheatstone bridge. Contours of *SN* for the optimal levels of $A$, $E$ and $F$ (after Box *et al.* 1990, p. 175)

In Fig. 9.8 the resistors $C$ and $D$ are given in their actual units (Ω) but the scales still reflect the logarithmic coding of the factor levels. Of the levels used in the experiment, the best result is given by taking $C = D = 10\,\Omega$, together with $A = 20\,\Omega$, $E = 30\,\text{V}$ and $F = 2\,\Omega$, but some further improvement can be gained if we take $C$ and $D$ to be about 5 Ω.

The contours are elliptical, and their principal axes are oblique to the $C$ and $D$ axes, confirming the strong $C \times D$ interaction. In fact there is a ridge oriented at about 45° to the axes, and movements along this ridge produce very small changes in *SN*. Table 9.11 gives a selection of values of *SN* for configurations that have $C = D$. As it happens, the first configuration in Table 9.11 is the one evaluated in row 9 of Table 9.9.

Taguchi and Wu (1979) did not attempt to measure interactions. Using a three-level orthogonal main effect plan based on the $L_{36}$ array, they selected the best of the three levels for each factor individually and arrived at the solution indicated in Fig. 9.8. As it happens, this solution is not markedly inferior to the true optimum, but this cannot be deduced from Taguchi and Wu's analysis.

## The role of the prediction equation

As we have indicated above, the second-order prediction equation summarized in Table 9.10 gives useful information about the way *SN* behaves as a function of *A*, *C*, *D*, *E* and *F*. On the other hand its predictions should not be taken literally. Figure 9.9 is like Fig. 9.8 but is based on predicted values of *SN*. The elliptical contours are again oriented at about 45° to the axes but the maximum value is over-predicted and there is a much steeper fall away from the maximum than in Fig. 9.8. The purpose of the prediction equation here is to describe the behaviour of *SN* in general terms, and perhaps to help locate

*Table 9.11* The Wheatstone bridge: some values of *SN* for *C* equal to *D*

| *A* | *C* | *D* | *E* | *F* | *SN* |
|---|---|---|---|---|---|
| 20 | 2 | 2 | 30 | 2 | 47.23 |
| 20 | 5 | 5 | 30 | 2 | 47.27 |
| 20 | 10 | 10 | 30 | 2 | 47.25 |
| 20 | 15 | 15 | 30 | 2 | 47.22 |
| 20 | 20 | 20 | 30 | 2 | 47.19 |
| 20 | 25 | 25 | 30 | 2 | 47.15 |
| 20 | 30 | 30 | 30 | 2 | 47.11 |
| 20 | 35 | 35 | 30 | 2 | 47.07 |
| 20 | 40 | 40 | 30 | 2 | 47.02 |
| 20 | 45 | 45 | 30 | 2 | 46.97 |
| 20 | 50 | 50 | 30 | 2 | 46.92 |

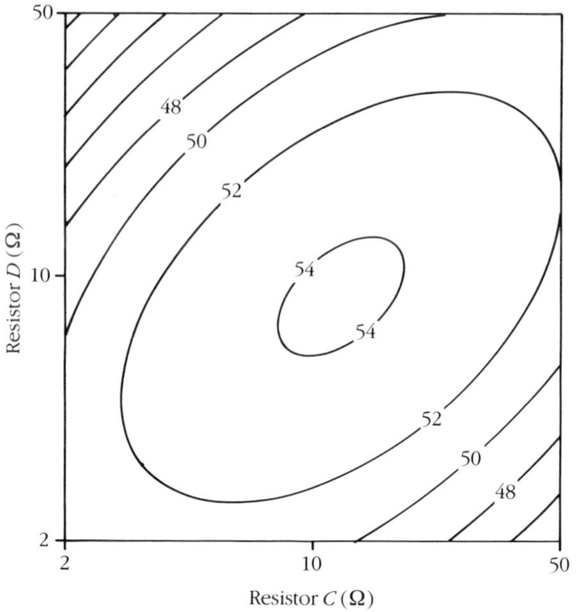


*Fig. 9.9* The Wheatstone bridge. Contours of a second-order approximation to $SN$

the maximum, not to predict accurately $SN$ at different points in the experimental region.

## Alternatives to [9.1]

We have criticized one-factor-at-a-time experiments on the grounds that they are inefficient in their use of data. Efficiency in this context means using the process of averaging as a counter-measure to the effect of random noise. In a simulation experiment this type of efficiency is not a concern, but in 'real' experiments it would be better to base the calculation of $s_y^2$ on an orthogonal outer array. For example, each factor could be given the levels nominal $\pm\ \sigma_i$, with $\Delta_i$ estimated as half the main effect. A run at the centre point could be added as a check on the approximate linearity of $y$.

## The role of the ammeter

Our analysis of the Wheatstone bridge is based on a mathematical model which has not, as far as we know, been checked by experimentation with real circuits. We have reservations about the assumption that errors that derive from the functioning or human reading of the ammeter can be represented by a constant standard deviation for the true current $X$. A more detailed analysis than we have space for here reveals that this assumption has a very important influence on the numerical results. Since energy is required to deflect the ammeter needle, it would seem more appropriate to express ammeter reading errors in terms of the power actually being dissipated in the ammeter when the needle appears to be at zero. We have not pursued the implications of this suggestion.

## Tolerance design

When the process of parameter design has been completed, further reduction in output variability can only be achieved by working on the input variables to reduce their variability. Taguchi calls this 'tolerance design' because in applications like the Wheatstone bridge it is possible to reduce variation in function by purchasing higher-grade components, manufactured to tighter tolerances.

We discuss tolerance design in general terms in Chapter 11. In essence, the quantities $\Delta_i$ that were combined to form $s_y^2$ are examined individually. The factor with the largest $\Delta_i$ is the one which contributes most to output variation, and — other things being equal — is the best candidate for action. In practice the costs of higher-grade components and materials must be taken into account, and balanced against the gains from reduced variation. Taguchi uses a quadratic loss function to facilitate this trade-off.

## SUMMARY OF CHAPTER 9

Experiments in parameter design are aimed at reducing the effect of noise on the function of a product or process. Sometimes it is feasible, for experimental purposes, to manipulate the sources of noise. There are then two types of factor, control and noise. Effective parameter design depends on the existence of interactions between control and noise factors.

In Taguchi's method of laying out this type of experiment, the control and noise factor settings are determined by the inner array and the outer array respectively. The number of runs can be reduced by using compounded noise in the outer array.

Taguchi advocates the same methods of analysis here as for the repetition data in Chapter 8. An alternative method is to measure each of the control × noise interactions individually. If there are only two noise conditions the latter approach is equivalent to studying the effects of the control factors on $\frac{1}{2}(y_- + y_+)$ and $\frac{1}{2}(y_- - y_+)$. This is a kind of location/dispersion analysis, except that 'robustness' is a better word than 'dispersion' in this context, and both sets of contrasts can be plotted on the same graph.

Many products and processes can be represented as input–output systems, in which variation of the inputs is transmitted into variation of the output. When a system consists of several components, piece-to-piece variation in a component is transmitted into variation of system outputs. This piece-to-piece variation can often be thought of as random, and modelled by a distribution centred on a nominal value. If the relationship between the input variables and the output $y$ is non-linear, the amount of variation transmitted to $y$ can be reduced by a suitable choice of nominal values. An experiment is conducted in which the control factors are the nominals for the components. $\sigma_y^2$, which measures the transmitted variation, can be estimated for any setting of the nominal values. The method involves an outer array that is often of the one-factor-at-a-time type, but could be an orthogonal array.

It will sometimes be useful to convert $\sigma_y^2$ into an S/N ratio. In the case of the Wheatstone bridge, fitting a second-order prediction equation to the S/N ratio shows that there is a strong interaction between the resistances $C$ and $D$. If $SN$ is considered as a function of $C$ and $D$ alone there is a ridge oriented at approximately 45° to the axes.

# CHAPTER 10

# More case studies

*This chapter is devoted to discussing some case studies. The object is to highlight non-standard features that were important in completing the analysis of these experiments.*

*The first case study concerns the welding of fuel tanks. One problem with this experiment was that the results for two of the runs were not reliable indicators of the overall effects of the factors. A simple method of replacing data and re-analysing the effects is one way to deal with the problem of 'bad' data.*

*The second case study concerns the manufacture of piston ring spacers, components that regulate the flow of oil over the surface of the piston. During an initial experiment (a saturated $L_8$), one of the supposed control factors turned out to be more of a noise factor. The technique of column fold-over was employed to try to establish interactions with the noise factor and thus to improve the robustness of the process.*

*We briefly return to the engine mapping experiment to discuss response and factor transformation.*

*Finally, an experiment to predict the air speed of a desk-top fan is presented. This experiment was carried out as part of an engineering training programme covering some of the methods in this book. Interesting features of this example include transformation of the response, and the use of residual analysis as a way to detect a problem with the experimental procedure.*

## 10.1 ANOTHER EXPERIMENT ON A WELDING PROCESS

This case study is an application of a fractional experiment to a process that stitch-seam welds the two halves of a fuel tank together. The experiment was run by George Basnett and Sam Pennington of the Ford Motor Co. Ltd. Improvement in weld quality was required to improve productivity — poor welds result in leaky tanks, which are inspected out before final assembly into the vehicle. For the purposes of the experiment, the quality of the weld is measured by two characteristics — seam width (measured in millimetres, mm) and weld strength (measured in kilonewtons, kN). Weld strength is related to the depth of the weld, and is easier to measure.

## Process

The welding process involves passing the flanges of the two halves of the tank between two welding wheels under pressure from hydraulic loading. An electric current is pulsed through the wheels, and the heat generated welds the two halves of the tank together. This process is illustrated in Fig. 10.1.

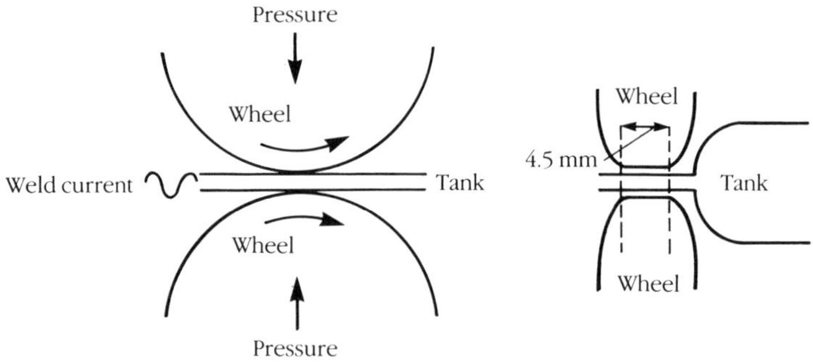


*Fig. 10.1* Welding process for fuel tanks

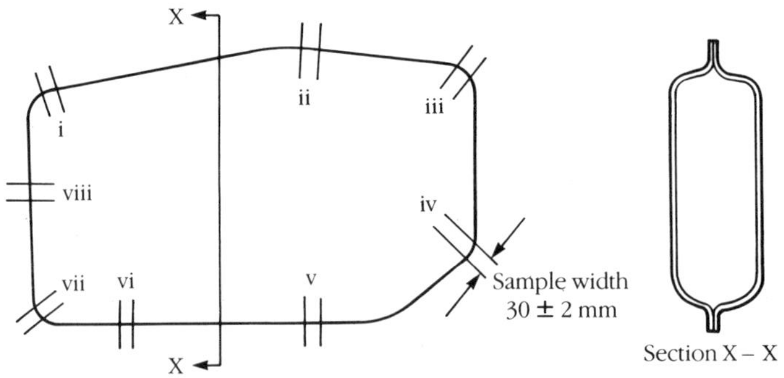


*Fig. 10.2* Fuel tank experiment. Positions of the eight sections cut from each tank

The two quality characteristics were measured by cutting eight sections (labelled i, ii, . . ., viii — see Fig. 10.2) and measuring the minimum seam width, and the strength of the weld, for each section. The position of the section on the tank can be considered a noise factor, since a good weld is required on the corners of the tank as well as the straight edges.

## Choice of factors

Six factors were chosen for investigation at two levels each:

| Factor | Level (−) | (+) |
|---|---|---|
| ($A$) Weld time, current on (cycles) | 3 | 5 |
| ($B$) Cool time, current off (cycles) | 2 | 3 |
| ($C$) Weld current (kA) | 14.4 | 18.7 |
| ($D$) Cradle speed ($\mathrm{m\,min^{-1}}$) | 2.3 | 2.5 |
| ($E$) Wheel condition | Old | New |
| ($F$) Wheel clamping pressure (bar) | 3 | 5 |

In addition to these factors, it was decided that three interactions were of primary interest, namely $B\times D$, $D\times E$ and $C\times E$. Measuring interactions with factor $E$ is potentially useful, because $E$ (wheel condition) is really a noise factor. If there exists, between $E$ and another control factor, an interaction of the type illustrated in Fig. 9.1, then this can be exploited to make weld quality robust to the condition of the welding wheel.

Since there are nine contrasts of primary interest (six main effects and three interactions), the $L_{16}$ array is the smallest standard array that will accommodate this experiment (remember, $L_{12}$ cannot be used to measure interactions). Not knowing about orthogonal array tables, the experimenters used Taguchi's linear graph method to allocate the interactions to particular columns in the array. The linear graph that the experimenters used here is shown in Fig. 10.3, taken from Taguchi (1986).

This is yet another type of linear graph for $L_{16}$, different in structure to the ones shown in Fig. 7.1. Factor $A$ was allocated to column 15, factor $B$ to column 8, factor $C$ to column 4, $D$ to column 1, $E$ to 2, and $F$ to 10. This layout keeps the required interactions clear of main effects. This can be verified from the linear graph by looking at links between nodes: $B\times D$ is measured in column 9, $D\times E$ in column 3, and $C\times E$ in column 6. However, these are not the only interactions measured in these columns *but we cannot tell from the linear graph what these other interactions are.*

Even more seriously, we cannot tell from the linear graph whether a main effect is confounded with an interaction that has not yet been considered. It

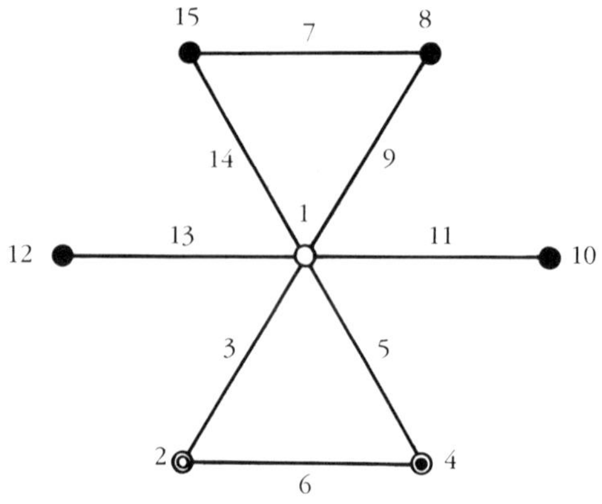


*Fig. 10.3* Fuel tank experiment. The linear graph that was used to allocate factors to the columns of $L_{16}(2^{15})$ (after Taguchi 1986)

turns out that, in this experiment, the main effect of $B$ is confounded with the $E \times F$ interaction, $F$ with the $B \times E$ interaction, and $E$ with the $B \times F$ interaction — a resolution III experiment. The full confounding pattern (ignoring, as usual, the higher-order interactions) is as follows:

| Column | Effects measured |
|---|---|
| $c_1$ | $D$ |
| $c_2$ | $E + B \times F$ |
| $c_3$ | $D \times E$ |
| $c_4$ | $C$ |
| $c_5$ | $D \times C + A \times F$ |
| $c_6$ | $C \times E$ |
| $c_7$ | $A \times B$ |
| $c_8$ | $B + E \times F$ |
| $c_9$ | $B \times D$ |
| $c_{10}$ | $F + B \times E$ |
| $c_{11}$ | $A \times C + D \times F$ |
| $c_{12}$ | $B \times C$ |
| $c_{13}$ | $A \times E$ |
| $c_{14}$ | $A \times D + C \times F$ |
| $c_{15}$ | $A$ |

However, the experimenters could have obtained a resolution IV experiment in four factors, as Table 4.6(b) of this book shows. This table tells us to put factor $A$ in column 1, factor $B$ in column 2, $C$ in 4, $D$ in 8, $E$ in 7 and $F$ in 11. The required interactions are then as follows: $B \times D$ in column 10, $D \times E$ in

15, and $C \times E$ in 3. Furthermore, because this layout is of resolution IV, no other interaction is confounded with a main effect. So we can see that using linear graphs can produce designs that have a more complicated confounding pattern than necessary.

## Array and data

For each experimental run, two tanks were welded, and sectioned according to the picture in Fig. 10.2. The raw data for each run in the experiment are given in Appendix 10.1. Figure 10.4 shows plots for each quality characteristic across the 16 runs of the experiment. Within these plots, the two tanks measured in each run are shown with a different symbol. The purpose of presenting the data in this way is to show that there is no 'tank effect' — that is, there appears to be similar scatter, around a particular mean, for both tanks within each run of the experiment (the interpretation of Fig. 10.4 is similar to that of Fig. 1.12). Using some statistical jargon, we can say that the overwhelming source of variation present for each run in the experiment is *within-tank*, rather than *between-tank* variation, so we can treat the data arising from the $2 \times 8 = 16$ sections of tank as if they were just one sample. (This conclusion can be reinforced by using the method of anova discussed in Chapter 3, but we think that, in this case at least, the message from Fig. 10.4 is clear.)

Table 10.1 shows the resolution III experimental layout together with the average and standard deviations (actually $-20\log_{10}(s)$ as in Chapter 8) for both width and strength. Note that the array used in this experiment is Taguchi's $L_{16}$. Just to recap, in Table 10.1, $c_3 = -(c_1 \times c_2)$, for example, so that the contrast labelled $c_3$ actually measures *minus* the $D \times E$ interaction as we have defined it. The same is true for all other interactions. This is not a problem, as long as we remember.

## Initial analysis

The analysis of this data set, as for any experiment, is greatly facilitated by graphical methods, and, before we calculate contrasts and draw Daniel plots, we begin with some more fundamental plots.

For example, if we were to consider each quality characteristic separately, we might well assume that each one is a larger-the-better characteristic. However, when we draw an $x$–$y$ scatter plot of the averages of the two quality characteristics for each experimental run, as in Fig. 10.5, we see that there is a negative correlation between the two. That is, as the average seam width *increases*, the strength *decreases*, and vice versa.

This negative correlation can be explained by first noticing that there are two main clusters of points, which match almost exactly the pattern of $-/+$ signs in column 4 of Table 10.1. This column measures the main effect of

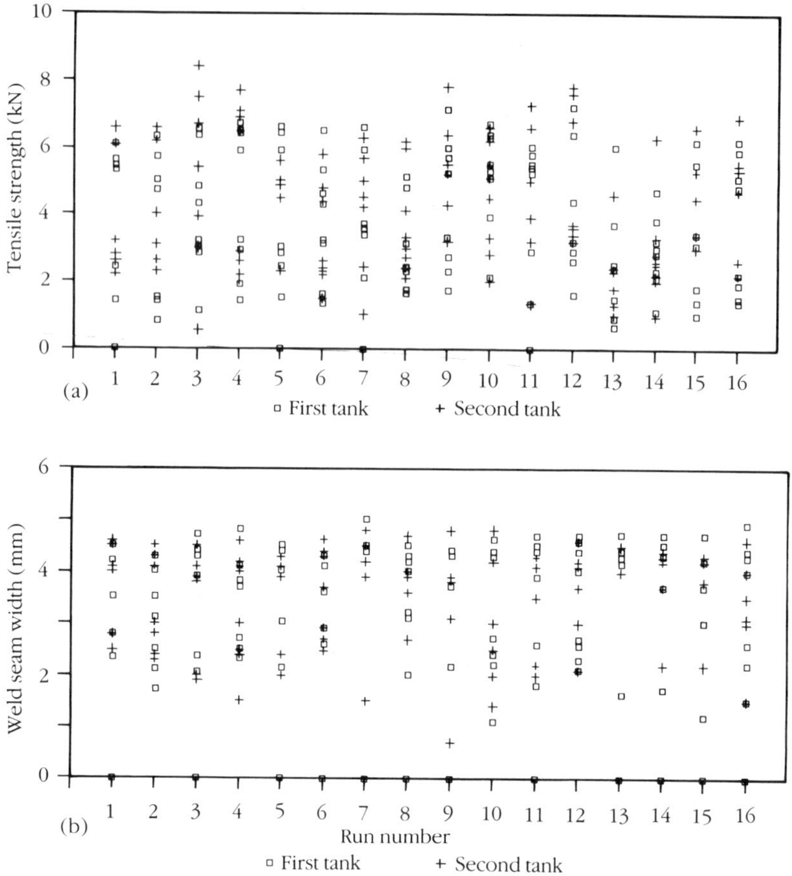


*Fig. 10.4* Fuel tank experiment. Results for (a) weld strength and (b) seam width (for a listing of the data see Appendix 10.1)

weld current (factor *C*). The cluster corresponding to a low seam width/high weld strength (runs 1, 2, 9, 10, 13, 14) has the weld current at the low level (14.4 kA), while the high seam width/low weld strength cluster (runs 3, 4, 7, 11, 12, 15, 16) has the weld current at the high level (18.7 kA). It turns out that, while the higher current produces a wider seam, it generates too much heat for the metal, which then burns, destroying the weld, giving poor strength. We can therefore be pretty sure based on Fig. 10.5 that weld current has a large effect on both quality characteristics.

Looking now at the remaining runs, Fig. 10.5 shows that the fuel tanks corresponding to runs 5 and 6 appear well away from the main body of data — they are strange observations that will need to be dealt with before we calculate effects and construct Daniel plots. Strange observations can be very influential in a statistical analysis; for example, they may make effects look larger (or smaller) than they should be, giving possibly misleading results.

*Table 10.1* Plan (and contrast) matrix for the fuel tank experiment

| | | | | | | | | | | | | | | | Strength | | Seam width | |
|---|---|---|---|---|---|---|---|---|---|---|---|---|---|---|---|---|---|---|
| Run* | *D* | *E* | $c_3$ | *C* | $c_5$ | $c_6$ | $c_7$ | *B* | $c_9$ | *F* | $c_{11}$ | $c_{12}$ | $c_{13}$ | $c_{14}$ | A | $\bar{y}$ | $-20\log(s)$ | $\bar{y}$ | $-20\log(s)$ |
| 1 | −1 | −1 | −1 | −1 | −1 | −1 | −1 | −1 | −1 | −1 | −1 | −1 | −1 | −1 | −1 | 4.86 | −5.54 | 0.93 | −1.12 |
| 2 | −1 | −1 | −1 | −1 | −1 | −1 | −1 | +1 | +1 | +1 | +1 | +1 | +1 | +1 | +1 | 5.86 | −2.64 | 1.77 | 1.29 |
| 3 | −1 | −1 | −1 | +1 | +1 | +1 | +1 | −1 | −1 | −1 | −1 | +1 | +1 | +1 | +1 | 3.50 | 0.95 | 4.24 | 15.33 |
| 4 | −1 | −1 | −1 | +1 | +1 | +1 | +1 | +1 | +1 | +1 | +1 | −1 | −1 | −1 | −1 | 2.18 | 1.31 | 4.01 | 8.67 |
| 5 | −1 | +1 | +1 | −1 | −1 | +1 | +1 | −1 | −1 | +1 | +1 | −1 | −1 | +1 | +1 | 1.35 | −4.84 | 0.16 | 3.74 |
| 6 | −1 | +1 | +1 | −1 | −1 | +1 | +1 | +1 | +1 | −1 | −1 | +1 | +1 | −1 | −1 | 0.39 | 4.19 | 0.00 | −† |
| 7 | −1 | +1 | +1 | +1 | +1 | −1 | −1 | −1 | −1 | +1 | +1 | +1 | +1 | −1 | −1 | 4.03 | −2.54 | 4.58 | 11.72 |
| 8 | −1 | +1 | +1 | +1 | +1 | −1 | −1 | +1 | +1 | −1 | −1 | −1 | −1 | +1 | +1 | 5.62 | −4.26 | 3.34 | −2.97 |
| 9 | +1 | −1 | +1 | −1 | +1 | −1 | +1 | −1 | +1 | −1 | +1 | −1 | +1 | −1 | +1 | 5.15 | −6.81 | 1.34 | −1.23 |
| 10 | +1 | −1 | +1 | −1 | +1 | −1 | +1 | +1 | −1 | +1 | −1 | +1 | −1 | +1 | −1 | 4.79 | −0.12 | 2.46 | 2.03 |
| 11 | +1 | −1 | +1 | +1 | −1 | +1 | −1 | −1 | +1 | −1 | +1 | +1 | −1 | +1 | −1 | 2.62 | 3.39 | 3.84 | 9.89 |
| 12 | +1 | −1 | +1 | +1 | −1 | +1 | −1 | +1 | −1 | +1 | −1 | −1 | +1 | −1 | +1 | 2.33 | 1.67 | 4.21 | 7.87 |
| 13 | +1 | +1 | −1 | −1 | +1 | +1 | −1 | −1 | +1 | +1 | −1 | −1 | +1 | +1 | −1 | 5.96 | 0.10 | 2.10 | −1.15 |
| 14 | +1 | +1 | −1 | −1 | +1 | +1 | −1 | +1 | −1 | −1 | +1 | +1 | −1 | −1 | +1 | 5.34 | −5.54 | 1.89 | −2.10 |
| 15 | +1 | +1 | −1 | +1 | −1 | −1 | +1 | −1 | +1 | +1 | −1 | +1 | −1 | −1 | +1 | 2.73 | 0.45 | 4.43 | 11.79 |
| 16 | +1 | +1 | −1 | +1 | −1 | −1 | +1 | +1 | −1 | −1 | +1 | −1 | +1 | +1 | −1 | 2.75 | −1.03 | 4.35 | 9.77 |

*Relative to the row order in this table (Taguchi's standard order) the actual run order was 2, 3, 1, 4, 12, 10, 9, 11, 14, 15, 13, 16, 6, 5, 8, 7. In the text and figures we refer to the runs by their numbers in this table

†All the data were zero for this run

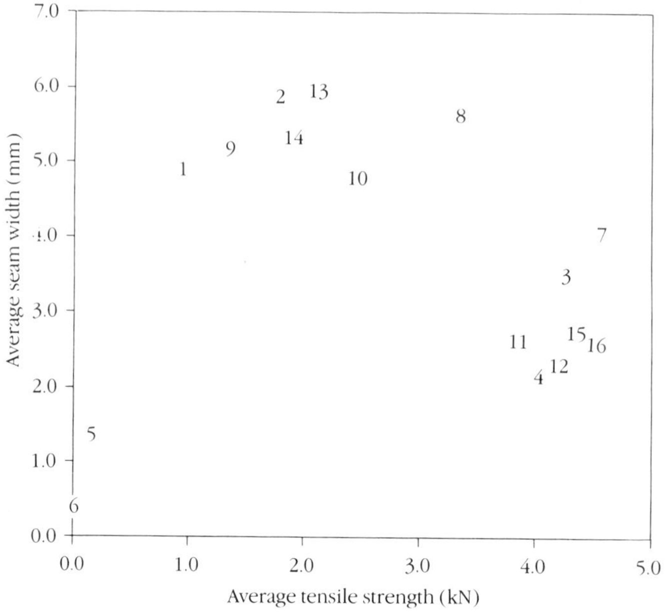


*Fig. 10.5* Fuel tank experiment. Average strength plotted against average seam width. The plotting symbols are the run numbers

Runs 5 and 6 have uniquely in common a slow cradle speed with a low weld current with a new wheel, and the process has failed to function under these conditions. This may be indicative of a three-way interaction between these factors (the $C \times D \times E$ interaction is measured by contrast $c_7$ in Table 10.1, which also measures the $A \times B$ interaction). Although this is an important finding in its own right, it does not help in determining the effects of the factors generally.

Also from Fig. 10.5, run 8 appears between the two clusters towards the top right of the plot. This is the area we would like to end up in (high strength and wide seam). This was not noticed at the time of the experiment, which is why it is *always* useful to plot data prior to any analysis. If the results of run 8 could have been reproduced, it may well have altered the course of the rest of the investigation.

## A more formal analysis — strength data

We start some more formal analysis by looking at the strength data. As we showed with the tee clamps in Chapter 8, a log–log plot of average and standard deviation is useful to determine whether there is any dependence between location and dispersion. Figure 10.6 is the plot for the strength data, and apart from runs 5 and 6, which we know to be suspect, there clearly is a

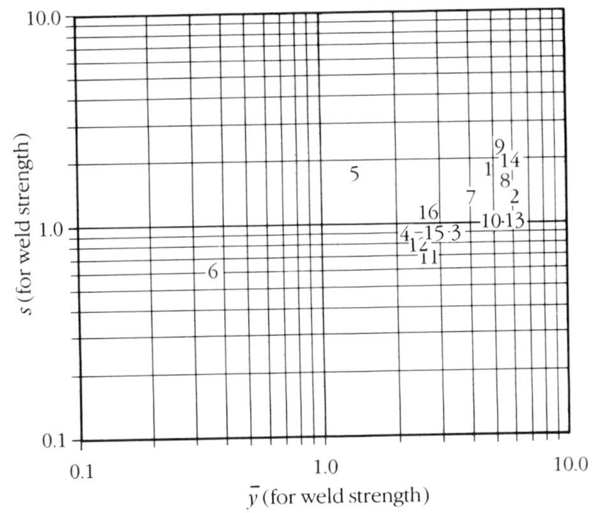


*Fig. 10.6* Fuel tank weld strengths. Plot of $s$ against $\bar{y}$ on logarithmic scales

strong link between location and dispersion. By eye, the gradient looks to be about 1 (the least-squares gradient is actually 0.7), so a logarithmic transformation of the data should be helpful in decoupling the link between mean and standard deviation.

After taking (natural) logs of the raw data in Appendix 10.1, the revised log–log plot of mean and standard deviation is given in Fig. 10.7. Runs 5 and 6 are missing from this plot because some of the raw data were zero. Figure 10.7 shows that there is now no obvious dependence between mean and dispersion, and we therefore choose to analyse the data for this experiment in the log metric. We refer to log strength as $Y = \ln(y)$. The summary data now become as in Table 10.2.

Before we calculate contrasts for $Y$ we need a way to deal with the missing data in runs 5 and 6. There are many ways to deal with missing data in statistical analysis. In Chapter 6 with the tyre experiment, we *replaced* the data from one of the runs based on a *prediction* from the other runs. A multiple regression procedure was needed to do this. There are many variants of this idea of replacing bad data by predictions, and we illustrate a simple one that works well with orthogonal arrays, provided that the amount of missing data is not too great. The method uses orthogonal contrasts, so regression programs are not needed. The procedure involves a repetitive sequence of replacing and predicting (generally called *iteration*), as follows:

- Step 1: Replace the missing data with the average of the data from the good runs. Call these the new data.
- Step 2: Calculate effects, based on the 'new data' in the usual way.

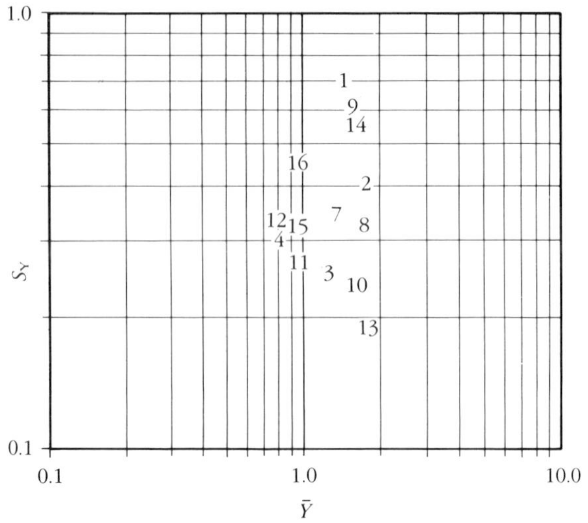


*Fig. 10.7* Fuel tank experiment. Plot of $s_Y$ against $\bar{Y}$, where $Y = \ln(\text{strength})$

*Table 10.2* Summary data for $Y = \ln(\text{strength})$

| Run | $\bar{Y}$ | $-20\log(s_Y)$ |
|---|---|---|
| 1 | 1.43 | 3.26 |
| 2 | 1.72 | 7.97 |
| 3 | 1.22 | 11.97 |
| 4 | 0.80 | 10.35 |
| 5* | – | – |
| 6* | – | – |
| 7 | 1.34 | 9.32 |
| 8 | 1.68 | 9.78 |
| 9 | 1.51 | 4.43 |
| 10 | 1.54 | 12.60 |
| 11 | 0.93 | 11.42 |
| 12 | 0.79 | 9.82 |
| 13 | 1.77 | 14.16 |
| 14 | 1.57 | 5.02 |
| 15 | 0.95 | 9.72 |
| 16 | 0.92 | 6.84 |

*Some of the strength data are zero, and these results have been ignored in calculating this table since ln(0) does not exist. For the plan (and contrast) matrix, see Table 10.1

- Step 3: Construct a Daniel plot of the effects calculated in step 2 and decide which effects are active and which are not.
- Step 4: Using only the active effects, predict the responses for the runs that were designated in step 1 as missing, and replace the data for these runs with the predictions. Hence the 'new data' are updated.
- Step 5: Repeat steps 2 to 4 until the sequence converges — that is, the predictions become equal to the values they are replacing.

We will illustrate this method using the strength data, and pay attention to *location* effects at first. Based on Fig. 10.5, we treat runs 5 and 6 as missing data. Remembering that we are working in the log metric, the average of all runs *except* 5 and 6 is 1.298, and so we initially replace runs 5 and 6 with this new value. Figure 10.8(a) is the corresponding Daniel plot, and we can see that factor $C$ (weld current) is apparently active, since it is just off the line (Fig. 10.8(b) is a full normal plot, which gives a clearer indication that factor $C$ is active). The effect of factor $C$ is calculated as $-0.437$. Now runs 5 and 6 have the same level for factor $C$ (level $(-)$) so the prediction for this configuration (see Chapter 2) is given by

$$\begin{aligned}\text{prediction} &= (\text{overall average}) + \tfrac{1}{2}(\text{level of factor } C) \times (\text{effect of } C)\\ &= 1.298 + \tfrac{1}{2} \times (-1) \times (-0.437)\\ &= 1.517\end{aligned}$$

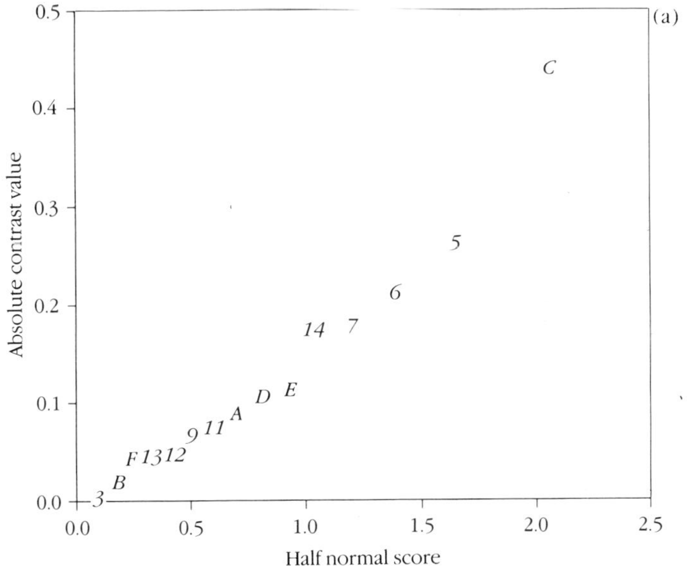


*Fig. 10.8* Fuel tank experiment. Location effects on ln(strength), treating runs 5 and 6 as missing data. (a) Daniel plot; (b) full normal plot. In this and all subsequent plots, numbers correspond to columns in $L_{16}(2^{15})$

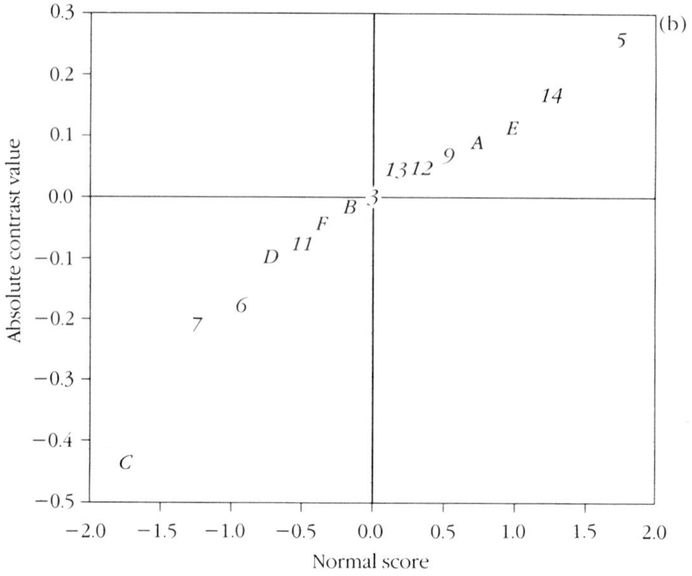


*Fig. 10.8* contd

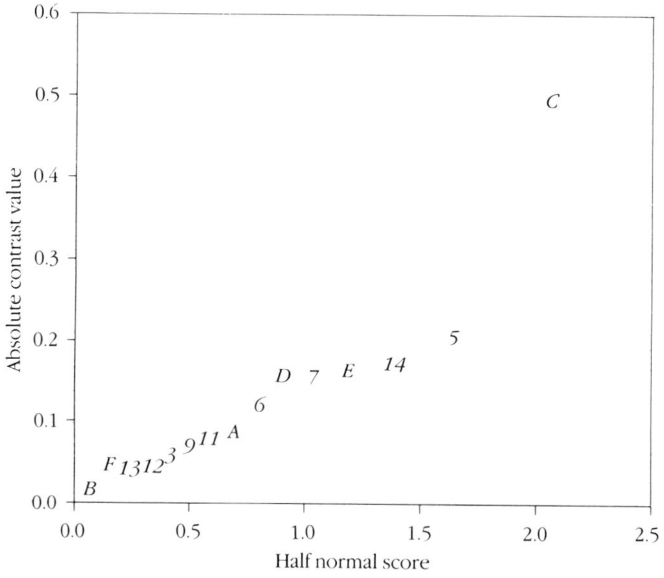


*Fig. 10.9* Fuel tank experiment. Location effects on ln(strength), after iteration 1 of the replacement/prediction method

Runs 5 and 6 are replaced with this prediction, and the sequence is then repeated. Figure 10.9 is a Daniel plot after runs 5 and 6 have been replaced with the prediction of 1.517, and now factor $C$ is definitely off the line.

In this case, only six iterations of the sequence are needed, and the final effect of factor $C$ is estimated as $-0.509$, with predictions for runs 5 and 6 given by 1.589. Table 10.3 details the effects and predictions for the entire set of iterations.

*Table 10.3* Location effects and predictions for $Y = \ln(\text{strength})$

| Iteration | $\bar{Y}$ | Prediction for runs 5 and 6 | Effect of factor $C$ |
|---|---|---|---|
| 0* | 1.299 | 1.298 | −0.437 |
| 1 | 1.326 | 1.517 | −0.491 |
| 2 | 1.333 | 1.572 | −0.505 |
| 3 | 1.335 | 1.585 | −0.508 |
| 4 | 1.335 | 1.589 | −0.509 |
| 5 | 1.335 | 1.590 | −0.509 |
| 6 | 1.335 | 1.590 | −0.509 |

*Iteration 0 is the situation immediately after step 1 of the sequence. It is an interesting fact that the algorithm that we have described actually ends up with the numbers which would have been obtained if we had used regression on the 14 'good' runs, taking account of only factor $C$

### Iteration with missing data

Iteration in a spreadsheet is straightforward. Calculate the contrast values initially by replacing the missing values with the average of the rest of the data. Then in the cells with the missing data, construct a prediction formula using the contrast values already calculated. The worksheet will now have a 'circular' calculation within it (probably indicated on the screen as a warning) since the results of two or more cells depend directly on each other through their current values. The spreadsheet will calculate one iteration at a time (sometimes more if required) and the convergence of the sequence of iterations will be seen to be complete when the contrast values and the predictions for the missing data values do not change from one iteration to the next.

Figure 10.10 is the final Daniel plot for the (logarithmic) strength location effects. This plot confirms the significance of weld current on tensile strength, which was deduced from Fig. 10.5.

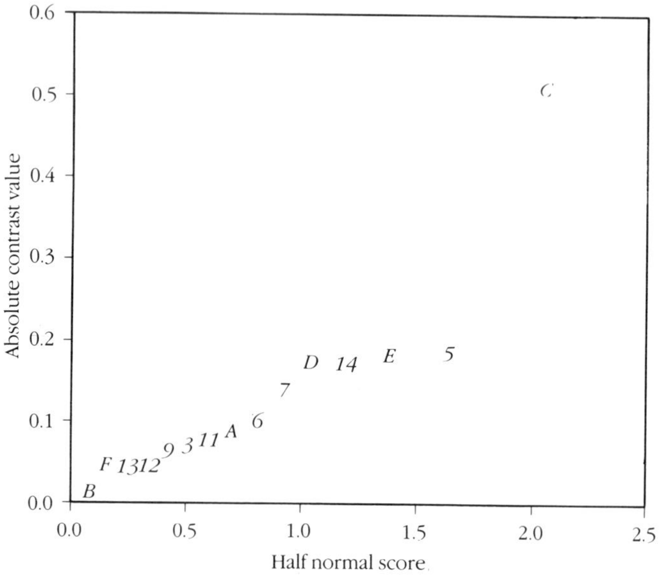


*Fig. 10.10* Fuel tank experiment. Location effects on ln(strength), after convergence of the replacement/prediction method

## Dispersion analysis of the strength data

Because the log transformation was designed to *decouple* the location and dispersion for the strength data, we can conduct a similar analysis for the dispersion effects, in the hope of finding some factors that reduce dispersion. We work with the quantity $-20\log(s_Y)$ as usual. To minimize dispersion, we need to maximize this quantity.

We again need to replace and predict the data for runs 5 and 6. Initially, we replace them with the average of the $-20\log(s_Y)$ values of the other 14 runs, which is 9.046. Figure 10.11(a) is a Daniel plot of the calculated effects. This plot gives a good impression of a straight line, making it difficult to

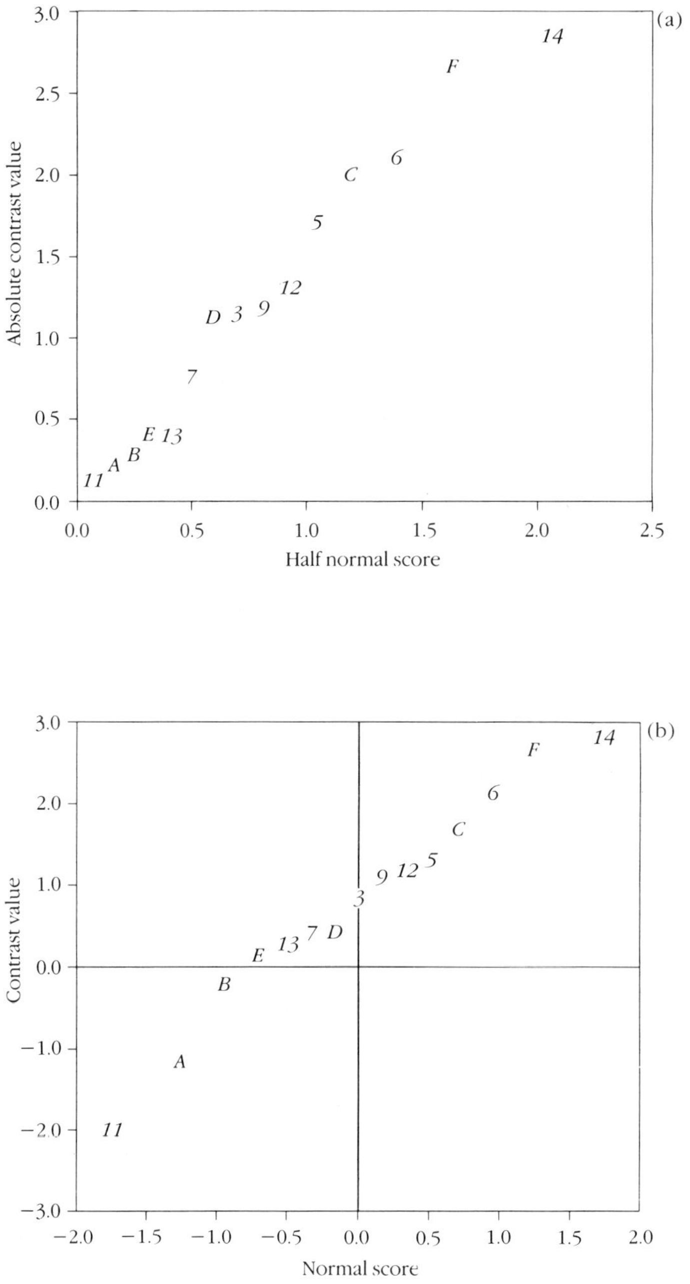


*Fig. 10.11* Fuel tank experiment. Dispersion effects on ln(strength), treating runs 5 and 6 as missing data. (a) Daniel plot; (b) full normal plot

judge whether any of the factors have an effect on dispersion. Figure 10.11(b) is a full normal plot, and this is no clearer. Note that the line misses the origin, which suggests that run 1 is slightly on the small side. We will choose to ignore the appearance of Fig. 10.11(b), and select from the Daniel plot the two largest contrasts, which correspond to column 14 (which measures minus the $C \times F$ and $A \times D$ interactions; the value of the contrast is 2.855) and factor $F$ (wheel pressure; the effect is 2.652). It is worth noting that these two contrasts remain the largest over a wide range of values substituted for runs 5 and 6. The sequence of predicting and replacing data is slightly more complicated now, because runs 5 and 6 have different configurations of factor $F$ and column 14, as follows:

| | $F$ | $c_{14}$ |
|---|---|---|
| Run 5 | + | + |
| Run 6 | − | − |

Hence different predictions will be attached to these runs.

Table 10.4 details the replacement and prediction sequence. At each stage, a Daniel plot was drawn to check whether column 14 and factor $F$ were still the largest effects, whether they moved off the line, and whether any other factor or interaction became significant. In this case column 14 and factor $F$ remained the only two 'significant' contrasts.

The final Daniel plot is shown in Fig. 10.12 with column 14 and factor $F$ clearly off the line. These two contrasts appear to influence dispersion, and an attempt to explain this should be made.

Since the effect of factor $F$ (wheel pressure) is positive, this means we need to choose $F$ at level (+) to maximize $-20\log(s_Y)$, i.e. to minimize $s_Y$. Why should factor $F$ affect dispersion? Well, some of the dispersion in strength comes about because corners are necessarily harder to weld than straight edges (this is because, at corners, the metal is generally deformed and wavy, and therefore harder to press together and achieve a good weld). The average strength of the sections from the straight edges is 3.964 kN and from the corners is only 2.952 kN, more than 1 kN less. Hence corners contribute to some of the variation in strength. Since factor $F$ is wheel pressure, and the dispersion analysis tells us to set this at the high level (5 bar), the two halves of the tank are being pressed together with more force. This helps to overcome the waviness in the metal and achieve a better weld at the corners.

The interaction is probably due to $C \times F$ rather than $A \times D$, because these two factors are active in their own right (although factor $C$ actually has a *location* effect, not a *dispersion* effect). Since the contrast corresponding to column 14 measures *minus* the $C \times F$ interaction, the interaction is actually negative, so needs to be set to 'level' (−) to help minimize dispersion. Since we would like factor $F$ to be at (+), we should set factor $C$ at (−), which is fortunate because we need factor $C$ at (−) to achieve maximum strength. Table 10.5 shows predictions for location and dispersion at these factor levels, using the results in Tables 10.3 and 10.4.

*Table 10.4* Dispersion effects and predictions of $-20\log(s_y)$, for $Y = \ln(\text{strength})$

| Iteration | Average of $-20\log(s_y)$ | Predictions Run 5 | Predictions Run 6 | Effect of factor $F$ | Effect of column 14 $-A\times D$ $-C\times F$ |
|---|---|---|---|---|---|
| 0* | 9.046 | 11.800 | 6.293 | 2.652 | 2.855 |
| 1 | 9.046 | 12.488 | 5.605 | 3.341 | 3.543 |
| 2 | 9.046 | 12.660 | 5.433 | 3.513 | 3.715 |
| 3 | 9.046 | 12.704 | 5.390 | 3.556 | 3.758 |
| 4 | 9.046 | 12.714 | 5.379 | 3.566 | 3.769 |
| 5 | 9.046 | 12.717 | 5.376 | 3.569 | 3.772 |
| 6 | 9.046 | 12.718 | 5.375 | 3.570 | 3.772 |
| 7 | 9.046 | 12.718 | 5.375 | 3.570 | 3.773 |
| 8 | 9.046 | 12.718 | 5.375 | 3.570 | 3.773 |

*Iteration 0 is the situation immediately after step 1 of the sequence

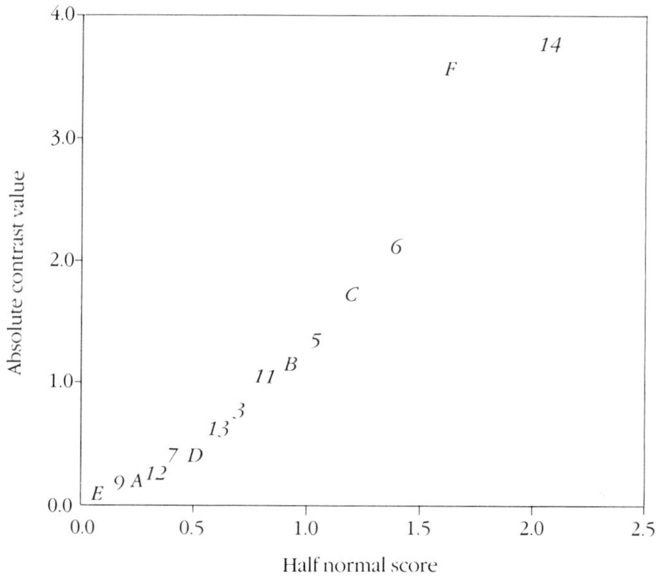


*Fig. 10.12* Fuel tank experiment. Dispersion effects on ln(strength), after convergence of the replacement/prediction method

*Table 10.5* Predictions for strength location and dispersion (for $C-$, $F+$)

| | |
|---|---|
| Predicted ln(strength) $= 1.590$, so strength $= e^{1.590} = 4.90$ kN | |
| Predicted $-20\log(s_Y) = 12.717$, so $s_Y = 10^{-12.717/20} = 0.231$, | |
| so $s_y \simeq 4.90 \times 0.231 = 1.133$* | |

*The reason for multiplying the predicted $s_Y$ by the predicted strength is explained in Chapter 11. See Table 11.1

## Analysis of the seam width data

To understand further the role of weld current in this experiment, we look at the seam width data, where another picture is useful. Figure 10.13 is a log–log plot of seam width location and seam width dispersion, for each experimental run except run 6, which contained all zero data. It shows that seam width variability *decreases* as the mean *increases* (drawing a line through the points by eye gives a gradient of about $-1$).

We know from Fig. 10.5 that increasing the weld current increases the seam width, but why does the seam width variability decrease? It turns out that, when the current is at the high level, the weld occurs across almost the entire width of the wheel (4.5 mm — see Fig. 10.1). Any disturbances, such as slight fluctuations in current, or movement of the wheel, will not result in much variation in seam width because there is enough energy to keep the seam equal to the width of the wheel (the seam cannot be wider than the wheel). For the lower current the average seam width is less than 2 mm, and therefore there is plenty of opportunity for the seam to vary under the wheel.

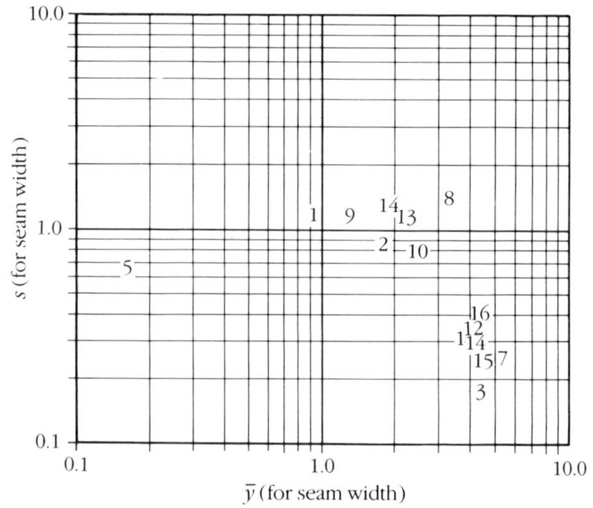


*Fig. 10.13* Fuel tank seam widths. Plot of $s$ against $\bar{y}$ on logarithmic scales

We choose to analyse just the location effects for seam width, and we do not transform the data (for an idea as to what transformation will decouple location and dispersion in Fig. 10.13, see Chapter 11). Runs 5 and 6 present a problem, but an application of predicting and replacing data as before eventually converges (after six iterations) on the following conclusion — factor $C$ has a strong positive effect (estimated at 2.376), with runs 5 and 6 predicted at 1.749. Since the $C$ effect was negative for strength, and is now positive for seam width, factor $C$ increases one characteristic while decreasing the other, which is obvious from Fig. 10.5.

Again the corners of the tank pose a problem. Figure 10.14 is a plot of the seam width at the different positions around the tank. This picture shows

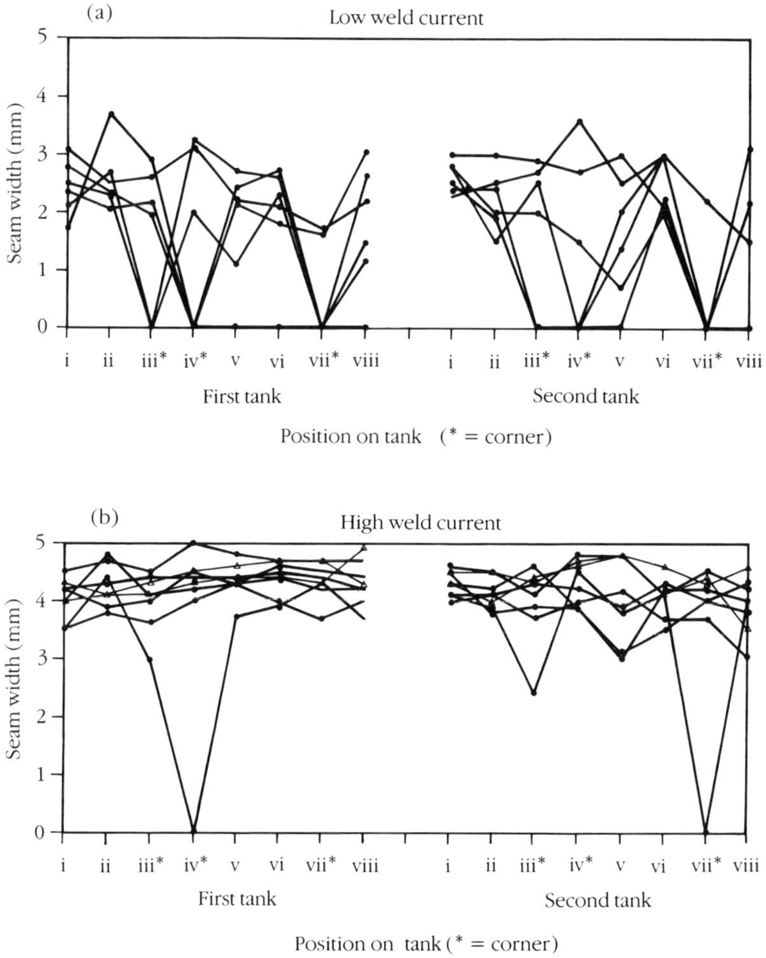


*Fig. 10.14* Fuel tank experiment. Seam width data for different locations on the tank. Each polygonal line corresponds to one tank in one run of the experiment

that in some cases the corner sections have a minimum width of zero (no seam) even with a high weld current. This is probably for the same reason as the lower strength at the corners — the tank sections are prone to undulations at the corners due to the forming process. Also welding around corners causes the welding wheel to skid.

Finally, Fig. 10.15 is a Daniel plot of seam width location effects *just for the corner sections* (sections iii, iv and vii in Fig. 10.2). This plot shows that, after weld current, the wheel clamping pressure is the next largest effect. This effect is positive. Although this contrast is actually on the line there is a suggestion that increasing the clamping pressure will help to increase the seam width at the corners, which is consistent with our observations about the effect of this factor on weld strength at the corners.

## Confirmation runs

An initial confirmation run with weld current set midway between the two levels used in the experiment (16.7 kA), and factors $A$, $B$, $D$, $E$ and $F$ set to 4 cycles, 2 cycles, 2.3 m min$^{-1}$, new and 3 bar, respectively, resulted in an average seam width of 3.7 mm and an average seam strength of 5.0 kN. This result is consistent with the plot in Fig. 10.5, assuming a linear relationship between the weld current and the two quality characteristics (which is all we can do because we only have a two-level experiment). However, having a

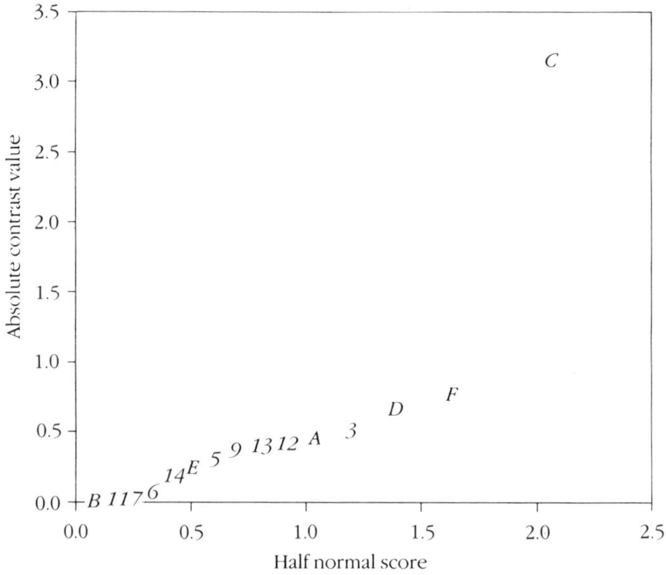


*Fig. 10.15* Fuel tank experiment. Location effects on seam width based on data from the corner sections only

current at 16.7 kA is something of a compromise in terms of seam width and strength. What is required is a seam with minimal variation in width and weld strength as large as possible. We *can* achieve a uniform weld width with the 4.5 mm wheel, but the current required is too high. But what about a narrower wheel? A narrower wheel would require less current to achieve a uniform weld, and less current improves strength. A narrower wheel would also assist in welding round corners. These hypothetical statements are really suggesting the need for a further experiment with a new set of factors, among them wheel width, and a new set of levels for some of the old factors like current and clamping pressure. Unfortunately, the experimenters used all their resources in the first experiment and it was not possible to try out these ideas. Chapter 1 of this book would have warned them!

As a final note, a recent article by Hamada and Wu (1991) suggests a slight modification to the iteration procedure described in this case study. They suggest choosing the effects that go into the prediction equation *before* adopting the iteration as described here, rather than relying on the iteration sequence itself to choose the prediction equation. In this example, we might choose just the main effects of the six factors as an initial prediction equation, and include all these effects even if they do not initially fall off the line on the Daniel plot. The final Daniel plot, after the sequence of iterations has converged, provides clues to the active factors in the usual way. The iteration process can then be applied again, for example by taking just the active main effects and their respective interactions in the prediction equation (if the confounding pattern allows). The final Daniel plot for this sequence of iterations may again suggest that effects should be added to or removed from the prediction equation, and so on.

## 10.2 AN EXPERIMENT ON OIL CONTROL PISTON RING SPACERS

This example concerns the variation in tangential load of oil control piston ring spacers. The experiment was organized by Michel Ferjoux of Ford France SA and Bruno Queval of Floquet Monopole, where the experiment was actually run.

The spacers fit around a piston in a groove, and are held in position by two rails. The spacers are designed to regulate the flow of oil over the surface of the piston, as shown in Fig. 10.16. If the spacers are too loose (i.e. tangential load is too low) then oil flows over the piston too freely and gets into the cylinder with the fuel. If the spacer is too tight, the pressure on the cylinder is higher, requiring more power to move the piston, which increases fuel consumption of the engine.

The specification for tangential load (measured in newtons) is 32.5 N with a tolerance of ±6 N. The process producing the piston rings resulted in

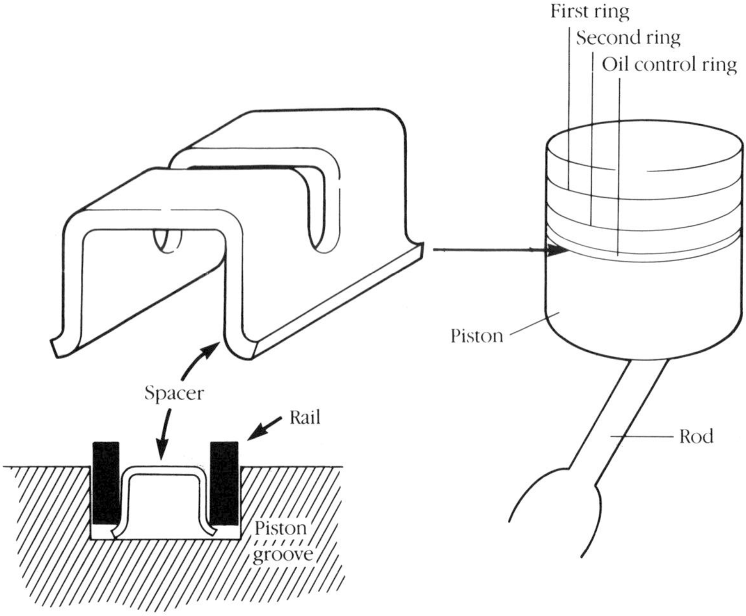


*Fig. 10.16* Oil control piston ring spacer: shape and function

around 20% of parts outside the specification: much effort was devoted to inspection of the process, with the machine slowed down so that the inspection could be managed. Figure 10.17 is a graph of scrap rates for a period of time before the experiment.

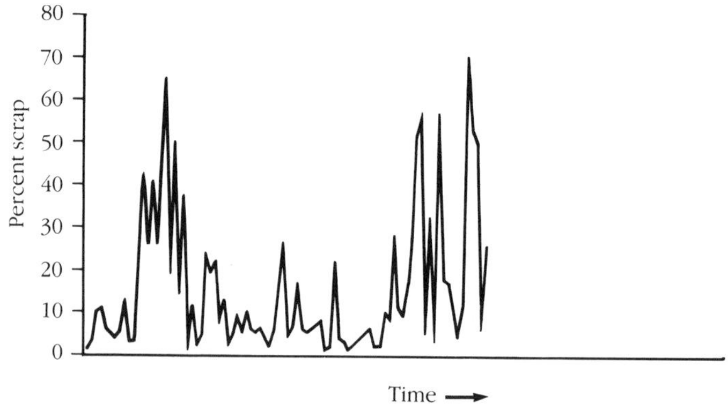


*Fig. 10.17* Scrap rates before the experiment on piston ring spacers

## Process and factors

The process works roughly as follows. An unformed strip of metal enters a press. The depth of the press (bottom dead centre) can be altered to adjust the aspect ratio of the cross-section of the finished spacer. The sides of the spacer are formed with an angle at the base (called the side-to-lug angle), and the strip of metal is then cut to length by utilizing the phase difference in the electric current.

The cut piece of metal is then passed into the generator phase where the length of the cut metal strip can be adjusted slightly with a manual length adjuster. The metal is tempered and formed into a piston ring spacer, and then hardened and heated with a HF power source. A final treatment involves the cooling of the formed spacer.

Seven process factors were identified, which were thought to have some bearing on the tangential load of piston ring spacers. These factors, and the levels selected for the experiment, were as follows:

| | Level | |
|---|---|---|
| Factor | (−) | (+) |
| (*A*) Bottom dead centre (mm) | 126.7 | 126.9 |
| (*B*) Side-to-lug angle | Min. | Max. |
| (*C*) Manual length adjust (mm) | Nominal − 0.3 | Nominal + 0.3 |
| (*D*) HF power (kW) | 850 | 880 |
| (*E*) Heat treatment speed | Slow | Fast |
| (*F*) Phase difference (cycles) | Nominal | Nominal + 0.4 |
| (*G*) Hardening temperature (°C) | 18 | 38 |

The objective is to achieve a tangential load of 32.5 N, and in order to measure the effects of the factors in the experiment, it was decided to make 30 piston ring spacers at every process setting, and use the mean and standard deviation as measures of the ability of the process to meet specification.

## Initial experiment

Initially, these factors were allocated to the $L_8$ orthogonal array (Taguchi's version), and the array and (summary) data are given in Table 10.6. Note that in Table 10.6, all the interactions are prefixed with a *minus* sign as a consequence of using Taguchi's array.

Figure 10.18 gives dot plots for the 30 spacers made in each of the eight runs. Note that all the distributions are roughly symmetrical with most data clustered towards the centre, so calculating a mean and a standard deviation is a reasonable thing to do. However, there is evidence of one or two outliers in the data, particularly in runs 1 and 8. The circled data in Fig. 10.18 were in

*Table 10.6* Initial piston ring spacer experiment

| Run | $A$ $-B \times C$ $-D \times E$ $-F \times G$ | $B$ $-A \times C$ $-D \times F$ $-E \times G$ | $C$ $-A \times B$ $-D \times G$ $-E \times F$ | $D$ $-A \times E$ $-B \times F$ $-C \times G$ | $E$ $-A \times D$ $-B \times G$ $-C \times F$ | $F$ $-A \times G$ $-B \times D$ $-C \times E$ | $G$ $-A \times F$ $-B \times E$ $-C \times D$ | $\bar{y}$ | $s$ | $-20\log(s)$ |
|---|---|---|---|---|---|---|---|---|---|---|
| 1 | −1 | −1 | −1 | −1 | −1 | −1 | −1 | 30.8 | 1.92 | −5.66 |
| 2 | −1 | −1 | −1 | +1 | +1 | +1 | +1 | 32.7 | 1.04 | −0.36 |
| 3 | −1 | +1 | +1 | −1 | −1 | +1 | +1 | 38.9 | 2.40 | −7.62 |
| 4 | −1 | +1 | +1 | +1 | +1 | −1 | −1 | 37.0 | 2.10 | −6.45 |
| 5 | +1 | −1 | +1 | −1 | +1 | −1 | +1 | 38.4 | 1.06 | −0.52 |
| 6 | +1 | −1 | +1 | +1 | −1 | +1 | −1 | 39.9 | 1.73 | −4.75 |
| 7 | +1 | +1 | −1 | −1 | +1 | +1 | −1 | 26.4 | 1.20 | −1.58 |
| 8 | +1 | +1 | −1 | +1 | −1 | −1 | +1 | 31.9 | 1.60 | −4.10 |
| Location effect | −0.70 | −1.89 | +8.12 | +1.74 | −1.76 | −0.07 | +1.97 | | | |

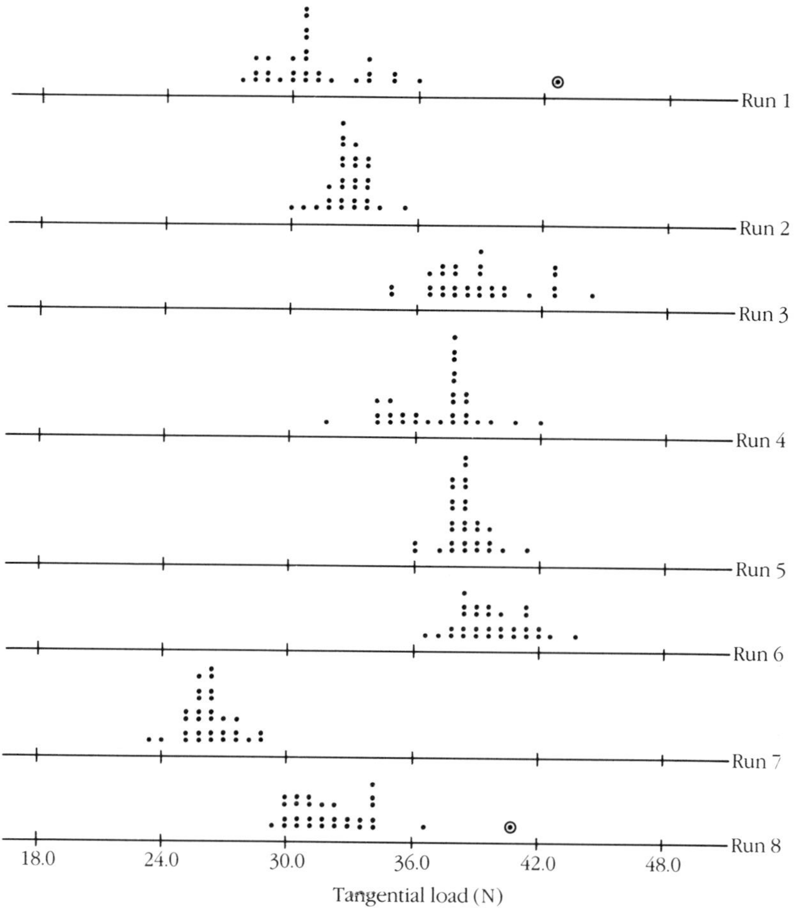


*Fig. 10.18* Initial experiment on piston ring spacers. Dot plots of tangential load

fact ignored when calculating the means and standard deviations in Table 10.6, since they would have quite an influence on the results. For example, including the extreme result in run 8 gives a mean of 32.395 and a standard deviation of 2.386, compared to 31.936 and 1.603 if it is left out. Also note from Fig. 10.18 that the spread in the dot plots is generally only about half as wide as the tolerance, so the within-run variation alone is not sufficient to explain the 20% scrap that was being observed.

Figure 10.19 is a Daniel plot of the location effects for the experiment in Table 10.6 (we will for the moment ignore dispersion effects). Because this experiment is saturated, it is of resolution III. No interaction information is separately available and therefore we initially make the assumption that contrasts measure main effects. Clearly from this picture, factor $C$ (manual length adjustment) has a large effect on tangential load, of nearly 8 N.

It was during the running of this $L_8$ experiment that the experimenters

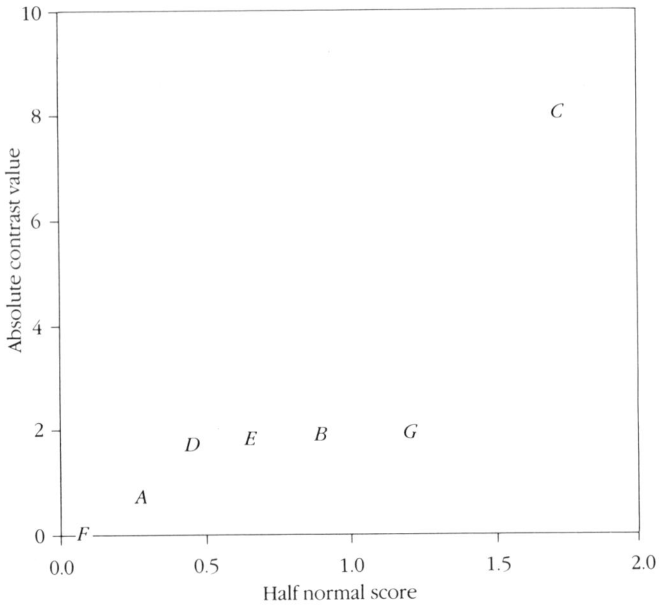


*Fig. 10.19* Initial experiment on piston ring spacers. Daniel plot of location effects

realized that factor $C$ was not very easy to adjust to the levels required, and in fact, if left unattended while producing piston ring spacers, had a tendency to wander around between the two levels (for the purposes of collecting experimental data, $C$ was *not* allowed to wander, by continuous monitoring and adjustment). Hence factor $C$ is really a noise factor. Coupled with the fact that $C$ has a large effect on the tangential load, the experimenters had, just by the act of running the experiment, discovered a main cause of variation in tangential load. Note that the size of the effect of factor $C$ (about 8) *added* to the natural piece-to-piece variation illustrated by the dot plots (a range of about 9) gives a total spread of $8 + 9 = 17$, wider than the tolerance of $\pm 6$ N — hence scrap will be produced. To improve the process two strategies are immediately available — reduce the *effect* of $C$, or reduce the piece-to-piece variation. A third strategy would be to control variation in $C$ better, which we will discuss briefly towards the end of this section.

This is an interesting example from the point of view of the discussion of process stability in Section 8.1. In normal production this process was unstable, partly because of the wandering of factor $C$. Controlling $C$ for the duration of the experiment brought the process much closer to stability, and therefore made $\bar{y}$ and $s$, the mean and standard deviation, much more useful measures of process performance.

## Follow-up experiment

Because the first experiment had thrown up an observation that the experimenters were not expecting (the discovery of a noise factor), the objective of the experiment *changed* from finding a (control) factor to reduce variability of tangential load to finding a factor that would *interact* with factor $C$ to nullify its effect (see Fig. 9.1 for an illustration of this idea). Interactions cannot be measured in an array that is saturated, so the experimenters chose to fold the design, conducting another eight-run experiment with all the levels of the factors reversed. The summary information from the extra eight runs (labelled runs 9 to 16) is shown in Table 10.7. A dot plot in Fig. 10.20 indicates one or two outliers in runs 10 and 13, which are again ignored when calculating a mean and standard deviation. The full data set for this experiment is given in Appendix 10.1.

Note that in the fold-over, the interactions now have a *plus* sign. This feature can be exploited when analysing the experiment as a whole, since if we *add* the effects based on Tables 10.6 and 10.7 the interactions will cancel

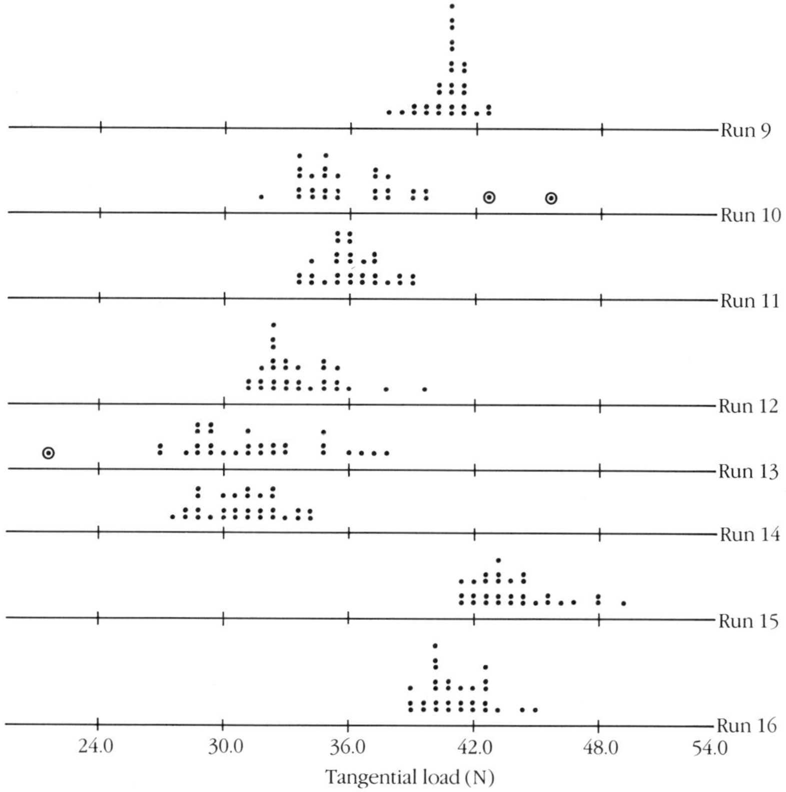


*Fig. 10.20* Data from the follow-up experiment on piston ring spacers

*Table 10.7* Eight extra runs obtained by fold-over

| Run | $A$<br>$B \times C$<br>$D \times E$<br>$F \times G$ | $B$<br>$A \times C$<br>$D \times F$<br>$E \times G$ | $C$<br>$A \times B$<br>$D \times G$<br>$E \times F$ | $D$<br>$A \times E$<br>$B \times F$<br>$C \times G$ | $E$<br>$A \times D$<br>$B \times G$<br>$C \times F$ | $F$<br>$A \times G$<br>$B \times D$<br>$C \times E$ | $G$<br>$A \times F$<br>$B \times E$<br>$C \times D$ | $\bar{y}$ | $s$ | $-20\log(s)$ |
|---|---|---|---|---|---|---|---|---|---|---|
| 9 | +1 | +1 | +1 | +1 | +1 | +1 | +1 | 40.7 | 1.10 | −0.81 |
| 10 | +1 | +1 | +1 | −1 | −1 | −1 | −1 | 35.7 | 2.04 | −6.17 |
| 11 | +1 | −1 | −1 | +1 | +1 | −1 | −1 | 36.2 | 1.47 | −3.33 |
| 12 | +1 | −1 | −1 | −1 | −1 | +1 | +1 | 33.7 | 1.93 | −5.73 |
| 13 | −1 | +1 | −1 | +1 | −1 | +1 | −1 | 31.6 | 3.07 | −9.74 |
| 14 | −1 | +1 | −1 | −1 | +1 | −1 | +1 | 31.0 | 1.85 | −5.33 |
| 15 | −1 | −1 | +1 | +1 | −1 | −1 | +1 | 44.0 | 2.13 | −6.55 |
| 16 | −1 | −1 | +1 | −1 | +1 | +1 | −1 | 41.2 | 1.48 | −3.43 |
| Location effect | −0.40 | −4.03 | +7.28 | +2.70 | +1.00 | +0.09 | +1.16 | | | |

out and we will be left with main effects, and if we *subtract* effects from Table 10.6 from those of Table 10.7, the main effects cancel out and we are left with interactions. Because we can now measure main effects separately from (combinations of) interactions, we see why folding over an $L_8$ that is resolution III produces an $L_{16}$ that is resolution IV, as we claimed in Chapter 4. Another way to get at the main effects and interactions is of course actually to combine Tables 10.6 and 10.7 into one larger array and work out the confounding pattern. Table 10.8 shows the contrast matrix for the 16 runs as a whole.

The factors and their two-way interactions generate 14 columns, and we have added an extra column that can be considered a 'block' contrast, because it measures the difference between the first eight runs and the second eight runs, which were carried out some time apart. The block contrast is orthogonal to all other contrasts.

All interactions between the control factors ($A$, $B$, $D$, $E$, $F$ and $G$) and the noise factor ($C$) are clear of main effects, but they are mixed up with other interactions. For an alternative plan which avoids this problem, the experimenters could have folded factor $C$ alone (see Section 4.2).

Figure 10.21 is a Daniel plot of the 15 available location contrasts. Note first that factor $C$ is definitely off the line and the size of the effect is similar to before (about 8), so the experimenters' intuition (based on their experimental experience) that the Daniel plot in Fig. 10.19 really did show a $C$ main effect (and not for example a $D \times G$ interaction) was correct.

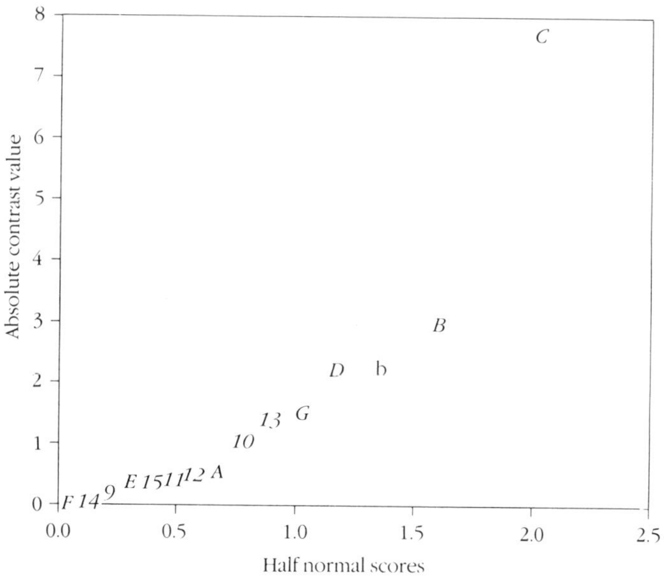


*Fig. 10.21* Experiment on piston ring spacers. Location effects based on all 16 runs. Italic numbers refer to the columns of $L_{16}(2^{15})$ — see Table 10.8

*Table 10.8* Contrast matrix for the complete 16-run piston ring spacer experiment*

| Run | *A* | *B* | *C* | *D* | *E* | *F* | *G* | b | **$B \times C$** $D \times E$ $F \times G$ *9* | **$A \times C$** $D \times F$ $E \times G$ *10* | $A \times B$ $D \times G$ $E \times F$ *11* | $A \times E$ $B \times F$ **$C \times G$** *12* | $A \times D$ $B \times G$ **$C \times F$** *13* | $A \times G$ $B \times D$ **$C \times E$** *14* | $A \times F$ $B \times E$ **$C \times D$** *15* |
|---|---|---|---|---|---|---|---|---|---|---|---|---|---|---|---|
| 1 | −1 | −1 | −1 | −1 | −1 | −1 | −1 | −1 | +1 | +1 | +1 | +1 | +1 | +1 | +1 |
| 2 | −1 | −1 | −1 | +1 | +1 | +1 | +1 | −1 | +1 | +1 | +1 | −1 | −1 | −1 | −1 |
| 3 | −1 | +1 | +1 | −1 | −1 | +1 | +1 | −1 | +1 | −1 | −1 | +1 | +1 | −1 | −1 |
| 4 | −1 | +1 | +1 | +1 | +1 | −1 | −1 | −1 | +1 | −1 | −1 | −1 | −1 | +1 | +1 |
| 5 | +1 | −1 | +1 | −1 | +1 | −1 | +1 | −1 | −1 | +1 | −1 | +1 | −1 | +1 | −1 |
| 6 | +1 | −1 | +1 | +1 | −1 | +1 | −1 | −1 | −1 | +1 | −1 | −1 | +1 | −1 | +1 |
| 7 | +1 | +1 | −1 | −1 | +1 | +1 | −1 | −1 | −1 | −1 | +1 | +1 | −1 | −1 | +1 |
| 8 | +1 | +1 | −1 | +1 | −1 | −1 | +1 | −1 | −1 | −1 | +1 | −1 | +1 | +1 | −1 |
| 9 | +1 | +1 | +1 | +1 | +1 | +1 | +1 | +1 | +1 | +1 | +1 | +1 | +1 | +1 | +1 |
| 10 | +1 | +1 | +1 | −1 | −1 | −1 | −1 | +1 | +1 | +1 | +1 | −1 | −1 | −1 | −1 |
| 11 | +1 | −1 | −1 | +1 | +1 | −1 | −1 | +1 | +1 | −1 | −1 | +1 | +1 | −1 | −1 |
| 12 | +1 | −1 | −1 | −1 | −1 | +1 | +1 | +1 | +1 | −1 | −1 | −1 | −1 | +1 | +1 |
| 13 | −1 | +1 | −1 | +1 | −1 | +1 | −1 | +1 | −1 | +1 | −1 | +1 | −1 | +1 | −1 |
| 14 | −1 | +1 | −1 | −1 | +1 | −1 | +1 | +1 | −1 | +1 | −1 | −1 | +1 | −1 | +1 |
| 15 | −1 | −1 | +1 | +1 | −1 | −1 | +1 | +1 | −1 | −1 | +1 | +1 | −1 | −1 | +1 |
| 16 | −1 | −1 | +1 | −1 | +1 | +1 | −1 | +1 | −1 | −1 | +1 | −1 | +1 | +1 | −1 |
| Location effect | −0.55 | −2.96 | +7.70 | +2.22 | −0.38 | +0.01 | +1.57 | +2.25 | +0.15 | −1.07 | −0.41 | +0.48 | +1.38 | +0.08 | −0.41 |

*We have highlighted the interactions that involve the noise factor *C*. The contrast labelled 'b' measures the difference between the results from each half of the experiment – the *block* effect. The other effects can also be calculated as half the sums and differences of effects from Tables 10.6 and 10.7

The next largest contrast measures a main effect due to factor $B$ (side-to-lug angle) with a value of about $-3$, but this contrast is on the line with the other contrasts pointing towards the origin. It is unfortunate that no interaction with factor $C$ is apparent, because this might lead to a way of nullifying its effect. The largest interaction is in fact measured by the contrast in column 13 of Table 10.8 and could be the $F \times C$ interaction. Factor $F$ is the phase difference, and assuming that this interaction might possibly be active, we have illustrated it in Fig. 10.22.

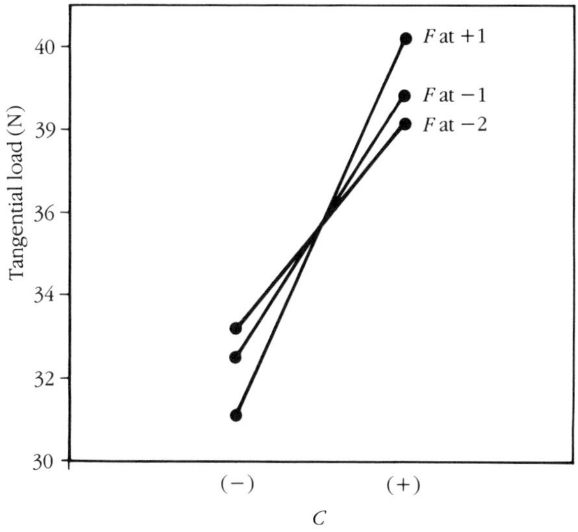


*Fig. 10.22* Experiment on piston ring spacers. A possible $C \times F$ interaction

Clearly, setting factor $F$ to level $(-)$ is better, since this reduces the effect of $C$, but reducing $F$ still further (to a coded level of $-2$ say, corresponding to Nominal $-$ 0.4 mm) might nullify the effect of factor $C$ still further. This was tried but unfortunately could not be confirmed, which might have been expected in the light of the Daniel plot in Fig. 10.21.

## Dispersion analysis

The next line of attack is to look for genuine dispersion effects in the data. Figure 10.23 is a log–log plot of the standard deviations and means from Tables 10.6 and 10.7. There is no apparent need to transform the data before looking for dispersion effects, because there is no trend in this plot. Hence we work directly with $-20\log(s)$, where $s$ is the standard deviation of the raw data.

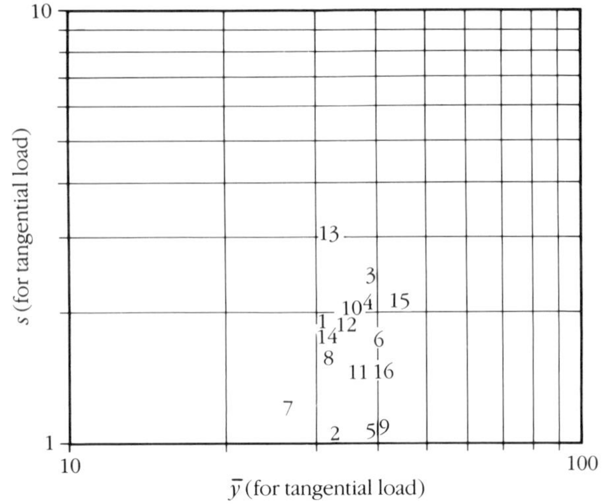


*Fig. 10.23* Experiment on piston ring spacers. Plot of $s$ against $\bar{y}$ on logarithmic scales

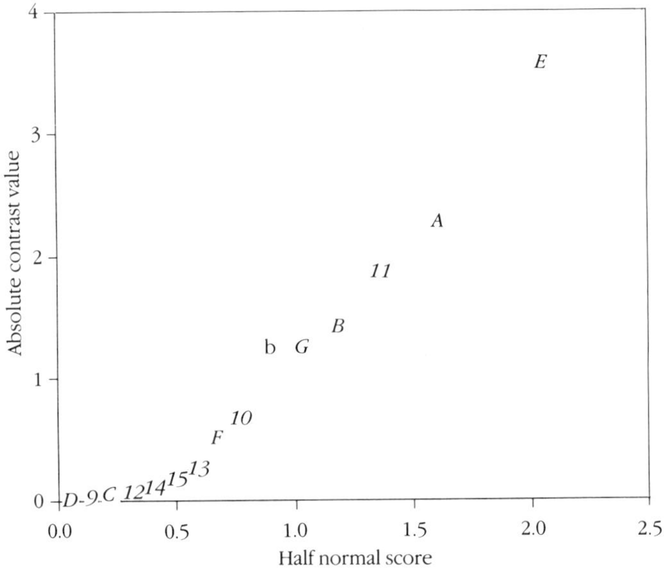


*Fig. 10.24* Experiment on piston ring spacers. Dispersion effects from the complete experiment

Figure 10.24 is the Daniel plot of the 15 dispersion effects from the complete experiment. This plot is not at all useful, in that the points do not form a straight line, and no effects appear unusually large. The largest effects are factor $E$ (heat treatment speed) and factor $A$ (bottom dead centre) and both of the effects are positive. If we tried to use these factors to reduce dispersion we would set them to their (+) levels to maximize $-20\log(s)$, i.e. reduce dispersion. The predicted dispersion is found as follows:

$$\text{predicted value of } -20\log(s) = -1.591$$
$$\text{which implies predicted } s = 1.201$$

Even if this prediction could be confirmed, however, it is not enough to ensure that the piston ring spacers will meet specification since the effect of factor $C$ (8) added to $\pm 3s$ is still about $8 + 6 \times 1.201 = 15.2$, somewhat wider than the tolerance of $\pm 6$ N.

## Application of SPC

Although it turned out that the experiment did not discover a factor that could remove the effect of factor $C$, and no strong dispersion effects were found, attention was focused on trying to control $C$ in a more precise way. SPC methods (control charts in this case) were initiated on the generator phase of the process, and special causes were identified and removed over a period of time. This is not a book on SPC so we will not give details (see Wheeler and Chambers 1986, or Owen 1989), but Fig. 10.25 shows that scrap was reduced to around 4% after the application of SPC to monitoring the length after the heat treatment.

Eventually this figure was reduced to under 1%. The strategy of SPC is one of removing causes rather than removing effects, but the experiment showed that removing effects was not going to be possible. Hence the

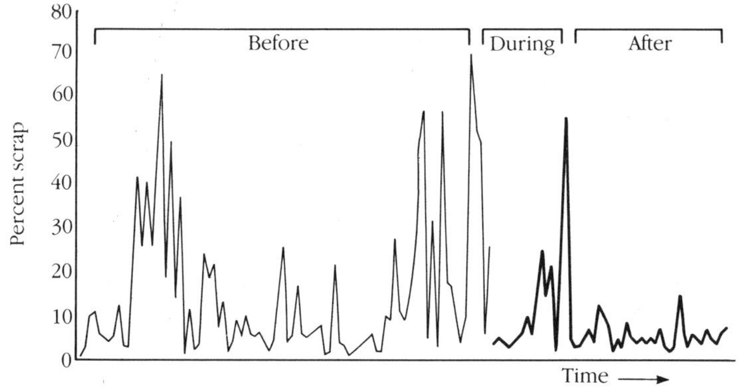


*Fig. 10.25* Scrap rates before, during and after the experiment on piston ring spacers

application of SPC was appropriate here, with the experiment indicating where to improve control of the process in order to reduce variation in the output.

## 10.3 A BRIEF RETURN TO THE ENGINE MAPPING EXPERIMENT

We briefly return to the engine mapping experiment to discuss a couple of points that would have got in the way in Chapters 5 and 6.

Recall that Figs 5.9(a) and (b) were Daniel plots of the contrasts available from the full factorial $3^3$ experiment for fuel flow, the data being in Table 5.9. These plots showed that a second-order model was not totally adequate for expressing fuel flow as a function of $R$ (engine speed), $T$ (torque) and $S$ (spark advance), because some third-order contrasts (namely $R_q \times S_\ell$ and $R_\ell \times S_q$) were active. However, the situation can be simplified by fitting a second-order equation to log(fuel). The Daniel plot is given in Fig. 10.26(a). In this plot, the two prominent contrasts measure *linear main effects*, and the next largest standardized contrast is also a linear main effect. Figure 10.26(b) is a re-plot with $R$ and $T$ removed. There is an indication that some other contrasts are off the line, but, compared to the size of the effects for $R$ and $T$, they are all small. Most if not all of the curvature can be captured by making an appropriate transformation of the data. Hence a log transformation for fuel simplifies the interpretation.

This conclusion can be reinforced by considering the physical theory involved. Since fuel consumption is related to the work done by the engine, and work done is given by force × distance (that is torque × engine speed), then a not unrealistic model from physical theory suggests

$$\text{fuel} \propto R \times T$$

or

$$\log(\text{fuel}) = \text{constant} + \log(R) + \log(T) \qquad [10.1]$$

Hence the system should be linear and additive after a log transformation has been made to the response *and to the factors R and T*. Here, we only transformed the response, which might explain why some of the contrasts in Fig. 10.26(b) were off the line even though they were small.

Transformations to the factors need to be considered *before* any experimentation is done. The levels of the factors must be equally spaced on a logarithmic scale if we wish to retain orthogonality in the contrasts which provide coefficients for the prediction equation. Since the levels here are equally spaced on a linear scale, we would need to use the method of multiple regression (see Chapter 6) to fit an equation of the type described by [10.1]. We do not give details here, but there are indications, based on the full 27-

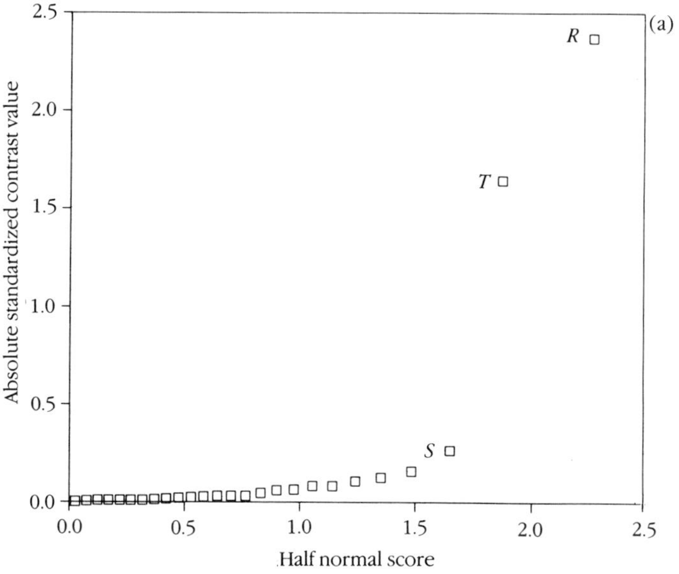


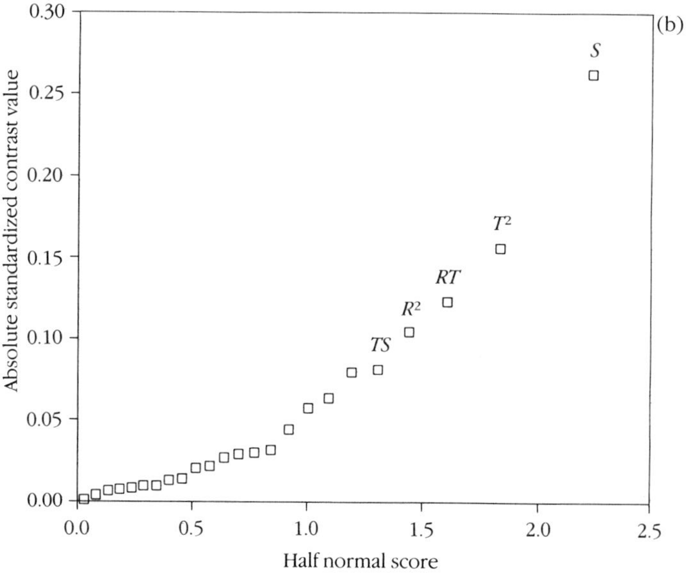


*Fig. 10.26* Engine mapping. Effects on ln(fuel): (a) 26 contrasts; (b) 24 contrasts ($R$ and $T$ removed)

run data set in Table 5.9, that a prediction equation of the form [10.1] performs at least as well as a second-order equation with no transformations.

Thus, *mechanistic knowledge* of the system under consideration can help the application of experimental design by simplifying the nature of the prediction equation.

## 10.4 PREDICTING THE AIR SPEED OF A DESK-TOP FAN

We have had the pleasure of giving courses about the methods in this book to groups of engineers in the Ford Motor Co. Ltd and supplier companies to Ford, and, as part of the training experience, we usually ask participants to conduct a small experiment. We would like to thank Chris Benton, Richard Parker, Adrian Stead and Martyn Whitehead, all of the Ford Motor Co. Ltd, for being enthusiastic about the ideas we were trying to teach them. The result is this experiment, and we have included it to show that the methods can be tried out on a small scale in order to familiarize engineers with planning, designing, running, analysing and predicting from experiments. This sort of experiment can be tried at home, for example, away from the pressures of everyday work.

The team of experimenters decided to try to predict the air speed of a desk-top fan as a function of factors that could easily be changed — fan speed, distance away from fan, and so on. The measured response ($y$) was chosen simply to be air speed in $\mathrm{m\,s^{-1}}$ (measured with a simple, cheap, hand-held device to the nearest $0.1\,\mathrm{m\,s^{-1}}$). The factors chosen for investigation, together with their respective levels, were as follows:

| | Level | | |
|---|---|---|---|
| Factor | (−) | (0) | (+) |
| ($S$) Speed of fan (actual values unknown) | 1* | 2* | 3* |
| ($D$) Distance from fan (m) | 0.5 | 1.0 | 1.5 |
| ($T$) Tilt angle (inches)† | −4 | 0 | +4 |
| ($R$) Rotation angle (inches)† | −4 | 0 | +4 |

*These speeds were pre-set by switches on the fan — intermediate speeds not available — and the speeds are asssumed to be equally spaced

†These distances were measured as the opposite side of a right-angled triangle dictated by tilting and rotating the fan — see Fig. 10.27

Three levels for each factor were used in order to find out whether air speed could, for the purposes of prediction, be well approximated by a second-order (quadratic) response equation in the four factors. The objective of the experiment, therefore, is to estimate a second-order equation to predict $y$ in terms of $S$, $D$, $T$ and $R$.

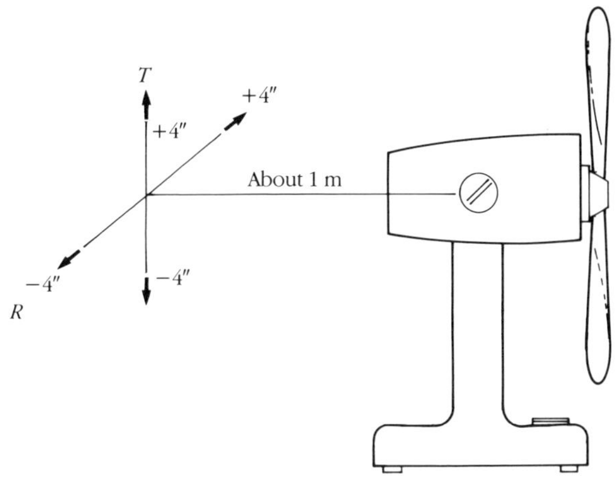


*Fig. 10.27* Schematic diagram of a desk-top fan, illustrating factors $T$ and $R$

The experimental plan chosen was the *composite design* consisting of a two-level array augmented with a centre point and star points — see Table 6.13. The resulting experiment and data collected are shown in Table 10.9. Note that the experiment was actually run twice as a genuine *replication* (i.e. all sources of experimental error, arising for example from set up, are equally well represented in both observations). There is good agreement between the two sets of results. Although there are really 50 runs, we will label the runs 1–25, and refer to replication 1 and replication 2. The experiment took about three hours to complete to the stage illustrated in Table 10.9.

In order to estimate the second-order equation, we will initially work with the average of the two air speed readings.

A total of 24 contrasts can be calculated from the averages $\bar{y}$. These consist of four linear contrasts, four quadratic contrasts, six linear by linear interaction contrasts and 10 checking contrasts, which test the adequacy of the second order model (see Chapter 6). Equation [5.8] can be used for the standardization of the contrasts, but we need to double the sums of squares (of coefficients in each contrast column) and double the divisors, because of the replication.

Figure 10.28 shows the Daniel plot of the 24 contrasts. Apart from the checking contrasts, we have labelled each point according to the corresponding term in the prediction equation. Some points are definitely off the 'line' formed by the others, these being obviously the linear effect of $D$ and of $S$, and the $D \times T$ interaction. Figure 10.29 is a re-plot of Fig. 10.28 with these three contrasts removed.

This plot does not look at all friendly — contrasts that measure quadratic effects of three of the factors (labelled $D^2$, $S^2$, and $T^2$) are all 'off the line' as well as the linear effect of $T$ and the $S \times D$ interaction. In addition one of the

*Table 10.9* Array and data for the desk-top fan experiment (two replications)

| | Factor | | | | Air speed ($m\,s^{-1}$) | | |
|---|---|---|---|---|---|---|---|
| Run | $S$ | $D$ | $T$ | $R$ | $y_1$ | $y_2$ | Average $\bar{y}$ |
| 1 | − | − | − | − | 2.6 | 2.8 | 2.70 |
| 2 | + | − | − | − | 5.2 | 5.5 | 5.35 |
| 3 | − | + | − | − | 0.05* | 0.05* | 0.05 |
| 4 | + | + | − | − | 0.1 | 0.1 | 0.10 |
| 5 | − | − | + | − | 2.4 | 2.7 | 2.55 |
| 6 | + | − | + | − | 4.8 | 4.8 | 4.80 |
| 7 | − | + | + | − | 0.2 | 0.7 | 0.45 |
| 8 | + | + | + | − | 2.0 | 2.0 | 2.00 |
| 9 | − | − | − | + | 2.9 | 2.8 | 2.85 |
| 10 | + | − | − | + | 5.4 | 5.7 | 5.55 |
| 11 | − | + | − | + | 0.05* | 0.05* | 0.10 |
| 12 | + | + | − | + | 0.2 | 0.1 | 0.15 |
| 13 | − | − | + | + | 2.7 | 2.4 | 2.55 |
| 14 | + | − | + | + | 4.4 | 3.9 | 4.15 |
| 15 | − | + | + | + | 0.7 | 1.0 | 0.85 |
| 16 | + | + | + | + | 3.0 | 2.9 | 2.95 |
| 17 | 0 | 0 | 0 | 0 | 3.1 | 2.8 | 2.95 |
| 18 | − | 0 | 0 | 0 | 2.3 | 2.6 | 2.45 |
| 19 | + | 0 | 0 | 0 | 4.7 | 4.0 | 4.35 |
| 20 | 0 | − | 0 | 0 | 2.8 | 2.6 | 2.70 |
| 21 | 0 | + | 0 | 0 | 0.5 | 0.5 | 0.50 |
| 22 | 0 | 0 | − | 0 | 2.0 | 1.8 | 1.90 |
| 23 | 0 | 0 | + | 0 | 2.1 | 2.2 | 2.15 |
| 24 | 0 | 0 | 0 | − | 2.2 | 2.3 | 2.25 |
| 25 | 0 | 0 | 0 | + | 3.2 | 3.3 | 3.25 |

*Actually between 0.0 and 0.1 $m\,s^{-1}$

checking contrasts (labelled $CC_5$ on the plot, which actually measures the $S_\ell \times D_\ell \times T_\ell$ interaction) is also 'off the line', which indicates that the second-order assumptions are not entirely adequate for making predictions about the air speed of the fan. Also, the rest of the contrasts in Fig. 10.29 do not form a very straight line in themselves.

In order to deal with some of these concerns, and to simplify the interpretation of the data, the experimenters tried some *transformations* of the data. For this experiment, a logarithmic transformation turns out to be useful (the appropriate transformation was determined quite quickly by trial and error using a spreadsheet on a lap-top computer). Figure 10.30 is a plot of all 24 standardized contrasts based on the average of the two replications per run, *after* the log transformation has been made to the raw data. Contrasts that measure the linear effect of $D$, $T$, and $S$ are clearly off the line, as are the

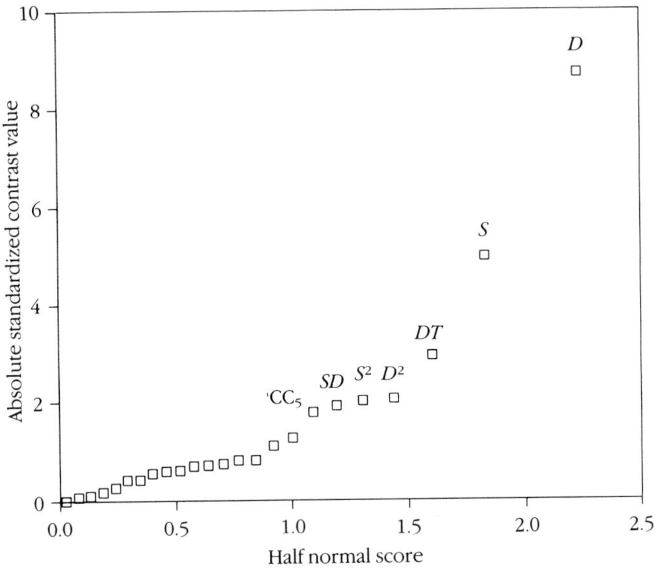


*Fig. 10.28* Fan experiment. Daniel plot of 24 contrasts based on the run averages

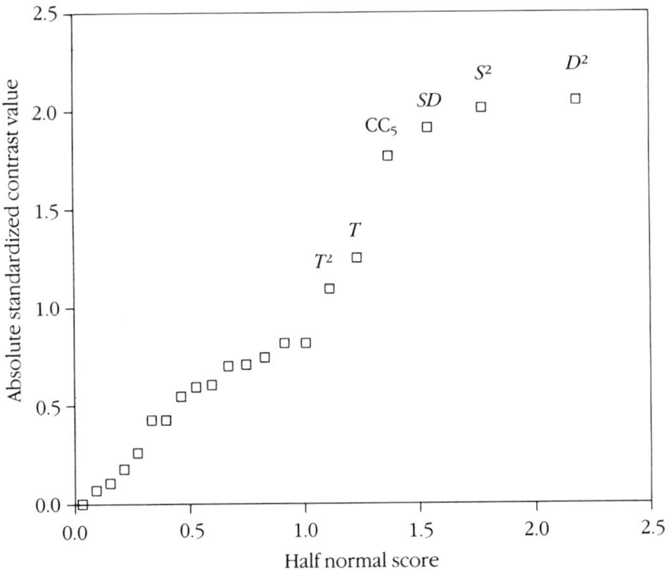


*Fig. 10.29* Fan experiment. Re-plot of Fig. 10.28 with three contrasts removed

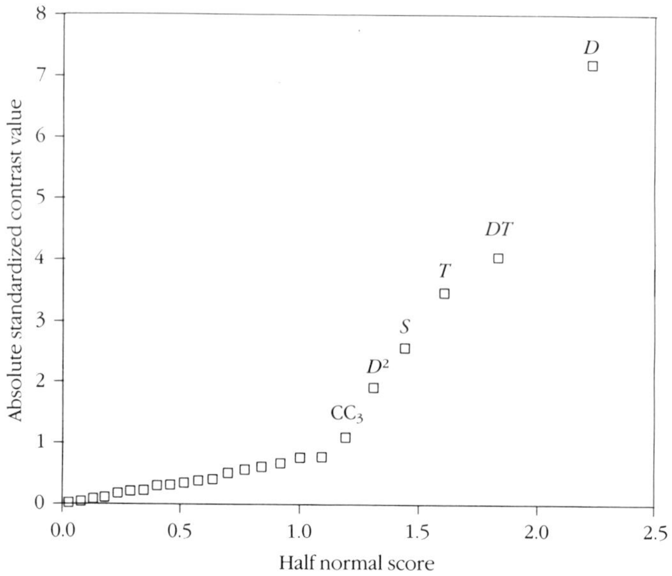


*Fig. 10.30* Fan experiment. Effects on ln(air speed)

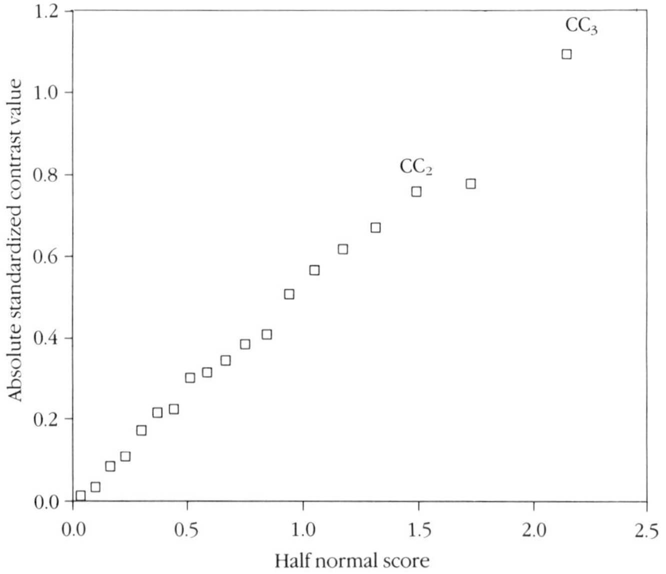


*Fig. 10.31* Fan experiment. Re-plot of Fig. 10.30 with five contrasts removed

$D \times T$ interaction and the quadratic effect of $D$ (labelled $D^2$). Removing these contrasts and re-plotting (Fig. 10.31) shows a very well behaved straight line. In particular, in the log metric *no checking contrasts are active*, and so the second-order assumptions are more plausible here.

The fitted second-order equation (with the factors in the coded units $-1$ to $+1$) is then

$$\ln(y) = 0.98 + 0.42S - 1.20D + 0.58T - 0.92D^2 + 0.71DT$$

or

$$y = \exp(0.98 + 0.42S - 1.20D + 0.58T - 0.92D^2 + 0.71DT) \quad [10.2]$$

which can be used to predict air speed ($y$) as a function of fan speed ($S$), distance ($D$) and tilt angle ($T$). The effect of the rotation angle ($R$) was not measurable against the background of experimental 'error' or common cause variation.

Figure 10.32 shows the predicted air speed in terms of $S$ and $D$ for tilt angles of $-4''$, $0''$, and $+4''$ respectively.

Equation [10.2] was used for prediction very successfully. Other members of the group (who had all done their own experiments, all worthy of inclusion in this book) asked the experimenters to configure the fan to give certain air speeds. As an example, one such request was for $1.2\,\mathrm{m\,s^{-1}}$. Note that this air speed was not actually observed in the experiment, so the experimenters had to place trust in their prediction equation to decide on the levels of the factors to achieve the desired value. After some trial and error with the prediction equation, the team came up with:

| Factor | $S$ | $D$ | $T$ | $R$ |
|---|---|---|---|---|
| Level | $-1$ | 0.25 | 0 | 0 |

Prediction
$\exp\{0.98 - 0.42 - 1.20 \times 0.25 - 0.92 \times (0.25)^2\}$
$= e^{2.025}$
$= 1.22\,\mathrm{m\,s^{-1}}$

The actual reading when this combination of levels was tried was $1.2\,\mathrm{m\,s^{-1}}$, which was the result required. Hence the knowledge gained from the experiment could be used to tune the system to give the desired output.

## Further analysis

Although they were not studied at the time, some interesting features of this experiment can be highlighted by considering the replications, and analysing the residuals from model [10.2]. Remember that we are working with the data in the log metric.

Fitting the second-order equation required interpretation of 24 (nearly

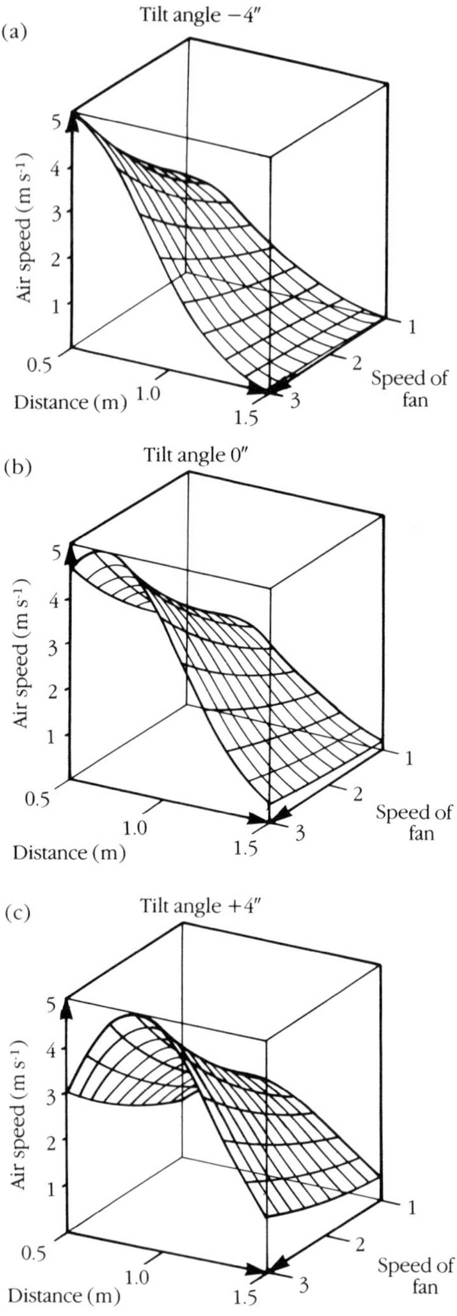


*Fig. 10.32* Fan experiment. Predicted air speed as a function of *S* and *D*, for three different tilt angles: (a) −4″; (b) 0″; (c) +4″

orthogonal) contrasts. Another 25 orthogonal contrasts are available (since 24 + 25 = 50 − 1 = 49), and these can be chosen to measure the difference between the pair of results for each run, so that the absolute contrast for each run is given by

$$\tfrac{1}{2}|\ln(y_1) - \ln(y_2)| \qquad [10.3]$$

Note that, on the original (untransformed) scale, this contrast becomes $\frac{1}{2}\ln(y_1/y_2)$ so that [10.3] refers to a *ratio* in the original data units.

Since the divisor is 2 for each of the 25 contrasts described by [10.3], they do not need to be standardized before plotting. However, we *will* standardize them (from [5.8], $k = 1/\sqrt{2}$) so that the resulting plot can be compared to Fig. 10.31.

Figure 10.33 is a Daniel plot of the standardized versions of [10.3], and two interesting facts emerge. First, we would expect this plot to resemble a straight line, because contrasts calculated from [10.3] should measure only experimental error. Clearly, however, the contrasts corresponding to runs 7, 12 and 15 are off the line, suggesting that the experimental noise in these runs is somewhat larger than expected. To some extent the log transformation hinders us here, because it *exaggerates* differences in results for small numbers, and runs 7, 12 and 15 all had low ($<1.0\,\mathrm{m\,s^{-1}}$) air speeds. For example, the two results from run 12 are 0.2 and 0.1, a difference of only 0.1 on the original scale, but $|\ln(0.2) - \ln(0.1)| = 0.693$ on the log scale. As a comparison, run 19 has the largest difference on the original scale (4.7 − 4.0 = 0.7) but $|\ln(4.7) - \ln(4.0)| = 0.161$, much less than 0.693.

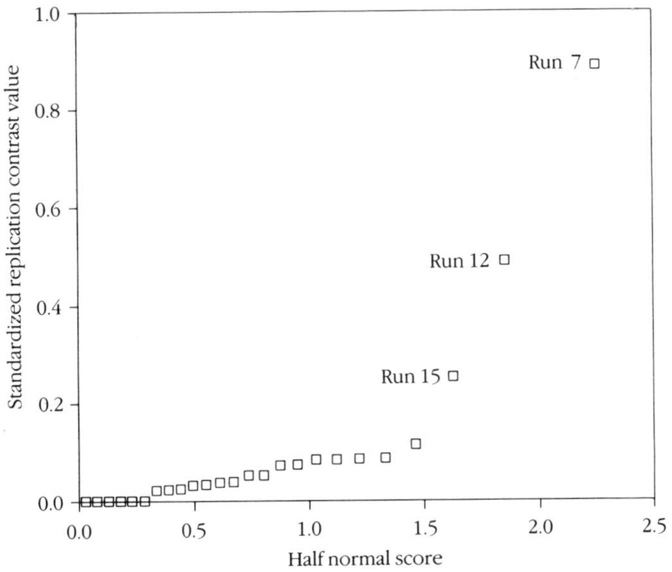


*Fig. 10.33* Fan experiment. Daniel plot of replication contrasts, one from each run

Another interesting feature of Fig. 10.33 is the *gradient*, which is a measure of $\sigma$, the experimental noise (see Chapter 6). From this plot, $\sigma$ is about 0.08. But another measure of $\sigma$ is the gradient of the Daniel plot of the inactive contrasts given in Fig. 10.31, which is about 0.6. There is a great disparity in these estimates, which suggests that the replication error cannot account for the slope formed by the inactive contrasts of Fig. 10.31. Indeed, if the slope in Fig. 10.33 is 'correct', then most of the contrasts in Fig. 10.31, including the checking contrasts, are off the line, which means that the second-order equation, looked at from the data analytic viewpoint, is not adequate (in practice of course it *is* adequate because it predicted satisfactorily, as our example showed).

We can get another handle on this 'lack of fit' by looking at *residuals*. Recall that residuals are observed values minus predicted values. We use equation [10.2] to provide predictions for each of the 25 configurations in the experiment, and calculate a residual for each of the 50 results (still in the log metric). Figure 10.34 is a run chart of the residuals in the order that the experiment was done.

Three residuals clearly stand out from this plot — the ones from runs 7 and 23 from the first set of results, and the residual from run 23 in the second set of results. Since run 23 stands out for both replications, and both residuals are about the same, this suggests that the prediction equation [10.2] does not do a good job at predicting this configuration. The prominent residual for replication 1 of run 7 is the reason why run 7 stood out on the Daniel plot of replication contrasts (Fig. 10.33).

Figure 10.35 is another way of presenting the residuals. It is a plot of the residuals from the first set of runs (on the $x$ axis) against the residuals from the second set of runs (on the $y$ axis). If the second-order equation explained

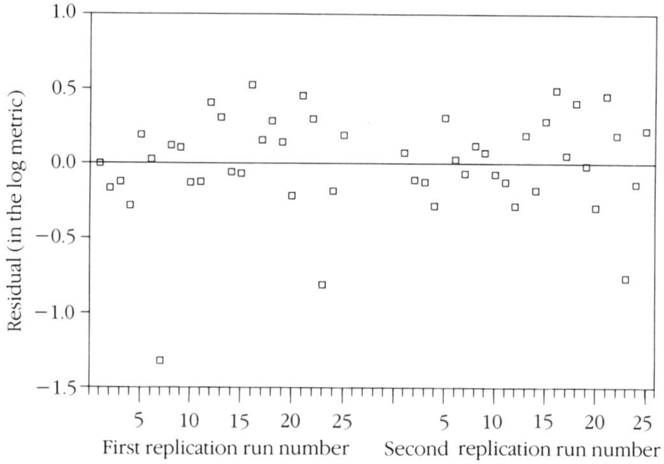


*Fig. 10.34* Fan experiment. Run chart of residuals, using equation [10.2] to predict ln(air speed)

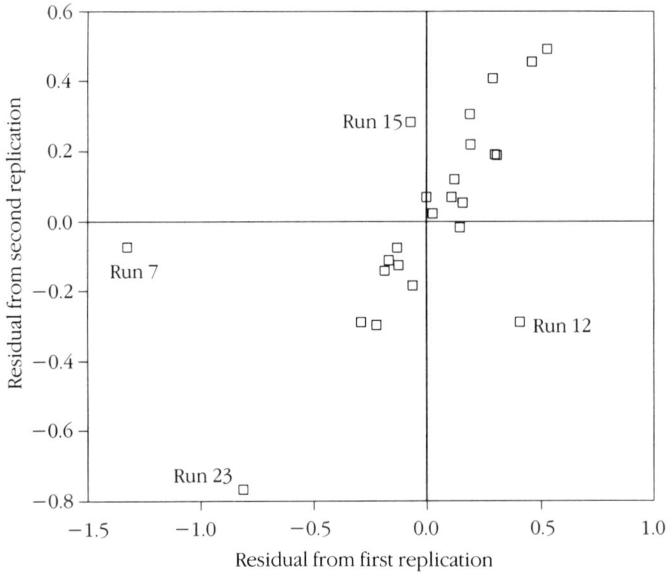


*Fig. 10.35* Fan experiment. For each run, the residual for the first replication is plotted against the residual for the second replication

the data apart from random noise, then this plot should show a random scatter of points. Clearly this is not the case. Apart from runs 7, 12 and 15, which were highlighted on the Daniel plot of replication contrasts, there is a strong positive correlation in the plot, suggesting that a positive residual from the first set of runs was repeated in the second set of runs, and similarly for the negative residuals — hence a *systematic* lack of fit from the second order model [10.2]. Note that run 23 fits in with the positive correlation but is a long way from the others, which is consistent with the run plot in Fig. 10.34.

When we discovered this, we quizzed the experimenters more closely, and they told us that, during the second set of 25 runs, the results for the first set were on display on a flip chart. The temptation to try to get a result close to the first must have been very strong and so some variation that might have been present ordinarily was almost certainly removed due to this bias. This helps to explain why the slope of the Daniel plot in Fig. 10.33 is less than the slope in Fig. 10.31.

## APPENDIX 10.1 DATA FROM TWO EXPERIMENTS

Table A10.1 contains the data from the fuel tank welding experiment of Section 10.1. Data from the piston ring spacer experiment of Section 10.2 are given in Table A10.2.

*Table A10.1* Data from the fuel tank experiment

(a) Tensile strength (kN)

| | First tank | | | | | | | | Second tank | | | | | | | |
|---|---|---|---|---|---|---|---|---|---|---|---|---|---|---|---|---|
| Run | i | ii | iii* | iv* | v | vi | vii* | viii | i | ii | iii* | iv* | v | vi | vii* | viii |
| 1 | 6.1 | 6.5 | 5.9 | 3.7 | 5.2 | 5.4 | 0.6 | 6.2 | 6.6 | 6.7 | 4.5 | 5.0 | 4.3 | 6.6 | 1.0 | 3.4 |
| 2 | 5.4 | 6.4 | 6.4 | 5.9 | 6.0 | 6.0 | 6.0 | 5.5 | 6.1 | 7.5 | 5.6 | 6.3 | 5.5 | 7.3 | 1.3 | 6.6 |
| 3 | 2.4 | 3.2 | 2.8 | 3.4 | 3.3 | 2.9 | 2.4 | 3.1 | 3.2 | 3.9 | 4.9 | 4.5 | 5.2 | 3.9 | 2.4 | 4.5 |
| 4 | 1.4 | 2.9 | 3.0 | 2.1 | 2.3 | 1.3 | 1.5 | 1.8 | 2.6 | 3.0 | 2.3 | 2.4 | 3.2 | 3.2 | 1.8 | 0.0 |
| 5 | 0.0 | 4.3 | 0.0 | 0.0 | 2.7 | 5.8 | 2.4 | 1.4 | 2.2 | 0.6 | 0.0 | 1.0 | 0.0 | 1.3 | 0.0 | 0.0 |
| 6 | 0.0 | 1.1 | 1.5 | 0.0 | 1.7 | 0.0 | 0.9 | 1.0 | 0.0 | 0.0 | 0.0 | 0.0 | 0.0 | 0.0 | 0.0 | 0.0 |
| 7 | 5.3 | 3.1 | 2.4 | 3.6 | 5.7 | 5.2 | 2.5 | 3.1 | 2.8 | 5.4 | 4.5 | 4.2 | 6.4 | 5.0 | 2.3 | 3.0 |
| 8 | 5.6 | 4.8 | 6.6 | 6.6 | 7.1 | 5.5 | 3.7 | 3.4 | 2.5 | 8.4 | 5.0 | 5.7 | 7.8 | 7.3 | 4.6 | 5.3 |
| 9 | 6.3 | 6.4 | 4.3 | 3.1 | 6.4 | 6.4 | 1.1 | 6.2 | 6.4 | 7.7 | 1.5 | 2.4 | 6.2 | 7.8 | 3.3 | 6.9 |
| 10 | 5.0 | 5.9 | 4.6 | 5.1 | 5.1 | 4.4 | 3.8 | 4.8 | 6.2 | 6.5 | 4.4 | 4.1 | 5.1 | 3.6 | 2.5 | 5.5 |
| 11 | 1.5 | 2.9 | 1.6 | 2.4 | 3.9 | 2.9 | 3.0 | 2.2 | 2.3 | 2.2 | 2.4 | 3.3 | 2.8 | 3.7 | 2.8 | 2.0 |
| 12 | 4.7 | 1.4 | 1.3 | 1.7 | 2.1 | 2.6 | 2.3 | 1.5 | 2.3 | 2.6 | 2.3 | 2.1 | 2.0 | 3.4 | 2.6 | 2.3 |
| 13 | 5.7 | 6.7 | 5.3 | 4.8 | 6.3 | 7.2 | 3.2 | 5.9 | 6.6 | 6.9 | 5.8 | 6.0 | 6.6 | 6.8 | 6.3 | 5.3 |
| 14 | 6.3 | 6.5 | 6.5 | 1.6 | 6.7 | 7.2 | 4.7 | 5.1 | 4.0 | 7.1 | 4.8 | 6.2 | 5.5 | 7.6 | 1.0 | 4.7 |
| 15 | 1.4 | 3.2 | 3.1 | 2.3 | 5.5 | 1.6 | 2.8 | 1.9 | 3.1 | 2.9 | 2.2 | 2.7 | 3.3 | 3.2 | 2.2 | 2.2 |
| 16 | 0.8 | 1.9 | 3.2 | 3.1 | 5.3 | 3.2 | 2.1 | 1.4 | 2.6 | 2.0 | 2.6 | 3.0 | 4.5 | 3.7 | 2.0 | 2.6 |

*Sections from the corners of the tank — see Fig. 10.2

(b) Seam width (mm)

| | First tank | | | | | | | | Second tank | | | | | | | |
|---|---|---|---|---|---|---|---|---|---|---|---|---|---|---|---|---|
| Run | i | ii | iii* | iv* | v | vi | vii* | viii | i | ii | iii* | iv* | v | vi | vii* | viii |
| 1 | 2.8 | 2.4 | 2.0 | 0.0 | 0.0 | 0.0 | 0.0 | 1.2 | 2.5 | 1.9 | 0.0 | 0.0 | 0.0 | 2.2 | 0.0 | 0.0 |
| 2 | 2.4 | 2.1 | 2.2 | 0.0 | 2.2 | 1.8 | 1.6 | 3.0 | 2.8 | 2.0 | 2.0 | 1.5 | 0.7 | 2.0 | 0.0 | 2.2 |
| 3 | 4.2 | 4.3 | 4.4 | 4.4 | 4.4 | 4.5 | 4.4 | 4.2 | 4.0 | 4.1 | 4.3 | 4.2 | 3.9 | 4.3 | 4.0 | 4.3 |
| 4 | 4.2 | 3.9 | 4.0 | 4.5 | 4.3 | 4.4 | 4.2 | 4.2 | 4.5 | 3.8 | 3.9 | 3.9 | 3.1 | 3.5 | 4.0 | 3.8 |
| 5 | 0.0 | 0.0 | 0.0 | 0.0 | 0.0 | 2.6 | 0.0 | 0.0 | 0.0 | 0.0 | 0.0 | 0.0 | 0.0 | 0.0 | 0.0 | 0.0 |
| 6 | 0.0 | 0.0 | 0.0 | 0.0 | 0.0 | 0.0 | 0.0 | 0.0 | 0.0 | 0.0 | 0.0 | 0.0 | 0.0 | 0.0 | 0.0 | 0.0 |
| 7 | 4.5 | 4.7 | 4.5 | 5.0 | 4.8 | 4.7 | 4.7 | 4.7 | 4.6 | 4.5 | 4.1 | 4.8 | 4.8 | 4.1 | 4.5 | 4.2 |
| 8 | 3.5 | 4.4 | 3.0 | 0.0 | 3.7 | 3.9 | 4.3 | 3.7 | 4.1 | 3.9 | 2.4 | 4.5 | 3.8 | 4.1 | 0.0 | 4.2 |
| 9 | 2.5 | 2.3 | 0.0 | 2.0 | 1.1 | 2.3 | 0.0 | 1.5 | 2.4 | 2.4 | 0.0 | 0.0 | 2.0 | 3.0 | 0.0 | 0.0 |
| 10 | 3.1 | 2.5 | 2.6 | 3.1 | 2.2 | 2.1 | 1.7 | 2.2 | 3.0 | 3.0 | 2.9 | 2.7 | 3.0 | 2.1 | 0.0 | 3.1 |
| 11 | 3.5 | 3.8 | 3.6 | 4.0 | 4.3 | 4.0 | 3.7 | 4.0 | 4.1 | 4.1 | 3.7 | 4.0 | 4.2 | 3.7 | 3.7 | 3.0 |
| 12 | 4.0 | 4.8 | 4.1 | 4.2 | 4.3 | 4.6 | 4.5 | 4.4 | 4.3 | 4.2 | 4.6 | 3.9 | 3.0 | 4.2 | 4.2 | 4.0 |
| 13 | 2.1 | 2.7 | 0.0 | 3.2 | 2.7 | 2.6 | 0.0 | 0.0 | 2.3 | 2.5 | 2.7 | 3.6 | 2.5 | 3.0 | 2.2 | 1.5 |
| 14 | 1.7 | 3.7 | 2.9 | 0.0 | 2.4 | 2.7 | 0.0 | 2.6 | 2.8 | 1.5 | 2.5 | 0.0 | 1.4 | 3.0 | 0.0 | 3.1 |
| 15 | 4.0 | 4.1 | 4.1 | 4.3 | 4.4 | 4.4 | 4.3 | 4.9 | 4.5 | 4.6 | 4.3 | 4.7 | 4.8 | 4.6 | 4.3 | 4.6 |
| 16 | 4.3 | 4.1 | 4.3 | 4.5 | 4.6 | 4.7 | 4.7 | 4.3 | 4.3 | 4.0 | 4.4 | 4.6 | 4.8 | 4.1 | 4.4 | 3.5 |

*Sections from the corners of the tank — see Fig. 10.2

*Table A10.2* Data from the piston ring spacer experiment: tangential load (N)

| Run 1 | 2 | 3 | 4 | 5 | 6 | 7 | 8 | 9 | 10 | 11 | 12 | 13 | 14 | 15 | 16 |
|---|---|---|---|---|---|---|---|---|---|---|---|---|---|---|---|
| 33.0 | 32.2 | 37.3 | 36.2 | 37.8 | 41.9 | 25.2 | 31.1 | 40.6 | 34.3 | 36.9 | 32.2 | 33.0 | 29.0 | 43.2 | 42.2 |
| 30.6 | 33.7 | 37.8 | 34.3 | 38.2 | 37.5 | 23.6 | 37.0 | 40.9 | 37.8 | 37.9 | 31.4 | 29.7 | 28.4 | 43.0 | 41.4 |
| 27.9 | 32.3 | 42.6 | 37.7 | 35.9 | 41.0 | 28.2 | 33.3 | 41.0 | 32.1 | 38.5 | 32.3 | 35.0 | 32.5 | 43.8 | 39.2 |
| 32.0 | 32.3 | 37.2 | 35.3 | 38.4 | 39.7 | 27.8 | 31.9 | 39.2 | 39.5 | 34.9 | 34.6 | 29.5 | 30.5 | 42.6 | 41.6 |
| 28.3 | 32.3 | 39.9 | 39.5 | 37.8 | 41.7 | 26.3 | 32.1 | 41.5 | 34.6 | 37.2 | 32.4 | 29.2 | 33.5 | 41.8 | 41.8 |
| 30.9 | 33.5 | 38.1 | 34.7 | 39.5 | 39.3 | 26.6 | 30.2 | 41.0 | 39.1 | 36.2 | 32.6 | 29.0 | 30.2 | 44.7 | 40.0 |
| 28.7 | 31.8 | 39.3 | 38.4 | 39.6 | 40.4 | 25.6 | 31.0 | 40.6 | 33.9 | 37.0 | 39.8 | 29.4 | 28.6 | 45.4 | 42.7 |
| 31.0 | 34.2 | 42.9 | 36.5 | 38.8 | 41.7 | 27.1 | 32.4 | 41.2 | 33.4 | 36.3 | 33.0 | 31.2 | 32.7 | 42.5 | 44.2 |
| 28.2 | 32.3 | 40.1 | 37.7 | 38.7 | 43.9 | 27.2 | 29.8 | 41.7 | 35.0 | 35.2 | 33.5 | 34.8 | 30.1 | 46.0 | 42.7 |
| 30.6 | 32.5 | 37.9 | 37.6 | 38.4 | 38.7 | 27.4 | 30.9 | 39.4 | 37.1 | 35.9 | 35.3 | 30.7 | 29.1 | 41.8 | 42.5 |
| 29.9 | 32.8 | 39.0 | 37.4 | 38.4 | 39.0 | 25.9 | 32.3 | 41.8 | 33.6 | 34.4 | 31.7 | 31.2 | 30.2 | 45.7 | 40.3 |
| 30.6 | 30.1 | 37.1 | 34.0 | 39.3 | 38.4 | 26.6 | 33.5 | 39.6 | 35.2 | 36.0 | 37.7 | 32.6 | 32.5 | 44.2 | 40.6 |
| 30.3 | 32.1 | 37.8 | 37.7 | 38.2 | 38.3 | 26.4 | 31.0 | 40.9 | 35.1 | 33.5 | 33.1 | 32.0 | 28.8 | 42.5 | 39.7 |
| 29.6 | 32.2 | 39.0 | 34.5 | 36.2 | 41.6 | 24.3 | 30.4 | 41.2 | 35.7 | 35.4 | 32.5 | 27.1 | 32.0 | 44.6 | 44.9 |
| 30.6 | 33.5 | 34.6 | 41.8 | 40.2 | 40.0 | 25.4 | 33.9 | 40.5 | 38.1 | 36.7 | 35.6 | 26.8 | 32.5 | 47.1 | 40.2 |
| 30.0 | 32.9 | 36.5 | 37.7 | 37.6 | 40.2 | 25.2 | 31.8 | 40.4 | 34.6 | 34.5 | 33.8 | 28.4 | 30.7 | 41.2 | 42.0 |
| 34.6 | 32.2 | 38.4 | 38.5 | 38.1 | 38.0 | 25.9 | 34.2 | 37.7 | 45.6 | 39.0 | 32.4 | 28.6 | 34.5 | 45.0 | 40.8 |
| 30.4 | 31.5 | 39.5 | 37.6 | 39.8 | 42.2 | 28.8 | 32.6 | 38.6 | 37.6 | 35.8 | 31.2 | 32.8 | 31.2 | 43.7 | 39.4 |
| 34.7 | 33.6 | 41.2 | 35.7 | 39.1 | 42.7 | 25.5 | 34.2 | 41.4 | 34.8 | 33.6 | 32.8 | 29.9 | 31.6 | 42.8 | 42.4 |
| 33.5 | 33.3 | 36.4 | 34.6 | 38.6 | 39.0 | 25.9 | 34.5 | 40.6 | 33.7 | 35.2 | 35.1 | 32.4 | 29.4 | 48.0 | 41.0 |
| 30.4 | 35.6 | 37.2 | 38.2 | 38.4 | 38.8 | 26.2 | 33.2 | 42.7 | 37.0 | 37.5 | 35.2 | 36.0 | 28.2 | 43.5 | 42.9 |
| 29.1 | 32.9 | 40.5 | 38.0 | 37.8 | 41.1 | 26.5 | 34.1 | 41.0 | 33.6 | 35.5 | 33.6 | 35.0 | 30.5 | 43.1 | 39.2 |
| 33.4 | 33.7 | 42.6 | 35.0 | 38.0 | 38.4 | 25.8 | 31.2 | 40.4 | 35.2 | 35.7 | 32.1 | 36.7 | 34.2 | 43.4 | 40.4 |
| 30.6 | 31.9 | 38.6 | 37.7 | 37.8 | 37.7 | 27.8 | 29.6 | 42.7 | 37.0 | 39.2 | 32.6 | 29.1 | 33.4 | 41.8 | 41.2 |
| 32.3 | 32.8 | 36.8 | 38.2 | 38.2 | 38.5 | 26.3 | 30.6 | 40.9 | 38.0 | 38.2 | 35.1 | 28.8 | 31.0 | 49.5 | 40.4 |
| 31.4 | 33.1 | 38.8 | 37.8 | 38.7 | 39.8 | 29.0 | 40.7 | 41.1 | 39.0 | 35.8 | 31.7 | 37.9 | 27.7 | 41.7 | 40.2 |
| 28.8 | 32.4 | 34.7 | 39.2 | 38.1 | 36.6 | 26.1 | 29.8 | 40.0 | 34.0 | 36.4 | 33.1 | 31.8 | 31.6 | 41.2 | 39.0 |
| 28.4 | 32.8 | 44.4 | 32.1 | 38.9 | 39.7 | 26.3 | 30.6 | 39.2 | 39.9 | 35.7 | 36.0 | 31.2 | 31.2 | 44.4 | 43.0 |
| 35.9 | 30.8 | 39.2 | 40.7 | 37.2 | 39.7 | 25.7 | 34.2 | 41.7 | 37.5 | 36.5 | 34.2 | 37.4 | 31.0 | 43.9 | 40.5 |
| 33.7 | 33.7 | 42.7 | 36.0 | 41.2 | 41.4 | 27.1 | 29.8 | 40.6 | 33.8 | 34.4 | 34.7 | 21.6 | 33.0 | 48.2 | 40.6 |

## *CHAPTER* 11

# Topics in quality engineering I

*This chapter is devoted to a variety of topics that are all related in one way or another to the effective use of experimentation for quality improvement. Each topic can also be seen as one component of the approach to engineering that Taguchi calls 'quality engineering'. Taguchi's approach is summarized in the final section.*

*Much of this chapter is more speculative than the rest of the book, intended to be thought-provoking, asking questions without always supplying answers. However, we do offer some further technical information about the relationship between signal-to-noise ratios and data transformations, about the selection of a transformation, and about 'untransforming' predictions so that they can be expressed in the same units as the original response.*

*We have a further look at the Wheatstone bridge example, using it to illustrate the possibility of eliminating interactions by transforming the factors.*

## 11.1 THE CHOICE OF QUALITY CHARACTERISTIC

It is important to separate the *objective* of an experiment from the *response* or *quality characteristic* to be measured. Often, the link between the two might be direct (as in the glove box experiment for example), but on other occasions the response may not be a direct measure of the objective (as in the fuel tank experiment). With 'quality engineering' experiments in particular, the response may bear little resemblance to the objective — see Chapter 12 for an example concerning an experiment on engine starting.

Some careful thought in selecting the response is repaid many times over during the experiment. Selecting the wrong thing to measure either makes the experimental process redundant, in the sense that the conclusions from the experiment are obvious, or the experiment becomes more and more difficult to complete.

One example of the former situation that we have come across was an experiment conducted to achieve a particular torque value for an adjusting screw. The *objective* of the experiment was to achieve a particular torque, and the team chose as their quality characteristic (QC) *torque*. The choice of this QC led to factors such as size of screw, size of bore, shape of bore, type of thread, and so on. Two levels were chosen for each factor, and an $L_{16}$ experiment was conducted. The results told the engineers only that the size of the bore and the size of the screw are the two most important factors that influence torque. *But this conclusion could have been reached on the basis of established engineering knowledge!*

A better strategy in this situation would have been to decide, prior to any statistical experimentation, what the nominal values for the screw size and bore size should be to achieve the desired torque. This in itself may well require experimentation of one kind or another, but probably not a multi-factor experiment. The problem for the engineer then becomes how to make screws and bores with as little variation as possible around these nominal values. The list of factors that is likely to be generated from these QCs will be very different from that originally developed when the QC was torque, and hence a completely different experiment would be conducted — *but the objective of the experiment remains the same.*

As an example in which the experimental procedure became harder and harder to administer, an experiment was run that was concerned with the measurement of oil leaks from an engine. The objective of course is not to have any oil leaks at all. The team chose as their response the amount of oil leaked from the engine. Factors affecting oil leaks concern dimensional relationships between engine components, and properties such as grade of finish on metal surfaces. Not surprisingly the plan matrix contained various combinations of dimensions and surface finishes, which meant that special engines had to be made to achieve the particular configurations dictated by the experimental plan. Experiments where special parts have to be made can be very expensive and time consuming, and before one commits to an experiment of this sort, it must be clear that the experiment has a good chance of success. Re-examining the QC and choosing one that will still satisfy the objective of the experiment but provide easier and cheaper ways of experimentation is much preferable. This is an engineering challenge.

With regard to the engine experiment, during the experiment some engines leaked oil and some did not. Some typical questions that arose were: How long should an engine be tested to see if it leaks? Should the amount of oil be measured or just the fact that it leaked? Is the most important factor that which changes an engine from one that leaks to one that does not leak, or a factor that affects the *amount* of oil leaked? The steps of the experimental procedure (outlined in Chapter 1) became more and more difficult to complete. To counter these complications to some extent, the team eventually

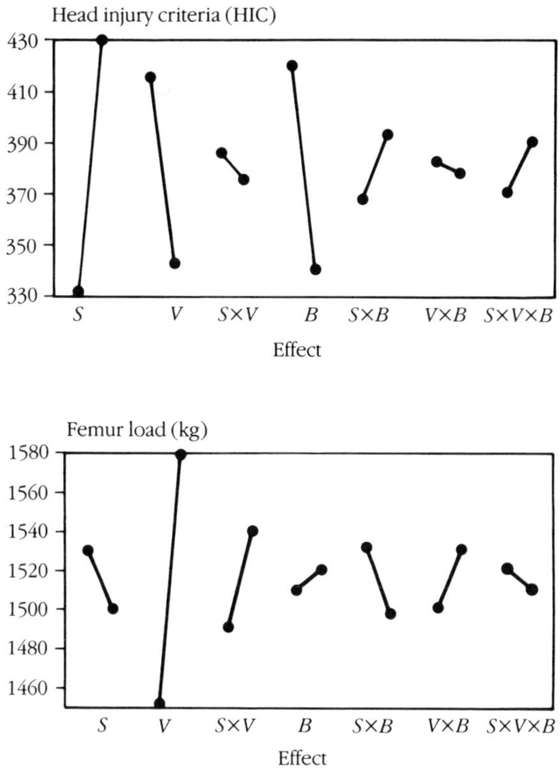


*Fig. 11.1* Air bag (sled test) experiment. Effects plots for HIC and femur load. Note that the effects on HIC all have opposite sign to the effects on femur load

chose as their QC a rating scale from 1 to 20, which described the severity of the leak, from no leak, through evidence of oil on the engine exterior, to a lot of oil leaking. At the end of this particular exercise, no factorial effect could be established owing to the extent of experimental variation, made worse by the fact that the QC itself was not an ideal measure. Outcomes of this sort are devastating to those concerned, since much effort is invested in planning and running the experiment and there is dismay when no useful conclusions can be drawn. Such experiences may put engineers off the idea of ever running a designed experiment again.

From both of these types of scenario it should be clear that giving some thought as to what to *measure* so that the *objective* of the experiment can be accomplished is well worth while. One guiding rule in establishing a 'good' QC is to measure something that *is* wanted, rather than something that *is not* wanted.

As an example of this, Fig. 11.1 shows effects plots (main effects and interactions) of two other quality characteristics that were measured in the (complete $2^3$) passenger air bag experiment. Apart from the chest $g$ force, which we looked at in Chapter 2, the experimenters also measured an HIC index (head injury criteria) and femur load. These characteristics are smaller-the-better as far as the car driver is concerned. Note that, in Fig. 11.1, all the effects for the two quality characteristics have opposite sign — there is a conflict therefore in achieving low values for HIC and femur load with the same air bag design.

Conflicts like this often arise in experiments where several characteristics are measured at the same time, and when the characteristics themselves do not measure what the system is meant to do, but rather what the system is not meant to do (in this case cause injury). What is the air bag meant to do? The air bag is designed to absorb the energy of the passenger before the passenger makes contact with something rigid like a dashboard or windscreen. These parts of the car are not good at absorbing energy, which is why personal injury results. Ideally deceleration should take place smoothly over the maximum time possible and without subjecting the body to point loads. It would, therefore, be more efficient to measure the energy absorption characteristics of the bag (what is wanted) rather than the energy absorption characteristics of the passenger (what is not wanted), manifesting as injury. We expand on the idea of measuring energy in a wanted state rather than an unwanted state in the next section.

## 11.2 IDEAL FUNCTION AND THE TRANSFER OF ENERGY

Experimental design under the banner of 'Taguchi methods' has received much attention in the last few years. In our view, the close identification of 'Taguchi methods' with the design and analysis of experiments leads to two types of mis-understanding. At one extreme, people call *any* experiment involving an orthogonal array a 'Taguchi experiment'; while at the other extreme, people view 'Taguchi methods' as nothing more than well-known experimental design methods that have been around for years. Less attention has been paid to another aspect of 'Taguchi methods': the idea of *engineering in function* rather than *engineering out problems*, which on the face of it has little to do with experimental design at all. In fact it is better not to talk about Taguchi methods, but rather to talk in broader terms of *quality engineering*. Taguchi has made the observation that all engineering systems involve a transfer of energy, and that, if the system is functioning as intended, this energy transfer will be direct from an input state to an output state. This transfer of energy is called *ideal function*.

For example, a brake on a car has the job of converting the kinetic energy of the vehicle into heat. This is the ideal function of the braking system. Of course, the car driver measures function in terms of stopping distance in a straight line. It is necessary to translate the *voice of the customer* into an engineering measure of ideal function, and techniques like *quality function deployment* (see Burn 1990) can help in this regard. If the transfer of energy is disrupted for some reason, problems may occur; for example, the braking system may cause judder and noise. The job of the engineer is to ensure that energy being transferred to the desired state (heat in this case) is *maximized*, which, because of the laws of energy conservation, means that energy left over to cause problems is *minimized*. This is why problem solving in engineering is often difficult — minimizing energy in an unwanted state is no guarantee that energy in the wanted state is increased. The energy may get diverted into another unwanted state to cause another problem.

One way to think of any transfer of energy is as an input–output device dictated by an engineering system:

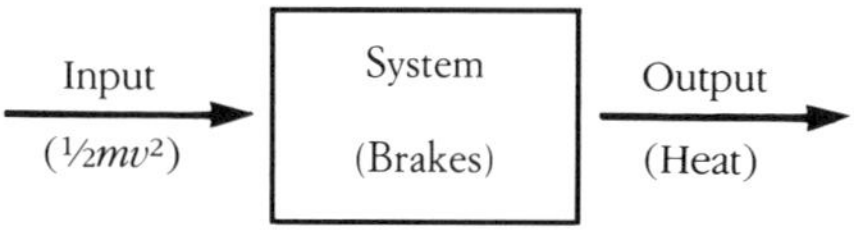


In most engineering applications, this energy transfer is required to be *dynamic*. In the brake example, the faster the car is travelling, the faster the rate at which kinetic energy needs to be converted to heat by the braking system, to stop the car in a safe distance. We talk more about dynamic systems in Chapter 12.

## 11.3 SIGNAL-TO-NOISE RATIOS AND RESPONSE TRANSFORMATIONS

In Chapter 8 we introduced some signal-to-noise formulae popularized by Taguchi. From the engineering perspective, it is useful to think of the S/N ratio as a measure of ideal function; it is the ratio of the amount of energy in the required state (the signal) to the amount of energy in the unwanted states (the noise). What is more controversial is whether this general engineering concept justifies the routine use of the particular formulae that Taguchi has promoted. For example, the nominal-is-best S/N ratio can be written

$$SN = 20\log_{10}(\mu_y/\sigma_y) \qquad [11.1]$$

Here we have replaced the observed mean $\bar{y}$ and standard deviation $s$ by their theoretical counterparts $\mu_y$ and $\sigma_y$. Box (1988) has pointed out that this quantity is very nearly equivalent to

$$SN' = -20\log_{10}(\sigma_Y) \qquad [11.2]$$

where $Y = \ln(y)$ is a logarithmic transformation of the response variable and $\sigma_Y$ is the standard deviation of $Y$, the transformed variable.

When $Y$ has a normal distribution, the relationship between $\sigma_y/\mu_y$, the coefficient of variation of $y$, and $\sigma_Y$ is as illustrated in Fig. 11.2. This relationship is virtually linear over a very wide range, and so the two

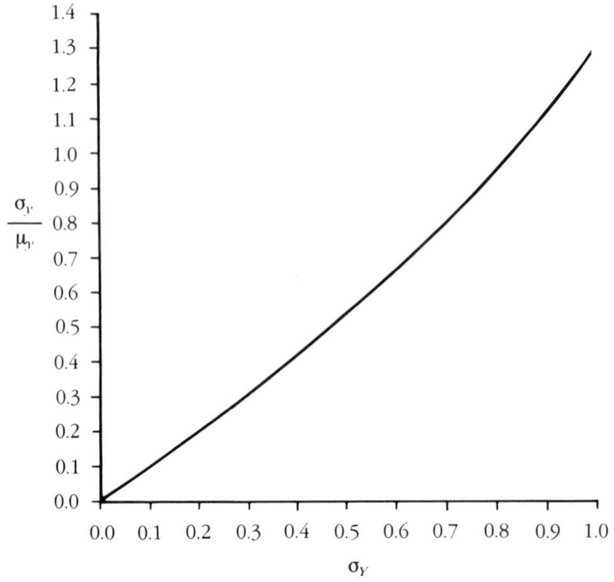


*Fig. 11.2* The relationship between the coefficient of variation of $y$ and $\sigma_Y$, when $Y = \ln(y)$ has a normal distribution

quantities [11.1] and [11.2] are almost equivalent. In fact this is often true in practice even if $Y$ does not have a normal distribution. Therefore an analysis of Taguchi's signal-to-noise ratio [11.1] is very nearly equivalent to an analysis of dispersion, after first making a logarithmic transformation, and using the 'signal-to-noise ratio' [11.2].

It is well known that Taguchi strongly advocates the use of the S/N ratio [11.1] when analysing experimental data, as a way to find control factors to achieve robustness. Other authors cite the connection between [11.1] and [11.2] to suggest that Taguchi's S/N ratio is generally too restrictive, and that other transformations, *including no transformation*, should be considered. Logothetis and Wynn (1989) describe several case studies in which alternative transformations are useful.

The reason for considering a data transformation in this context is the one we introduced in Chapter 8: to eliminate the dependence between mean and standard deviation, rather than to achieve as simple a prediction equation as possible (as in some of the transformations in Chapter 10). If $\sigma_y \propto \mu_y^p$, i.e. $\sigma_y$ is proportional to some power of $\mu_y$, a transformation can be found that will eliminate the dependence, at least to a good approximation. Depending on what $p$ is (or is estimated to be), a different transformation is required to separate mean and dispersion. In general, we call the transformed variable $Y = h(y)$.

If an analysis is eventually conducted in a transformed metric, it is virtually always necessary to express the predictions from the experiment in terms of the original units. As far as predictions for the average are concerned, applying the inverse transformation to the prediction in the transformed scale is usually all that is required, i.e. $\mu_y \sim h^{-1}(\mu_Y)$. To apply predictions for dispersion we can use the approximate result $\sigma_y \simeq \sigma_Y/|h'(\mu_y)|$ where $h'(.)$ is the derivative of the transformation. See Table 11.1 for the sorts of transformations $h(y)$ required for different values of $p$ and details of how to convert predictions for location and dispersion in the transformed metric to predictions in the original metric. An example was given in the fuel tank experiment in Chapter 10.

*Table 11.1* Transformations to remove dependence between μ and σ

| $p$ | Transformation $Y = h(y)$ | Location in the original metric as a function of location in the transformed metric $\mu_y \simeq h^{-1}(\mu_Y)$ | Dispersion in the original metric as a function of dispersion in the transformed metric $\sigma_y \simeq \sigma_Y/\lvert h'(\mu_y)\rvert$ |
|---|---|---|---|
| −1 | $y^2$ | $\mu_Y^{1/2}$ | $\sigma_Y/2\mu_y$ |
| 0 | $y$ | $\mu_Y$ | $\sigma_Y$ |
| 0.5 | $y^{1/2}$ | $\mu_Y^2$ | $2\sigma_Y(\mu_y)^{1/2}$ |
| 1 | $\log(y)$ or $\ln(y)$ | $10^{(\mu_Y)}$ or $\exp(\mu_Y)$ | $\sigma_Y\mu_y$ |
| 1.5 | $y^{-1/2}$ | $\mu_Y^{-2}$ | $2\sigma_Y(\mu_y)^{3/2}$ |
| 2 | $y^{-1}$ | $\mu_Y^{-1}$ | $\sigma_Y(\mu_y)^2$ |

The purpose of the log–log plot of $s$ against $\bar{y}$, which we introduced in Section 8.3, is to determine $p$ experimentally. If $\sigma_y \propto \mu_y^p$ then $\log(\sigma_y) = q + p\log(\mu_y)$ for some constant $q$, so that $p$ is the *gradient* of this plot. It is usually best to estimate $p$ from these plots by *least squares* (easily done in a spreadsheet using the regression facility). George Box has proposed an alternative method of selecting a transformation, based on a so-called λ *plot* (Box 1988).

On the face of it the assumption that $\sigma_y \propto \mu_y^p$ appears to rule out the possibility of separating or decoupling the location and dispersion effects of different factors, but our assumptions can easily be extended to allow for this. To keep things simple, suppose that $\mu_y$ is a function of a single control factor $A$, and $q$ is a function of $B$. Then

$$\log(\sigma_y) = q(B) + p\log\{\mu_y(A)\} \qquad [11.3]$$

$\sigma_y$ is a function of both $A$ and $B$, and $A$ cannot be used to adjust $\mu_y$ without affecting $\sigma_y$. But if $Y$ is a transformed variable chosen according to Table 11.1, $\sigma_Y$ is not a function of $A$ (to a first approximation at any rate).

If there is an active factor $B$, [11.3] implies that a log–log plot of $\sigma_y$ against $\mu_y$ would be a mixture of parallel lines, one for each level of $B$, all with slope $p$. Hence an empirical log–log plot, based on $\bar{y}$ and $s$, should still have a discernible linear pattern with slope roughly equal to $p$.

The log–log plot for the fuel tank experiment (Fig. 10.6) was of this type, with slope roughly 1, and the log transformation was successful (Fig. 10.7) in decoupling location and dispersion. However, a first analysis of dispersion effects on the transformed scale failed to find any significant influences on dispersion, over and above the link to the mean. We were able, after replacing some suspect data, to identify two apparently significant effects (a main effect and an interaction) but we have found that in practice 'factor $B$' in [11.3] often turns out to be elusive. Insight into factors affecting dispersion is harder to achieve than into those which affect location. In our experience, engineers tend to think in terms of location rather than dispersion, but this must change.

The approximate equivalence between S/N analysis and dispersion analysis on a new scale extends beyond the case of the log transformation. The S/N ratio [11.1] can be thought of as a special case of

$$SN = 20\log_{10}(\mu_y^p/\sigma_y) \qquad [11.4]$$

which for many sets of data will be nearly equivalent to using [11.2] with the transformed variable $Y$ chosen according to Table 11.1.

Our own investigations suggest that the log–log plot works best when $p$ is around 1, so this plot is a useful tool to check for the appropriateness of the ordinary S/N formula [11.1].

## S/N ratios and the transfer of energy

Taguchi argues that, for quality characteristics that are related to the transfer of energy, the ordinary S/N formula (or equivalently a log transformation) is always appropriate. We can show this to be true for the simplest of physical systems, a gas in a container. Here we will take the *input* as heat and the *output* as the velocity of the gas molecules:

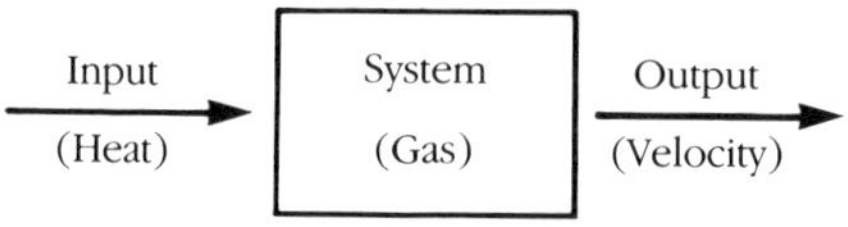


In this simple system, as the heat increases then so does the velocity of the gas molecules. We will assume that there are a lot of molecules in the container. They will not all have exactly the same velocity of course, and the distribution of velocities among the molecules is described by the *Maxwell distribution* after the scientist who first established the result. The distribution is shown in Fig. 11.3.

The Maxwell distribution is closely related to the normal distribution. Maxwell suggested that at any particular time the velocities in the $x$, $y$ and $z$ directions (denoted by $v_x$, $v_y$ and $v_z$) have independent normal distributions with the same mean and the same standard deviation. The absolute velocity (i.e. speed) is given by the equation $v = \sqrt{(v_x^2 + v_y^2 + v_z^2)}$, and the distri-

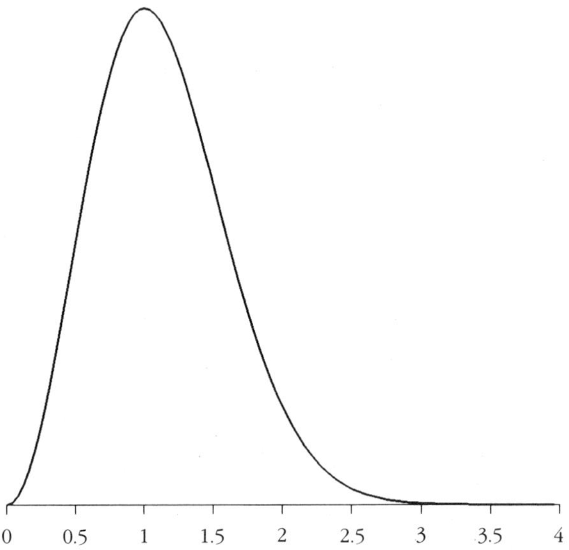


*Fig. 11.3* The Maxwell distribution

bution of $v$ is the Maxwell distribution. An expression for the mean velocity of a gas molecule (denoted by $\mu_v$) is given by

$$\mu_v = \sqrt{\{8kT/(\pi m)\}} \qquad [11.5]$$

and the standard deviation of the velocity (denoted by $\sigma_v$) is

$$\sigma_v = \sqrt{\left\{\frac{kT}{m}\left(3 - \frac{8}{\pi}\right)\right\}} \qquad [11.6]$$

where $m$ is the mass and $kT$ is the average kinetic energy of a gas molecule.

From [11.6], as the input energy ($kT$) increases, the standard deviation of the velocity also increases. More importantly, $\sigma_v \propto \mu_v$ since dividing equation [11.6] by [11.5] leaves $\sqrt{(\frac{3}{8}\pi - 1)}$, which is a constant not depending on the amount of energy in the system. Taguchi's S/N ratio [11.1] therefore can be justified in this case. It would be beyond the scope of this book to show this to be true for other more complicated systems, but such research would be worth while. This simple example illustrates the point that the condition $\sigma \propto \mu$ is sensible for energy-related measures, and gives some statistical justification to the S/N ratio. Note that in this description of the system $kT/m$ plays the role of factor $A$ in [11.3], but there is no factor $B$ with which to influence the S/N ratio.

## Achieving additivity of the S/N ratio

As we suggested in Chapter 4, Taguchi places great emphasis on the need to reduce or eliminate interactions, in other words to achieve additivity. Most people would agree that additivity is a preferable state of affairs because such situations are easier to understand, and require less experimentation to investigate. According to Taguchi, additivity also greatly increases the chance that experimental findings can be successfully transferred to the real world of manufacturing and customer use.

It is sometimes argued that because S/N ratios should be calculated for energy-related quality characteristics, they ought to be additive because energy itself is an additive quantity. However, additivity is not ensured just by an appropriate QC and S/N ratio. Apart from the obvious objection that *ratios* of energy measures are not inherently additive, it is clear that the factors and levels need to be chosen to reflect the energy transfer in the system and to exploit the additive nature of energy. For example, the experiment on the passenger air bag had *sliding levels* for the factor vent size — that is the vent sizes of small and large were chosen *relative to the size of the bag and inflation speed*. The reason for doing this is that the characteristics of air bag inflation and deflation upon impact will be affected by the size of the vents relative to the bag size and inflation speed. Note from Fig. 11.1 that in this experiment the interactions were generally smaller than the main effects, particularly for HIC, even though the quality characteristics are not ideal.

The chances of achieving additivity of effects can be greatly enhanced by considering the energy transfer in the system. However, even in the case of energy-related measures, there seems to be no theoretical backing for the idea that the S/N ratio is automatically additive, or that factors and levels can be chosen to make it additive, without experimentation to provide some initial understanding as to *why* the system as it is currently understood is not additive, so that it can be made so.

Taguchi is of the view that, if an engineer cannot create an additive S/N ratio via an appropriate quality characteristic, then he does not understand the engineering system well enough to conduct efficient experimentation, and that if interactions are uncovered (by lack of confirmation), he should re-think his factors and levels, and even the QC, and run another experiment. Our view, first presented in Chapter 4, is that further experimentation with the *same* factors and QC to discover the types of interactions that are present would itself be a strategy to develop further understanding and knowledge of the system, rather than going right back to square one and re-thinking factors and QCs.

The Wheatstone bridge example, which we pursue in the next section, shows how the discovery of a particular interaction can motivate a different way of describing a system. In this new framework, interactions are substantially reduced.

## 11.4 FACTOR TRANSFORMATIONS AND ADDITIVITY

In the Wheatstone bridge example discussed in Chapter 9, we uncovered an interaction between resistors $C$ and $D$ that could not be detected by Taguchi's original method of analysis. In view of our comments in the previous section, can we eliminate the need to measure interactions in this circuit by modifying our thinking of the Wheatstone bridge system, and in particular the resistors $C$ and $D$?

One possibility that is generally worth trying is experimenting with products and ratios of factors. For example, we can define two new factors ($P$ and $R$ say), where $P = CD$ and $R = C/D$. This is a form of factor transformation. To fit in with the previous discussion we take the levels for $P$ and $R$ to be equally spaced on a logarithmic scale: 10, 100, 1000 for $P$ and 0.1, 1, 10 for $R$. The resulting levels of $C$ and $D$ are a bit of a mess (e.g. we need $C = 3.16$ and $D = 31.6$ to give $P = 100$ and $R = 0.1$), but this is not a barrier to us calculating $\sigma_C$ and $\sigma_D$ as before from equation [9.5] and then calculating $s_y^2$ as a measure of the variation in $y$, the estimated value of the unknown resistance. We should point out that the method we used to calculate $s_y^2$ in this chapter was slightly different from the method summarized in [9.1] and [9.2] (it was based on partial differentiation of $y$ in [9.3] rather than the finite differences in [9.1]). Agreement between the two methods is very close. As before, $s_y^2$ is converted into an S/N ratio using [9.7].

Our new parameter design experiment (again a five-factor composite plan) is laid out in Table 11.2. Based on these results, a second-order prediction equation for *SN* would have the coefficients listed in Table 11.3. Like the other factors, $P$ and $R$ are now measured on the coded scale $-1$ to $+1$.

Comparison with Table 9.10 shows that the interaction terms are generally smaller than before. The coefficient of $PR$, which measures the interaction between the product and ratio of $C$ and $D$, is now almost negligible. It is clear that the relative importance of the interaction effects has been reduced by thinking of the factors in a different way. In addition, note that $P$ has a very small influence on the S/N ratio. The effect of $C$ and $D$ is manifested almost entirely through $R$, their ratio. The quadratic term in $R$ is about twice the linear term in $R$, and they are both negative, which points to a value of $R$ around the mid-level as being the optimum. Now the mid-level is 1, and a ratio of 1 means that $C = D$. Since the product $P$ is not too critical, it seems we are free to choose $C$ and $D$ as whatever we like subject to them being about the same.

This conclusion should not be surprising — when we drew the contour plot of the S/N ratio in the $C$–$D$ plane (Fig. 9.8), we saw that there was almost a ridge along the line $C = D$. Contour plots for other values of $\varrho$, the unknown resistance, are similar. What is special about a circuit with $C = D$? Well this implies a symmetry in the circuit since if $C = D$ then $y = B$, i.e. the variable resistor $B$ must be set equal (or in practice approximately equal) to

*Table 11.2* The Wheatstone bridge: an alternative parameter design experiment

| Run | Resistance *A* | Product *P* | Ratio *R* | Voltage *E* | Resistance *F* | *SN* |
|---|---|---|---|---|---|---|
| 1 | 20 | 10 | 0.1 | 1.2 | 50 | 0.16 |
| 2 | 500 | 10 | 0.1 | 1.2 | 2 | −4.74 |
| 3 | 20 | 1000 | 0.1 | 1.2 | 2 | 20.63 |
| 4 | 500 | 1000 | 0.1 | 1.2 | 50 | −26.14 |
| 5 | 20 | 10 | 10 | 1.2 | 2 | 26.41 |
| 6 | 500 | 10 | 10 | 1.2 | 50 | −16.22 |
| 7 | 20 | 1000 | 10 | 1.2 | 50 | 14.44 |
| 8 | 500 | 1000 | 10 | 1.2 | 2 | 0.60 |
| 9 | 20 | 10 | 0.1 | 30 | 2 | 45.78 |
| 10 | 500 | 10 | 0.1 | 30 | 50 | 0.60 |
| 11 | 20 | 1000 | 0.1 | 30 | 50 | 26.59 |
| 12 | 500 | 1000 | 0.1 | 30 | 2 | 23.77 |
| 13 | 20 | 10 | 10 | 30 | 50 | 38.10 |
| 14 | 500 | 10 | 10 | 30 | 2 | 27.46 |
| 15 | 20 | 1000 | 10 | 30 | 2 | 46.36 |
| 16 | 500 | 1000 | 10 | 30 | 50 | 18.03 |
| 17 | 100 | 100 | 1 | 6 | 10 | 26.68 |
| 18 | 20 | 100 | 1 | 6 | 10 | 38.35 |
| 19 | 500 | 100 | 1 | 6 | 10 | 13.14 |
| 20 | 100 | 10 | 1 | 6 | 10 | 24.90 |
| 21 | 100 | 1000 | 1 | 6 | 10 | 26.61 |
| 22 | 100 | 100 | 0.1 | 6 | 10 | 14.07 |
| 23 | 100 | 100 | 10 | 6 | 10 | 24.41 |
| 24 | 100 | 100 | 1 | 1.2 | 10 | 12.73 |
| 25 | 100 | 100 | 1 | 30 | 10 | 39.86 |
| 26 | 100 | 100 | 1 | 6 | 2 | 34.45 |
| 27 | 100 | 100 | 1 | 6 | 50 | 14.67 |

*Table 11.3* Coefficients in prediction equation for *SN* based on Table 11.2

| Term | Coefficient | Term | Coefficient |
|---|---|---|---|
| Intercept | 26.6 | *AP* | 0.7 |
| *A* | −12.2 | *AR* | −0.3 |
| *P* | 0.5 | *AE* | 1.3 |
| *R* | 4.4 | *AF* | −0.7 |
| *E* | 13.3 | *PR* | 0.0 |
| *F* | −8.4 | *PE* | −0.1 |
| $A^2$ | −0.9 | *PF* | 0.9 |
| $P^2$ | −0.9 | *RE* | −0.1 |
| $R^2$ | −7.4 | *RF* | −2.4 |
| $E^2$ | −0.3 | *EF* | 0.7 |
| $F^2$ | −2.1 | | |

the unknown resistance ϱ. The function of the circuit is to achieve balance, and therefore the idea that $C = D$ and $y = B$ is sensible in functional terms. This argument has been used for other symmetrical circuits (see Phadke 1989) in which nominals for components in each half of the circuit are chosen to be the same to facilitate function.

If we had the knowledge to choose $C = D$ at the outset, the number of factors would effectively be reduced from five to four — resistor $A$, resistor $F$, voltage $E$ and resistors $C$ and $D$ together (call this 'resistor' $T$).

To illustrate the application of parameter design in this situation, we model the errors in the components as before (in Chapter 9) and run a four-factor composite plan (given in Table 6.13). The actual factor levels and values of $SN$ are given in Table 11.4, and the coefficients derived from these results are in Table 11.5.

The interaction coefficients are all relatively small, with the linear effects of $A$, $E$ and $F$ pretty much as before — they now dominate the list. $T$ has very small coefficients by comparison but it is essentially quadratic with no linear term. This interpretation gives the following circuit to maximize $SN$: $A(-)$,

*Table 11.4* The Wheatstone bridge: parameter design experiment with $C = D$

| Run | Resistance $A$ | Resistance $T$ $(= C = D)$ | Voltage $E$ | Resistance $F$ | $SN$ |
|---|---|---|---|---|---|
| 1 | 20 | 2 | 1.2 | 2 | 32.28 |
| 2 | 500 | 2 | 1.2 | 2 | 5.25 |
| 3 | 20 | 50 | 1.2 | 2 | 28.34 |
| 4 | 500 | 50 | 1.2 | 2 | 7.22 |
| 5 | 20 | 2 | 30 | 2 | 47.23 |
| 6 | 500 | 2 | 30 | 2 | 33.05 |
| 7 | 20 | 50 | 30 | 2 | 46.92 |
| 8 | 500 | 50 | 30 | 2 | 34.93 |
| 9 | 20 | 2 | 1.2 | 50 | 10.13 |
| 10 | 500 | 2 | 1.2 | 50 | −17.03 |
| 11 | 20 | 50 | 1.2 | 50 | 9.10 |
| 12 | 500 | 50 | 1.2 | 50 | −12.06 |
| 13 | 20 | 2 | 30 | 50 | 37.62 |
| 14 | 500 | 2 | 30 | 50 | 10.93 |
| 15 | 20 | 50 | 30 | 50 | 36.68 |
| 16 | 500 | 50 | 30 | 50 | 15.90 |
| 17 | 100 | 10 | 6 | 10 | 26.68 |
| 18 | 20 | 10 | 6 | 10 | 38.35 |
| 19 | 500 | 10 | 6 | 10 | 13.14 |
| 20 | 100 | 2 | 6 | 10 | 23.51 |
| 21 | 100 | 50 | 6 | 10 | 26.10 |
| 22 | 100 | 10 | 1.2 | 10 | 12.73 |
| 23 | 100 | 10 | 30 | 10 | 39.86 |
| 24 | 100 | 10 | 6 | 2 | 34.45 |
| 25 | 100 | 10 | 6 | 50 | 14.67 |

*Table 11.5* Second-order coefficients derived from Table 11.4

| Term | Coefficient |
|---|---|
| Intercept | 26.9 |
| $A$ | −10.8 |
| $T$ | 0.6 |
| $E$ | 12.6 |
| $F$ | −9.1 |
| $A^2$ | −1.2 |
| $T^2$ | −2.2 |
| $E^2$ | −0.7 |
| $F^2$ | −2.4 |
| $AT$ | 1.2 |
| $AE$ | 1.4 |
| $AF$ | −1.3 |
| $TE$ | 0.2 |
| $TF$ | 0.5 |
| $EF$ | 1.4 |

*Table 11.6* The Wheatstone bridge: optimization using the $L_9$ array

| Run | $A$ | $T$ | $E$ | $F$ | $SN$ |
|---|---|---|---|---|---|
| 1 | 20 | 2 | 1.2 | 2 | 32.28 |
| 2 | 20 | 10 | 6 | 10 | 38.35 |
| 3 | 20 | 50 | 30 | 50 | 36.68 |
| 4 | 100 | 2 | 6 | 50 | 10.79 |
| 5 | 100 | 10 | 30 | 2 | 45.00 |
| 6 | 100 | 50 | 1.2 | 10 | 12.15 |
| 7 | 500 | 2 | 30 | 10 | 23.65 |
| 8 | 500 | 10 | 1.2 | 50 | −12.90 |
| 9 | 500 | 50 | 6 | 2 | 21.19 |

| Term | Coefficient |
|---|---|
| Intercept | 25.2 |
| $A$ | −12.6 |
| $T$ | 0.5 |
| $E$ | 12.3 |
| $F$ | −10.6 |
| $A^2$ | 0.6 |
| $T^2$ | −0.7 |
| $E^2$ | −0.6 |
| $F^2$ | −2.5 |

*C*(0), *D*(0), *E*(+) and *F*(−), which is exactly the circuit obtained in Chapter 9.

If we had known that the circuit could be optimized without the need to test for interactions (i.e. if we had known to experiment with $C = D$), we could have used the $L_9$ orthogonal array. This experiment, and the coefficients derived from it, are given in Table 11.6.

In fact the results of the $L_9$ experiment (as well as the composite design in Table 11.4) show that the Wheatstone bridge can be viewed not only as an additive system but also as a *linear* one, at least approximately. Removing interaction has also removed the large quadratic effects. Interactions and quadratic effects are closely connected because they both represent *non-linear* effects, but in different directions in the factor space. This exposes an inconsistency in Taguchi's argument — while he advocates the need to eliminate interactions, he seems happy to live with the possibility of quadratic effects by using three-level orthogonal arrays like $L_{18}$ and $L_{27}$. But if a quadratic effect is detected, there may well be other types of curvature (interaction) present, which should be investigated. To be consistent, Taguchi's striving for additivity should also include *linearity*. This combination would mean that we need only use saturated (resolution III) two-level orthogonal arrays for experimentation.

## 11.5 COMPOUNDED NOISE

The Wheatstone bridge experiment is a good example of the exploitation of curvature in the relationship between response and factors to minimize variation caused by *inner noise*, that is piece-to-piece variation in the individual components. This idea of transmitted variation was illustrated in Fig. 9.6, which incorporates the assumption that the inner noise can be described quite simply in terms of a distribution.

The effects of *outer noise* (environmental variables such as temperature, customer usage patterns and so forth) are much harder to predict. One situation is depicted in Fig. 11.4, where, as in Chapter 9, $z$ represents a component dimension (or in general a control factor) and $y$ is a measure of function (a system output or response). In this section we will use the label $z$ throughout for different control factors.

In this case the outer noise nullifies the effect of the curvature, in the sense that the range of the variation in function is much the same for all nominals of $z$. There is no advantage to be gained by changing the nominal in an attempt to reduce the variability. On the other hand, the effects of outer noise can often be exploited, even when the relationship between factor and response is essentially linear, as Fig. 11.5 shows. Here, the outer noise changes the *slope* of the response, so that, in this situation, choosing the nominal of the factor as far to the left as possible provides for a more robust system. Note that both Figs 11.4 and 11.5 describe *interaction* between

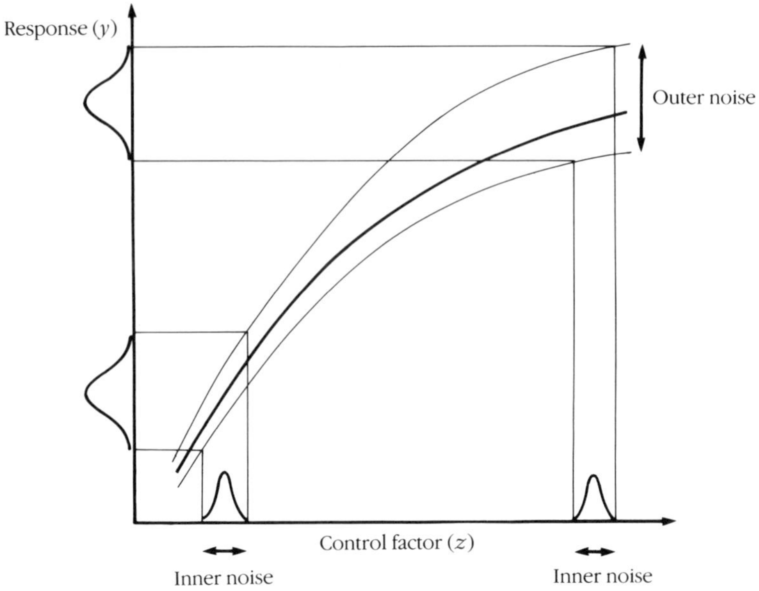


*Fig. 11.4* Transmission of variation from component to system output, with outer noise superimposed

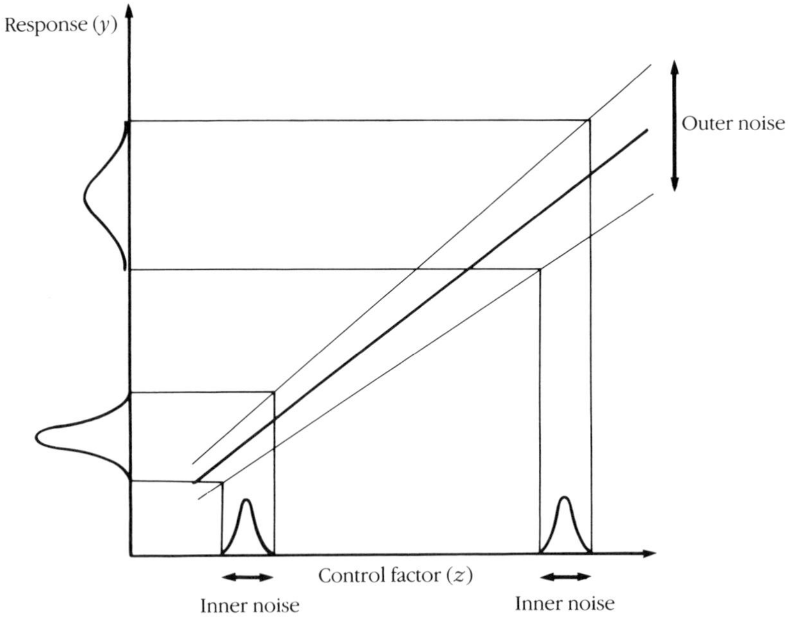


*Fig. 11.5* An opportunity for reduced variation in $y$ despite a linear response function

control and noise, which is crucial to parameter design. For this reason it is usually preferable to define the noise factors first, and then afterwards decide on control factors that are likely to interact with the noise.

We could draw many more pictures showing the hypothetical effects of outer noise, and in theory all these situations could be modelled mathematically by running a suitable experiment, followed by statistical analysis to estimate the coefficients in the various prediction equations. However, because of the many possible effects of outer noise, Taguchi has suggested that we do not need to model these situations with large experiments, but should merely *exploit* reduced variability when we find it.

The strategy for discovering such opportunities is to use compounded noise whenever we can, and in fact we have already illustrated this in Figs 11.4 and 11.5. In order to get a measure of the variability transmitted to the response from the inner and outer noise, it is only necessary to take the extreme left of the inner noise combined with the lowest level of outer noise, together with the extreme right of the inner noise combined with the uppermost outer noise. However, this strategy of compounding inner and outer noise is only safe if we know *a priori* the sign of the effect of the control factor on the response; compare Fig. 11.5 with Fig. 11.6, in which the extremes on the function scale are produced by a combination of the lowest level of inner noise and the highest level of outer noise, and vice versa.

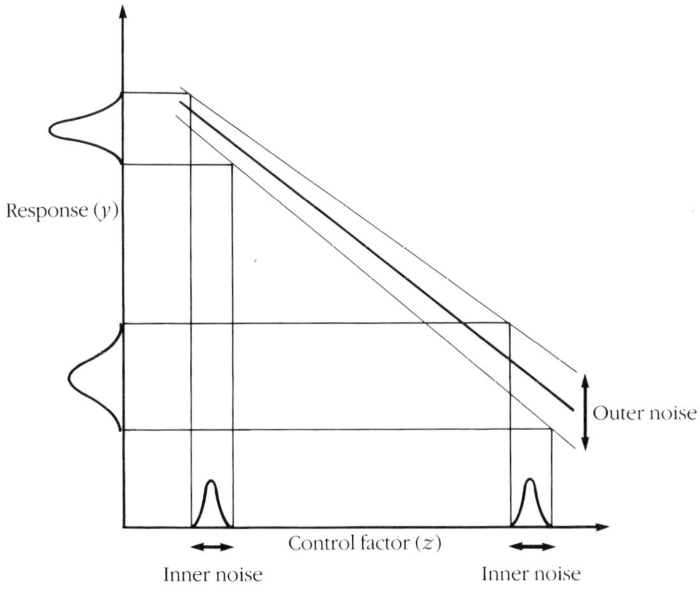


*Fig. 11.6* Compounding of inner and outer noise must take account of the sign of the response function gradient

Compounded noise is therefore most useful when *outer* noise factors are combined into two or three categories. We saw in the simulated rear seat belt example that the use of compounded outer noise factors can make experimentation more efficient by allowing us to test only two extremes, $N-$ and $N+$. However, in that example we also saw that although $N-$ was supposed to be least favourable, for some of the experimental runs $N+$ was actually *worse* than $N-$. In this case the idea of compounded noise does not work efficiently, since we may possibly have a situation like the one in Fig. 11.7. This is another form of interaction between control and noise factors, but this time the interaction is not helpful.

The energy connection is important in the application of compounded noise. Because they are monotonic, the situations illustrated in Figs 11.5 and 11.6 are likely to come about if the response and factors are related to energy transfer.

(Note: We have used the term 'inner noise' as a synonym for piece-to-piece variation. This is not in accord with Taguchi's terminology: he uses phrases like 'inner noise' to mean the deterioration that takes place over time in an individual component or system.)

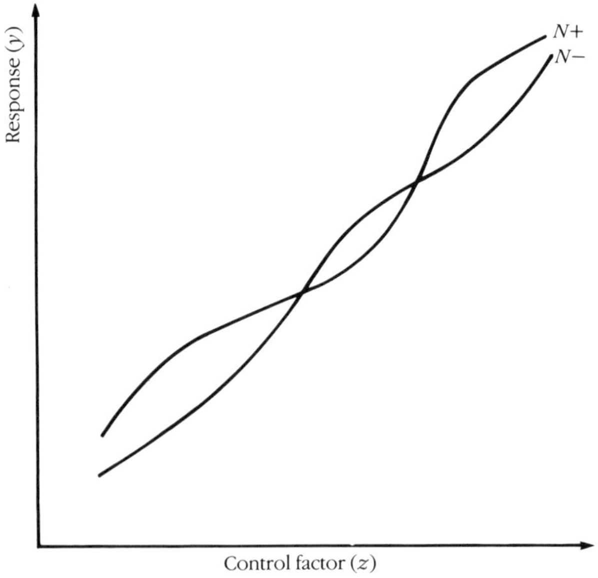


*Fig. 11.7* Interaction between control and noise is not always helpful

## 11.6 TWO ALTERNATIVE ENGINEERING STRATEGIES

Whatever the weaknesses in some of Taguchi's applications of experimental design, Taguchi has advocated a fundamental strategy that is really radical from the engineering perspective — to reduce variability first, and adjust to target afterwards. Because it is generally harder to reduce variability than it is to adjust to target, Taguchi argues, we should do this first, as far upstream as possible in the engineering process, where we are freer from restrictions. In this context, freer from restrictions means freer to try bold and original ideas.

At present, in Western companies, engineering strategy is often exactly the opposite way round — to get function on target, without considering the effects of noise, and then reduce variability afterwards. Because getting systems on target implies fixing nominals, the only strategy left to reduce variability in function is to work on the sources of the noise (both inner and outer). Reduction of inner noise requires a reduction of piece-to-piece (manufacturing) variability, which is generally expensive and not easy to accomplish, while reduction of the impact of outer noise requires actions such as up-grading materials — again expensive.

We label these two alternative engineering strategies A and B:

| Strategy A | Strategy B |
|---|---|
| Get function on target | Reduce variability |
| *then* | *then* |
| reduce variability | get function on target |

To clarify the implications of strategy B and to set it into the context of the general engineering process, Taguchi splits engineering into three constituent parts: system, parameter, and tolerance design.

*System design* is the act of selecting an appropriate technology to achieve the desired function. For example, is a speedometer going to be a mechanical magnet/spring system or an electronic system? Is the car radio antenna going to be a conventional whip aerial, or is it going to be incorporated into the heated rear screen? Will a fuel tank be welded metal or moulded plastic? System design can be an expensive stage of engineering because research may be required to establish new technology to deliver the function, or existing technology may need to be developed.

*Parameter design* is the act of selecting the nominals of the system once the system technology has been chosen. For example, if the magnet/spring system is chosen for the speedometer, we should experiment with magnet strengths, spring strengths and so on, to find a combination that is robust to sources of noise. An important concept at the parameter design stage is to experiment with the *cheapest components possible*, even if they exhibit much variability piece-to-piece (as in the Wheatstone bridge example). We may find a combination of nominals that is robust even in the presence of this variability. This is why tolerances should be kept as wide as possible at the parameter design stage.

*Tolerance design* is the act of tightening tolerances and up-grading materials to achieve a robust, high-quality system. For example, we may decide to up-grade the magnet quality in the speedometer because we just cannot achieve adequate robustness, even after parameter design with cheap magnets. But up-grading costs money, so this stage is very much a last resort. Tolerance design uses information from a parameter design experiment to select the components and materials to work on, taking into account the costs of up-grading and the benefits of reduced variation.

Of the three stages described here, two are expensive and one is cheap. The West is very good at, and spends much time doing, the two expensive ones. Parameter design, the only stage where cost can actually be reduced, is not done to any great extent.

If parameter design is not actively pursued before tolerance design, it is not possible to assess which dimensions of which components should be monitored and controlled in an effort to achieve low functional variability (these dimensions could be called *significant characteristics*). The tendency is to treat every component dimension as having equal importance, and to monitor its variation through a capability index or some other measure of variability.

Faced with no parameter design information, a product or process engineer often has to resort to measuring the function of the product as a means to ensure quality, rather than the significant characteristics. But by measuring function he cannot always control his process in the Shewhart sense, because he has no feel for which component dimensions or process settings are causing the variation in function. A 'control chart' on the functional variation really amounts to statistical inspection, and to implement this process of inspection, specification limits (decided by the engineer) are placed on functional variation. But customers do not place tolerances on function, they are concerned only with *nominal.* For this reason Taguchi developed the quality loss function as a means to measure the effects of variation in function. This moves us away from viewing quality of function as either good (within tolerance) or bad (outside tolerance), and points us towards reducing variation in function. Experimental design is the main tool for discovering *how* we reduce variation in function.

## SUMMARY OF CHAPTER 11

The best choice of response variable or quality characteristic may not be a direct measure of the objective of the experiment. A useful rule for selecting a quality characteristic is to measure something that is wanted rather than something that is not wanted.

Taguchi uses the phrase 'ideal function' to describe what is wanted from an engineering system. Ideal function is the transfer of energy from input to a desired output, without diversion into unwanted output states. The relative amounts of energy in wanted and unwanted states can be measured by a signal-to-noise ratio, but it is not clear that this justifies the formulae (introduced in Chapter 8) that Taguchi advocates for routine analysis of all types of data.

Using the nominal-is-best S/N ratio is usually equivalent to analysing dispersion after transformation to a logarithmic scale, but many other transformations are available. A log–log plot, in conjunction with Table 11.1, can be used to decide which transformation is appropriate, if any. It is unusual to find large dispersion effects on the transformed scale, but this may change as engineers get more practice in thinking about variation. Taguchi argues that there is a general connection between his nominal-is-best S/N formula and the transfer of energy. We make the connection in the particular case of a gas in a container, but we do not know whether this result can be generalized.

We agree with Taguchi in the emphasis that he places on reducing interactions (achieving additivity), but we have less faith than he does in the S/N ratio as a means to this end. Factors (and perhaps levels) have to be carefully chosen, and even in the case of an energy-related quality characteristic there is no reason to expect to be able to eliminate interactions without the benefit of knowledge that can only come from an experiment. We disagree with Taguchi's recommendation that an orthogonal array experiment should be used only as a numerical check for the existence of interactions, rather than as a means of understanding why the system is not additive.

The Wheatstone bridge example illustrates how the results of an experiment can promote a different way of thinking about a system, and hence lead to the elimination of interactions.

Models that describe the transmission of variation from components to system outputs (measures of function) become more complicated when outer noise is introduced. Taguchi suggests that, rather than try to describe this complexity in mathematical terms, we should merely exploit reduced variation when we find it. In order to discover such opportunities we need to make use of the strategy of compounded noise, but to use this strategy effectively we need some prior knowledge of the effects of noise.

Taguchi's engineering strategy is to reduce variability first, then adjust to target. In Western companies this sequence is often reversed. Taguchi's strategy offers greater opportunities for reducing variability at low cost. Taguchi splits his strategy into three parts: system design is concerned with the selection of an appropriate technology, parameter design is the selection of system nominals for maximum robustness, and tolerance design aims to achieve further reduction in variation by tightening and up-grading specifications on selected components and materials. Tolerance design uses information from a parameter design experiment, and the same type of information is needed for the effective use of process control to reduce functional variation.

# CHAPTER 12

# Topics in quality engineering II

*This chapter extends some of the discussion of Chapter 11 into the area which Taguchi calls 'dynamic engineering', where the function of the engineered system is to produce a variable output in response to a variable input signal. The input signal can be supplied directly by the user of the system to achieve an intended result, or may come from the output of another system.*

*We explore Taguchi's use of the signal-to-noise ratio for this type of situation, and offer an alternative based, as usual, on orthogonal contrasts. We make some connections between ideal function and transfer of energy, and the use of response transformations in the dynamic setting.*

## 12.1 DYNAMIC SYSTEMS

In Chapter 11 we used a representation of an engineering system as an input–output device. The input was described as a quantity of energy that the engineering system is required to transfer to a particular output state when it functions. Taguchi calls this transfer of energy *ideal function.*

In many applications, the input energy itself may vary depending on the *requirement* of the system, which is dictated by the *intention* of the user. For example, the requirement of a braking system is to reduce the speed of the vehicle either quickly or slowly depending on the intention of the driver. Similarly, the requirement of the air bag is to absorb the energy of a passenger in a collision — the quantity of energy needing to be absorbed will depend on the mass of the occupant and the impact speed in the collision.

These examples are meant to motivate the idea that if the quantity of energy at input is doubled, or trebled, or halved, then the energy in the ideal

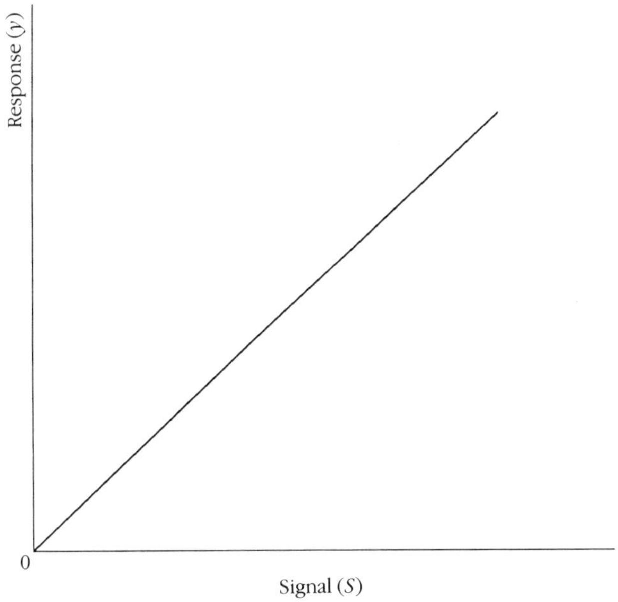


*Fig. 12.1* Linear relationship between input energy (signal) and output energy (response) for a dynamic system

output state will also double, or treble, or halve. We can capture this idea graphically, as in Fig. 12.1. This shows a *linear* relationship between input energy (called the *signal*) and output energy in the ideal state (*response*). It makes sense for this line to go through the origin, because if no energy is put in to the system, none can come out.

Figure 12.1 can be seen as describing a generalization of the nominal-is-best situation (Section 8.4): for a particular level of the signal, a particular (nominal) level of response is required.

The general system illustrated by Fig. 12.1 will of course be subject to noise. The noise may well affect the response by disrupting the signal, as well as the actual engineering system itself. For example, if the input signal is voltage, then this may be subject to fluctuations. Taguchi has extended his ideas of robustness to cover dynamic systems. Figure 12.2 shows some hypothetical data for a dynamic system subject to two levels of (possibly compounded) noise, $N-$ and $N+$.

In Fig. 12.2 we have labelled the input as a *signal factor* ($S$ for short), with three levels, coded as usual $-$, 0, $+$. Note, however, that level (0) does not mean that no signal is input. The true origin is somewhere to the left of the ($-$) level. Also, the levels of the signal factor do *not* have to be equally spaced, but usually it will be convenient for them to be so. Naming the input energy as a factor implies that it has a role to play in running experiments. We discuss this in more detail in Section 12.4. The reason for choosing three

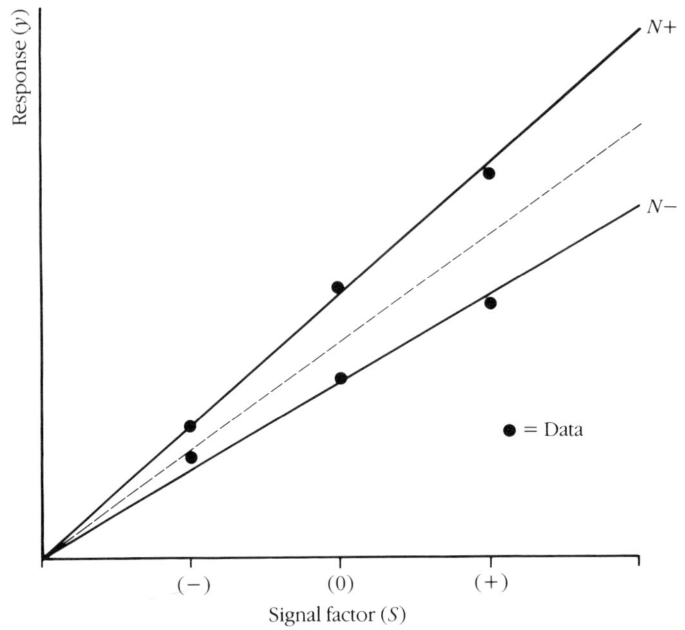


*Fig. 12.2* Hypothetical data from a dynamic system subject to noise. The effect of the noise increases with the level of the signal

levels for the signal factor is so that the linear nature of the input–output (signal–response) relationship suggested by Fig. 12.1 can be checked.

In Fig. 12.2 the broken line represents an 'average' linear relationship between signal and response, which lies midway between the two noise levels. We will explain what we mean by average in Section 12.2. The full lines represent the actual responses induced by the noise factor. The (hypothetical) experimental data are not exactly on the full lines because there will usually be some sources of experimental variability ('experimental error'). Note that in Fig. 12.2 there is an interaction between the signal factor and the noise factor, since we have assumed that the effect of the noise increases with the strength of the signal, and that all lines point to the real origin. Certainly, if there is zero signal, the effect of the noise must be zero since there is no output.

Table 12.1 shows a simple experimental plan for obtaining the data illustrated in Fig. 12.2.

## 12.2 SIGNAL-TO-NOISE RATIOS FOR DYNAMIC SYSTEMS

One way to capture the experimental relationship between the signal factor and the response is to summarize the data into convenient measures.

*Table 12.1* Plan matrix for an experiment on a dynamic system

| $S$ | $N$ | Response |
|---|---|---|
| − | − | $y_1$ |
| − | + | $y_2$ |
| 0 | − | $y_3$ |
| 0 | + | $y_4$ |
| + | − | $y_5$ |
| + | + | $y_6$ |

Assuming that the linear relationship is reasonable, we can propose a simple mathematical model

$$y = \beta S \qquad [12.1]$$

where as usual $y$ is the response (a measure of ideal function) and $S$ is the value of the signal factor. The quantity $\beta$ is the slope or gradient between $y$ and $S$. In [12.1], $S$ is measured on the *actual scale* of the input signal rather than on the coded scale $-1$ to $+1$ implied by the plan in Table 12.1.

Note that [12.1] is a very simple prediction equation, particularly when compared with some of the equations in earlier chapters. It has no intercept (because if nothing is put in to the system, we would expect nothing out) and no quadratic term.

The experimental data implied by Fig. 12.2 do not satisfy equation [12.1] exactly. Apart from experimental error, it is *intended* that the noise factor should cause variation, and there may be systematic non-linearity that [12.1] cannot represent. Hence we need to choose a value of $\beta$ ($\hat{\beta}$ say) that captures the essence of what the data are trying to convey.

One possibility is to choose $\hat{\beta}$ so that the sum of squared residuals (deviations from the chosen line $y = \hat{\beta}S$) is minimized. Then $\hat{\beta}$ is given by the equation

$$\hat{\beta} = \frac{\Sigma y_i S_i}{\Sigma S_i^2} \qquad [12.2]$$

where the summations are over the total number of data points (indexed by $i$) in the plot (six in Fig. 12.2). This is called a constrained least-squares solution: 'least-squares' because it is based on the sum of squares of the residuals, and 'constrained' because the line is forced to pass through the origin. The broken line in Fig. 12.2 has a slope calculated using [12.2], so that $\hat{\beta}$ is an 'average slope' calculated across the levels of the noise factor.

Just knowing $\hat{\beta}$ is not good enough, however. We need also to capture the extent of variation around the fitted equation $y = \hat{\beta}S$. For the moment, we use a convenient measure that looks very much like a standard deviation for a single sample (see Section 8.1), which we will write as

$$s_r = \sqrt{\left(\frac{1}{n-1}\sum(y_i - \hat{\beta}S_i)^2\right)} \qquad [12.3]$$

We use $s_r$ in this context to distinguish [12.3] from the ordinary standard deviation; $\hat{\beta}S_i$ is a prediction of the response value when the signal takes the value $S_i$, $(y_i - \hat{\beta}S_i)$ is the corresponding residual, and $\Sigma(y_i - \hat{\beta}S_i)^2$ is the *residual sum of squares*.

Taguchi has combined $\hat{\beta}$ from [12.2] and $s_r$ from [12.3] into a signal-to-noise ratio that he defines as

$$SN = 10\log_{10}\left(\frac{\hat{\beta}}{s_r}\right)^2 \qquad [12.4]$$

**Dynamic S/N ratios**

Dynamic S/N ratios given by equation [12.4] are easily calculated in a spreadsheet, since $\hat{\beta}$ is a regression coefficient and $s_r$ is the (square root of) the residual sum of squares divided by $n - 1$. Both of these quantities should be available as part of any regression output. To calculate the required $\hat{\beta}$ and $s_r$, set the (actual) levels of the signal factor as the 'independent' or $x$ variable, and the corresponding response data as the 'dependent' or $y$ variable. If the regression facility has the option, instruct the spreadsheet to perform regression through the origin. Then combine $\hat{\beta}$ and $s_r$ according to equation [12.4]. If there is no option to perform regression through the origin the regression program can be tricked into doing it by duplicating the signal factor levels and the data and multiplying by $-1$ (in other words performing *reflection*). Then the original and reflected signal and response data should be submitted to regression and the correct $\hat{\beta}$ will be calculated. The residual sum of squares will be inflated by a factor of 2, so this number needs to be taken into account before employing [12.4] to calculate the S/N ratio.

There is a strong similarity between the S/N ratio [12.4] and the S/N ratio for the nominal-is-best situations given originally by [8.1] and discussed further in Chapter 11. As in the case of [8.1], the formula we have given here is a slight simplification of Taguchi's actual formula. Recall from the discussions in Chapter 11 that we suggested that the S/N ratio as given by Taguchi was appropriate for analysing dispersion effects when a log–log plot of $s$ against $\bar{y}$ had a discernible linear pattern with a slope of roughly 1. In the dynamic framework the analogue of $s \propto \bar{y}$ is $s_r \propto \hat{\beta}$, which implies

$$\log_{10}(s_r) = q + \log_{10}(\hat{\beta}) \qquad [12.5]$$

Note that the S/N formula [12.4] can be rearranged as

$$\log_{10}(s_r) = -\frac{SN}{20} + \log_{10}(\hat{\beta})$$

which is equivalent to equation [12.5] with $q = -SN/20$. As in Chapter 11 we hope that $q$ is a function of at least one control factor $-B$ say — so that $q$, and hence $SN$, can be increased by setting $B$ appropriately. By analogy with the static framework, we should expect the S/N ratio [12.4] to be a sensible measure of the dynamic system if there are control factors that affect both $s_r$ and $\hat{\beta}$ proportionately, resulting in a log–log plot of $s_r$ against $\hat{\beta}$ which has a visible linear pattern with slope roughly 1. In this chapter we refer to [12.4] as the *dynamic* S/N ratio, and the nominal-is-best counterpart given by [8.1] as the *static* S/N ratio.

## 12.3 ORTHOGONAL CONTRASTS FOR DYNAMIC SYSTEMS

The dynamic S/N ratio is not the only way in which the relationships between signal and response in a dynamic system can be captured. Another way is to use orthogonal contrasts.

If we suppose that the plan in Table 12.1 is typical, with three (equally spaced) levels of the signal factor and two levels of noise, then five orthogonal contrasts are available to measure effects. These are $S_\ell$ and $S_q$ (linear and quadratic effects of the signal factor), a contrast to measure the effect of noise ($N$ say) and two interaction contrasts between the signal factor and noise, $S_\ell \times N$ and $S_q \times N$. Table 12.2 shows the contrast coefficients. It is worth noting that although $S_\ell$ can be interpreted as a slope (see Chapter 5), it is not quite the same thing as $\hat{\beta}: S_\ell$ is found by measuring the slope between the average response for $S-$ and the average for $S+$, whereas $\hat{\beta}$ is the slope of a line that is forced to pass through the origin. In some applications, in particular when the levels of the signal factor are clustered a long way from its true origin, it would be preferable to replace $\hat{\beta}$ by $S_\ell$ in the signal-to-noise analysis of Section 12.2.

If the relationship between the signal factor and response is linear, then we would expect $S_\ell$ to be a comparatively large contrast and $S_q$ to be small. Also, providing the levels of the noise factor have been well chosen, the $N$ effect would be large. If Fig. 12.2 represents the system well, $S_\ell \times N$ would also be relatively large, since $S$ and $N$ interact, but the idea of a *robust* system is that this interaction is as small as possible. On the other hand, the $S_q \times N$ contrast would be small for any linear system. Potentially, orthogonal contrasts contain more information than the signal-to-noise ratio, which, as always, combines a lot of experimental information into one summary measure. The S/N ratio [12.4] can be thought of (approximately) as comparing (on a log scale) the magnitude of the $S_\ell$ contrast with the average

*Table 12.2* A set of contrasts for the plan matrix in Table 12.1

| | $S_\ell$ | $S_q$ | $N$ | $S_\ell \times N$ | $S_q \times N$ | |
|---|---|---|---|---|---|---|
| | −1 | +1 | −1 | +1 | −1 | $y_1$ |
| | −1 | +1 | +1 | −1 | +1 | $y_2$ |
| | 0 | −2 | −1 | 0 | +2 | $y_3$ |
| | 0 | −2 | +1 | 0 | −2 | $y_4$ |
| | +1 | +1 | −1 | −1 | −1 | $y_5$ |
| | +1 | +1 | +1 | +1 | +1 | $y_6$ |
| Divisor | 4 | 4 | 3 | 2 | 2 | |

of the other four contrasts in Table 12.2. We should not use an S/N ratio unless we are fairly sure that it will work for us — otherwise using the information from contrasts would be a more sensible approach. The signal-to-noise ratio is likely to do a reasonable job for systems that can be described by a picture like Fig. 12.3. Here the control factor $C$ has an effect on the slope *and* on the noise effect. We have deliberately chosen to highlight two features in Fig. 12.3: (i) the effect of the noise increases proportionally with the effect of the signal, and (ii) the effect of the noise increases proportionally

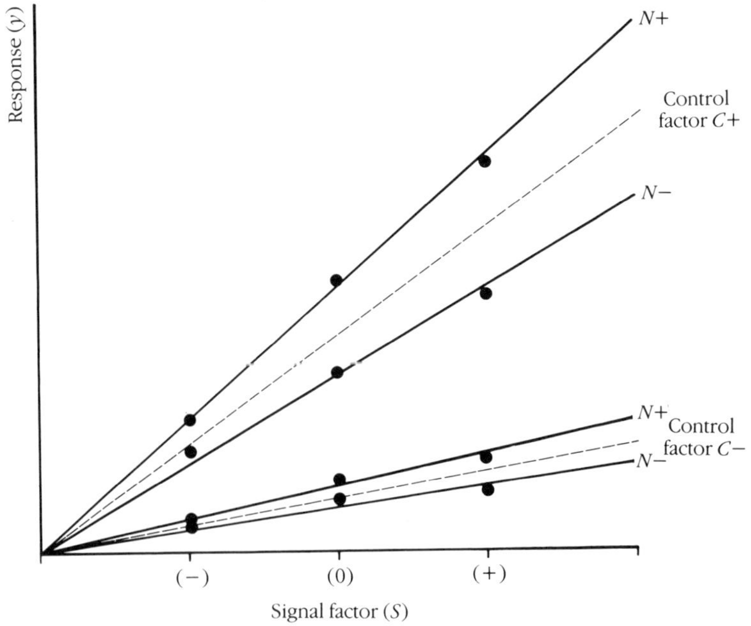


*Fig. 12.3* Control factor $C$ has an effect on the slope and on the noise effect. The noise effect increases proportionally with the slope

with the slope. These two features can be justified to some extent from our discussions in Chapter 11 concerning levels of energy and resulting variability.

## 12.4 EXPERIMENTATION WITH DYNAMIC SYSTEMS

Not surprisingly, Taguchi recommends that, as in the nominal-is-best situation, engineers should run experiments to discover robust dynamic systems by changing control factors.

The purpose of experimenting with control factors is to try to reduce the interaction between signal and noise, i.e. bring the full lines in Fig. 12.3 closer together. This should be done by reducing the effect of the noise rather than the effect of the signal. If a control factor $C$ does have an effect on the $S \times N$ interaction, then a robustness effect is measured by the (three-factor) interaction $C \times S \times N$.

The effect of the signal may eventually need to be adjusted to achieve the desired slope between the signal factor and the response, so we should also look for factors that change the slope.

Taguchi advocates measuring the robustness effect with the dynamic S/N ratio [12.4]. Once the S/N ratio has been calculated for each control factor setting, each effect is found by contrasting S/N ratios in the usual way. In Fig. 12.3 both control factor settings have the *same* S/N ratio, because although $\hat{\beta}$ has quadrupled in going from $C-$ to $C+$, so has the effect of the noise.

As an alternative to the S/N ratio, the five contrasts in Table 12.2 could be calculated for each control factor setting. Any differences between the contrast values for the different settings of the control factors would be indicative of an interaction involving the control factor. In particular, a three-factor $C \times S_\ell \times N$ interaction can be exploited to achieve robustness. Because in Fig. 12.3 all lines point to the origin, the presence of a three-factor interaction $C \times S \times N$ will imply that the lower-order effects are also present, that is $C \times S$, $S \times N$ and $C \times N$, and the individual main effects for these factors. We discuss this further below.

When there is more than one control factor, Taguchi utilizes the idea of an inner and outer array (see Table 9.1 for a generic example) to conduct experimentation on dynamic systems, and S/N ratios like [12.4] to analyse for control factor effects.

In Taguchi's formulation, the outer array is made up of the plan matrix given by Table 12.1. The inner array consists of an orthogonal array (or more generally some other design) with a number of control factors. As usual the control factors and their levels are chosen with a view to discovering a robust system. Table 12.3 shows a typical experimental layout. To keep the discussion as simple as possible, we have shown an $L_4$ as the control factor (inner) array, with three control factors allocated. We will also assume for simplicity that the control factors do not exhibit interaction. In practice the

*Table 12.3* Experimental layout for a dynamic system ($L_4$ used as an example)

| | Inner array $L_4$: control factors | | | Outer array: noise and signal factors | | | | | | |
|---|---|---|---|---|---|---|---|---|---|---|
| | | | | – | + | – | + | – | + | *N* |
| Run | *A* | *B* | *C* | – | – | 0 | 0 | + | + | *S* |
| 1 | – | – | + | $y_1$ | $y_2$ | $y_3$ | $y_4$ | $y_5$ | $y_6$ | |
| 2 | + | – | – | $y_7$ | $y_8$ | $y_9$ | $y_{10}$ | $y_{11}$ | $y_{12}$ | |
| 3 | – | + | – | $y_{13}$ | $y_{14}$ | $y_{15}$ | $y_{16}$ | $y_{17}$ | $y_{18}$ | |
| 4 | + | + | + | $y_{19}$ | $y_{20}$ | $y_{21}$ | $y_{22}$ | $y_{23}$ | $y_{24}$ | |

array is likely to be substantially larger, and interactions between control factors may well be present. Taguchi recommends the following strategy to analyse experiments of the type shown in Table 12.3.

First calculate $\hat{\beta}$ and $s_r$ for each row of (in this case six) $y$ values for each run from the inner array using equations [12.2] and [12.3]. As is usual with this approach, these calculations are done without regard for the effect of the noise factor. Then with $\hat{\beta}$ and $s_r$ calculate the S/N ratio for each row using equation [12.4], and establish the effects of the control factors by calculating contrasts in the usual way. The objective is to find control factor settings which as before *maximize* the S/N ratio. Factors that affect $\beta$ but not *SN* can be used as tuning factors so that the gradient of the signal to the response can be tuned to ensure function.

The alternative to Taguchi's approach that we hinted at above involves calculating contrasts for control factors and noise factors and signal factors and various sets of interactions. Table 12.4 shows a different way to lay out the experiment presented in Table 12.3.

The layout of Table 12.4 has the signal factor incorporated into the inner array. Note that the inner array looks very much like one of Margolin's designs – see Table 7.10. Margolin's designs may offer a way to reduce the number of runs for a dynamic experiment, particularly if interactions between control factors are of interest. Since the inner array now consists of essentially 12 runs, with each run repeated across the noise factor, there are 11 contrasts available from this array. These contrasts measure main effects of *A*, *B*, *C*, and the main effect of *S*, separated as usual into $S_\ell$ and $S_q$. All interactions between the control factors and *S* are also available, namely $A \times S_\ell$, $B \times S_\ell$ and $C \times S_\ell$, and $A \times S_q$, $B \times S_q$ and $C \times S_q$. This is the total of 11 contrasts. Note that the layout as presented in Table 12.4 looks very much like a conventional parameter design experiment of the sort described by Table 9.1.

By converting the $y$ values for each 'run' in Table 12.4 into a measure of dispersion (such as a static S/N ratio or a standard deviation, or even a simple difference as in the seat belt experiment in Chapter 9), we can analyse the layout of Table 12.4 for robustness effects, since any measure of dispersion is a measure of the noise effect. We would expect control factors that contribute to robustness to show up with strong main effects. With regard to the S/N

*Table 12.4* A different way to lay out the experiment of Table 12.3

| | Inner array: control and signal factors | | | | Outer array: noise factor | | |
|---|---|---|---|---|---|---|---|
| Run | $A$ | $B$ | $C$ | $S$ | $-$ | $+$ | $N$ |
| 1 | − | − | + | − | $y_1$ | $y_2$ | |
| 2 | + | − | − | − | $y_7$ | $y_8$ | |
| 3 | − | + | − | − | $y_{13}$ | $y_{14}$ | |
| 4 | + | + | + | − | $y_{19}$ | $y_{20}$ | |
| 5 | − | − | + | 0 | $y_3$ | $y_4$ | |
| 6 | + | − | − | 0 | $y_9$ | $y_{10}$ | |
| 7 | − | + | − | 0 | $y_{15}$ | $y_{16}$ | |
| 8 | + | + | + | 0 | $y_{21}$ | $y_{22}$ | |
| 9 | − | − | + | + | $y_5$ | $y_6$ | |
| 10 | + | − | − | + | $y_{11}$ | $y_{12}$ | |
| 11 | − | + | − | + | $y_{17}$ | $y_{18}$ | |
| 12 | + | + | + | + | $y_{23}$ | $y_{24}$ | |

ratio, we would hope not to see effects involving the signal factor $S$ at all, since we require factors with robustness effects for all levels of the signal factor. If a robustness main effect for $S$ did show up (either linear or quadratic), it may well be an indication that transformation of the $y$ values is needed before the analysis is conducted. We talk more about transformations in the dynamic framework in Section 12.5.

Converting the $y$ values for each run into a measure of location (such as the average $\bar{y}$ across the noise factor) enables us to look for location effects. We would expect to see a large $S_\ell$ contrast but not $S_q$ if our assumption of a linear relationship is true. An interaction between $S_\ell$ and a control factor would mean that that particular factor could be used to adjust the gradient of the signal–response relationship. And as we suggested above, any control factor exhibiting interaction with $S_\ell$ will also have a main effect in its own right because the signal–response graph is anchored at the origin. We would not expect to see any large interaction contrasts involving $S_q$.

Refer back to Chapters 8–10 for more discussion about analysing experiments for location and dispersion effects. In its essence, the layout described in Table 12.4 is identical to those in Chapters 8 and 9 except for the presence of the signal factor. In the dynamic framework we need to make sure that we can interpret any contrasts involving the signal factor as the need arises.

A final way to lay out an experiment with a dynamic response is illustrated in Table 12.5. Here all the factors are allocated to one array, which yields an experiment in 24 'runs'. There are of course 23 orthogonal contrasts available from the layout in Table 12.5. These contrasts are all location

*Table 12.5* Another way to lay out the experiment in Table 12.3

| | Control, signal and noise factors | | | | | |
|---|---|---|---|---|---|---|
| Run | *A* | *B* | *C* | *S* | *N* | |
| 1 | − | − | + | − | − | $y_1$ |
| 2 | + | − | − | − | − | $y_7$ |
| 3 | − | + | − | − | − | $y_{13}$ |
| 4 | + | + | + | − | − | $y_{19}$ |
| 5 | − | − | + | 0 | − | $y_3$ |
| 6 | + | − | − | 0 | − | $y_9$ |
| 7 | − | + | − | 0 | − | $y_{15}$ |
| 8 | + | + | + | 0 | − | $y_{21}$ |
| 9 | − | − | + | + | − | $y_5$ |
| 10 | + | − | − | + | − | $y_{11}$ |
| 11 | − | + | − | + | − | $y_{17}$ |
| 12 | + | + | + | + | − | $y_{23}$ |
| 13 | − | − | + | − | + | $y_2$ |
| 14 | + | − | − | − | + | $y_8$ |
| 15 | − | + | − | − | + | $y_{14}$ |
| 16 | + | + | + | − | + | $y_{20}$ |
| 17 | − | − | + | 0 | + | $y_4$ |
| 18 | + | − | − | 0 | + | $y_{10}$ |
| 19 | − | + | − | 0 | + | $y_{16}$ |
| 20 | + | + | + | 0 | + | $y_{22}$ |
| 21 | − | − | + | + | + | $y_6$ |
| 22 | + | − | − | + | + | $y_{12}$ |
| 23 | − | + | − | + | + | $y_{18}$ |
| 24 | + | + | + | + | + | $y_{24}$ |

contrasts (a dispersion measure cannot be calculated from a single $y$ value) and they are calculated directly from the $y$ values. The contrast set includes main effects for $A$, $B$ and $C$, and also $S_\ell$ and $S_q$ relating to the signal factor. The effect of noise $N$ is also now available. The other contrasts are made up of interactions between the control, signal, and noise factors, namely $A \times S_\ell$, $B \times S_\ell$, $C \times S_\ell$, $A \times S_q$, $B \times S_q$, and $C \times S_q$; $A \times N$, $B \times N$ and $C \times N$; $N \times S_\ell$ and $N \times S_q$; and finally three-factor interactions $A \times N \times S_\ell$, $B \times N \times S_\ell$, $C \times N \times S_\ell$, $A \times N \times S_q$, $A \times N \times S_q$ and $A \times N \times S_q$.

One way to interpret these contrasts relative to contrasts already discussed is as follows. The set of contrasts based on Table 12.5 form two groups (leaving $N$ aside). Any contrast that involves an interaction with $N$ measures essentially the same thing as the corresponding dispersion contrast from Table 12.4. Any contrast that does not involve $N$ arises from averaging over the levels of $N$, and gives exactly the same result as the corresponding location contrast from Table 12.4.

As usual we would expect $N$ to have a strong main effect. Also the $N \times S_\ell$ interaction contrast will be active because the effect of the noise will depend on the level of the signal factor. We would expect that a three-way interaction involving a control factor with $S_\ell$ and $N$ would be active if robustness effects were present. However, the corresponding two-way interactions and main effects would also be active, which makes it harder to interpret contrasts for robustness effects than in the static case of previous chapters. In Section 12.5 we consider how transformations may help to make robustness contrasts easier to interpret.

Hence Taguchi's use of experimentation with a dynamic system can be seen within the context of orthogonal contrasts, rather than S/N ratios, if necessary. The S/N ratio is essentially a confounding of interactions between control factors and noise factors together with measures of non-linearity.

As a final note in this section, it is very easy in a spreadsheet to arrange the experiment and the data into any of the layouts in Tables 12.3, 12.4 and 12.5.

## 12.5 TRANSFORMATIONS IN THE DYNAMIC SETTING

In Chapter 11 we suggested that in many cases a log transformation can be used to simplify the interpretation of effects in an experiment. The log transformation helps to achieve a separability of location effects and dispersion effects when $\mu$ and $\sigma$ are *linked* by an equation like [11.3] with $p$ around 1. It also sets the static S/N ratio [8.1] in the context of the standard deviation, a more familiar measure of dispersion than the S/N ratio itself.

If we assume that Fig. 12.3 is typical for energy-related responses, then the log transformation works in the dynamic framework too. Taking logs of both sides of equation [12.1] yields

$$\log(y) = \log(\beta) + \log(S) \qquad [12.6]$$

That is, if we take logs of both the response *and the signal factor*, a plot of $\log(S)$ against $\log(y)$ will result in a line of unit gradient with intercept given by $\log(\beta)$. Hence a set of lines that diverge from the origin become parallel. Transforming Fig. 12.3 gives Fig. 12.4.

Figure 12.4 is much easier to interpret in terms of contrasts than Fig. 12.3 because in Fig. 12.4 we can see the following:

- $S$ still has a strong linear effect.
- There is no $S \times N$ interaction.
- Control factors that affect the slope show up as an interaction with $S_\ell$ in Fig. 12.3, but as a simple main effect in Fig. 12.4, since the slope is now equivalent to the intercept.
- Control factors that affect robustness show up as a three-factor interaction incorporating $S \times N$ in Fig. 12.3, but since this interaction is removed from

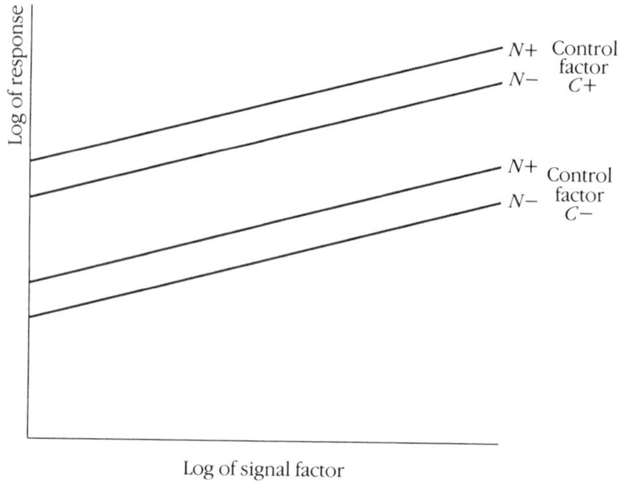


*Fig. 12.4* Taking logs of the response and the signal transforms the full lines in Fig. 12.3 into a set of parallel lines

Fig. 12.4, robustness contrasts will show up as an interaction with $N$ only (i.e. a pair of parallel lines will be closer together for one level of the control factor than another).

Hence the log transformations have eliminated the need to interpret three-factor interactions for robustness and two-factor interactions for adjusting the slope. The number of effects necessary to interpret the experiment has been reduced. This analysis suggests that we should experiment with the signal factor by making its three levels equally spaced on a log scale to enable the contrasts in Table 12.2 to retain a linear and quadratic interpretation.

Making the lines parallel in Fig. 12.4 is *analogous* to decoupling $\mu$ and $\sigma$ in the static framework. To see how this works, take the following simple model for the link seen in Fig. 12.3 between the slope and the noise effect:

$$\beta = n_-\beta_- \text{ for } C-, N- \qquad \beta = n_+\beta_- \text{ for } C-, N+$$
$$\beta = n_-\beta_+ \text{ for } C+, N- \qquad \beta = n_+\beta_+ \text{ for } C+, N+$$

Then in Fig. 12.4 the intercepts for $N-$ and $N+$ differ by the same amount ($\log(n_+) - \log(n_-)$) for both levels of $C$. This is telling us that, although factor $C$ has a robustness effect (Fig. 12.3), this can only be exploited at the expense of a lower slope. In the transformed picture the effect disappears. A robustness effect that survives after transformation to give a pair of parallel lines which are closer together *and* have larger intercepts is much more useful.

## 12.6 AN EXPERIMENT TO ACHIEVE A ROBUST ENGINE STARTING SYSTEM

We will pursue the use of orthogonal contrasts in experiments on dynamic systems by discussing a case study concerned with achieving a good start time for a cold engine irrespective of the ambient temperature. This experiment was initiated by a Quality Function Deployment team at the Ford Motor Co. Ltd under the leadership of Derek Eade, and executed in conjunction with Professor Paul Shayler, Jon Dixon, Jes Sage and Paul Tinwell in the Department of Mechanical Engineering at the University of Nottingham.

The air-to-fuel ratio (*AFR*) at the tip of the spark plug at the moment of spark was considered to be a vital quantity for start to be achieved. Therefore, although the objective of the experiment is to make the start time as insensitive as possible to temperature, the response is chosen as the air-to-fuel ratio.

The noise factor was ambient temperature, designated by the letter $N$, with two levels of $\pm 15$ °C (coded + and − as usual). The signal factor in this experiment is the injected fuel mass, designated by the letter $S$. The fuel mass is controlled by an electronic pulse delivered from the electronic engine management system — the wider the pulse, the more fuel is delivered. Factor $S$ has three levels designated by pulse widths of 30 ms, 45 ms and 60 ms. Fuel mass is a signal factor because the starting system needs to respond to different amounts of fuel that the engine management system decides to inject. In this experiment, the three levels of the signal factor are equally spaced on a linear scale.

Some control factors were determined, and these are listed in Table 12.6. For reasons of confidentiality, we cannot give details of the actual levels of these factors. However, there were six types of injector, which we will refer to as type 1, type 2, etc., so $A$ is a six-level factor. The other factors all had equally spaced (or nearly equally spaced in the case of $F$ and $G$) levels on a continuous scale. Hence we will refer to the levels of these factors on the usual coded scale of $-1$ to $+1$.

The array chosen to accommodate the control factors for this experiment was $L_{18}$ (Table 7.2). This array is the smallest one that will accommodate all the control factors at the desired levels. In particular, the six-level factor requires that the standard array be modified by combining and re-coding the first two columns of the array according to the rules explained in Section 7.2. Recall also from Chapter 7 that in general it is not possible to extract information on interactions from $L_{18}$.

In this application $L_{18}$ takes the role of the inner array (see Table 12.3). The outer array is a full factorial in $N$ and $S$ as illustrated in Table 12.1, which means six combinations of signal and noise. Hence a total of $18 \times 6 = 108$ tests are required. It was decided to repeat (*not* replicate) each test. In this application, we refer to each combination of control factors as an engine *build*, rather than an experimental *run*.

*Table 12.6* Control factors for the starting experiment

| Factor | Name |
|---|---|
| $(A)$ | Injector type |
| $(B)$ | Distance from injector tip to valve head |
| $(C)$ | Injection timing |
| $(D)$ | Valve timing |
| $(E)$ | Spark plug reach |
| $(F)$ | Spark timing |
| $(G)$ | Fuel rail pressure |

The experiment was conducted in a special laboratory, the temperature of which could be varied between the required extremes of ±15 °C. Using special instrumentation the experimenters were able to measure the quantity of fuel at the tip of the spark plug at the moment of spark by drawing off the air–fuel mixture into a special flask. The measured quantity is an air-to-fuel ratio. The amount of air can be considered a constant however, because the same volume of mixture was sampled for each experimental run. An important point is that there was no attempt to start the engine during this experiment even though the ultimate objective of the study is to obtain quick start times in hot and cold ambient conditions.

The experimental plan and data are shown in Table 12.7, p. 332. In this table we have used ordinary numerals to denote the levels of the six-level factor. Note that there are two numbers missing from Table 12.7, but this complication has been ignored in everything that follows. This is possible because of the repeat data.

In order to illustrate the basic nature of the data, it is worth constructing some simple plots. As an example, Fig. 12.5(a) is a plot of the data for build 3. This plot is nothing like a line pointing at the origin as we required in the discussion surrounding Fig. 12.2 and 12.3. However, if we work with the *reciprocal* of the data in Table 12.7 (the fuel-to-air ratio), things look much more encouraging — see Fig. 12.5(b). This plot fits in better with a system characterized by an input and an output (i.e. fuel in–fuel out, since the volume of air is constant). Furthermore, the *ideal* situation for this relationship is a linear one. Figure 12.5(b) shows a good linear relationship for each of the two noise levels (i.e. each temperature extreme), and both lines appear to point roughly at the origin (no fuel in–no fuel out). In everything that follows, we work with the fuel-to-air ratio.

Similar plots to Fig. 12.5 can be constructed for all the other runs. Plotting the data in this way enabled the experimenters to spot some results that looked unusual, and a few of the builds were re-tested. Table 12.7 incorporates the data from the re-tests.

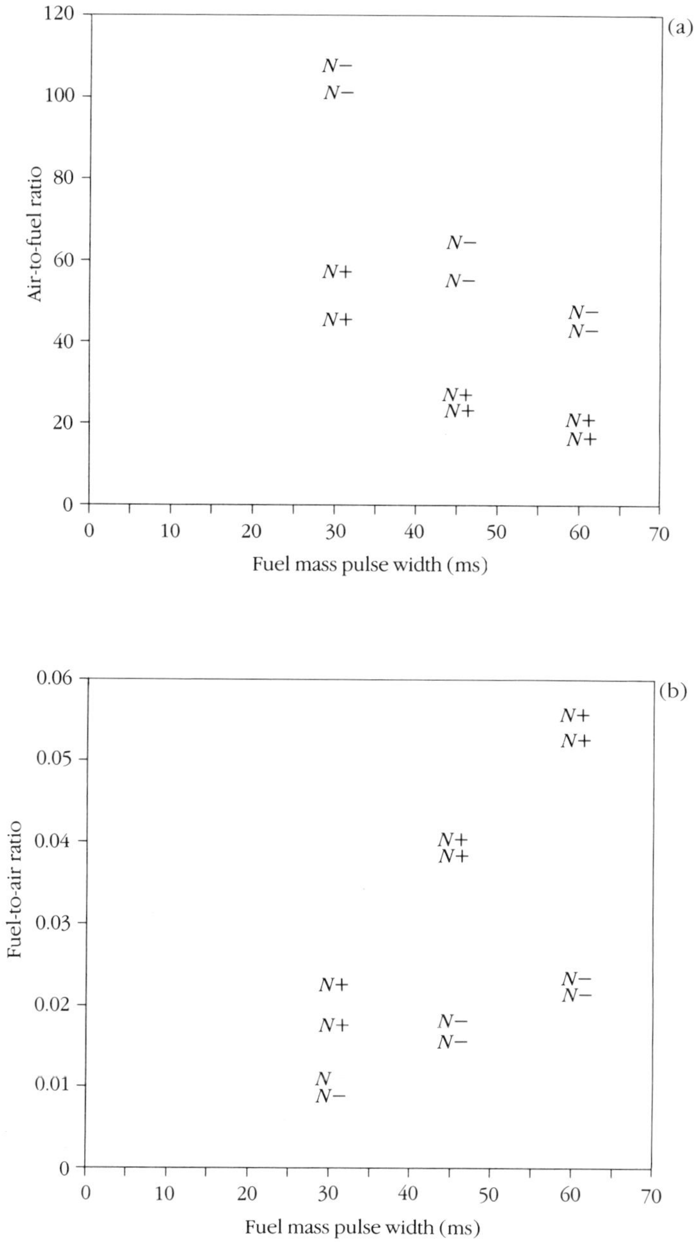


*Fig. 12.5* Starting experiment. The results for build 3: (a) raw data; (b) after taking reciprocals

*Table 12.7* Array and data (AFR) for the starting experiment

| | Inner array: control factors | | | | | | | Outer array: signal and noise factors | | | | | | |
|---|---|---|---|---|---|---|---|---|---|---|---|---|---|---|
| | | | | | | | | – | + | – | + | – | + | *N* |
| Build | *A* | *B* | *C* | *D* | *E* | *F* | *G* | – | – | 0 | 0 | + | + | *S* |
| 1 | 1 | – | – | – | – | – | – | 199.2 | 72.8 | 218.1 | 48.8 | 106.6 | 37.5 | |
| | | | | | | | | 285.3 | 72.9 | 153.4 | 52.7 | – | 39.0 | |
| 2 | 1 | 0 | 0 | 0 | 0 | 0 | 0 | 96.0 | 50.3 | 42.4 | 26.1 | 47.0 | 20.7 | |
| | | | | | | | | 156.3 | 61.7 | 58.3 | 27.5 | 51.5 | 20.0 | |
| 3 | 1 | + | + | + | + | + | + | 100.1 | 45.3 | 63.9 | 25.7 | 46.5 | 19.0 | |
| | | | | | | | | 107.2 | 57.3 | 54.8 | 25.4 | 42.8 | 18.0 | |
| 4 | 2 | – | – | 0 | 0 | + | + | 77.6 | 58.5 | 69.8 | 39.3 | 52.0 | 23.7 | |
| | | | | | | | | 146.0 | 57.2 | 58.3 | 26.9 | 45.7 | 22.8 | |
| 5 | 2 | 0 | 0 | + | + | – | – | 102.2 | 42.7 | 84.2 | 43.3 | 54.3 | 34.9 | |
| | | | | | | | | 104.1 | 76.1 | 86.1 | 42.8 | 59.8 | 30.8 | |
| 6 | 2 | + | + | – | – | 0 | 0 | 168.2 | 90.5 | 79.9 | 41.4 | 67.4 | 30.2 | |
| | | | | | | | | 150.4 | 102.0 | 60.4 | 42.1 | 59.2 | 29.8 | |
| 7 | 3 | – | 0 | – | + | 0 | + | 95.1 | 55.7 | 55.3 | 38.8 | 47.7 | 27.7 | |
| | | | | | | | | 174.9 | 68.1 | 69.3 | 37.7 | 58.6 | 29.9 | |
| 8 | 3 | 0 | + | 0 | – | + | – | 110.4 | 112.2 | 78.3 | 48.0 | 82.4 | 34.7 | |
| | | | | | | | | 164.8 | 93.8 | 99.1 | 48.8 | 69.8 | 34.8 | |
| 9 | 3 | + | – | + | 0 | – | 0 | 94.5 | – | 91.7 | 29.9 | 77.2 | 25.6 | |
| | | | | | | | | 192.2 | 52.9 | 84.3 | 31.8 | 75.9 | 24.3 | |

*Table 12.7* contd

| | Inner array: control factors | | | | | | | Outer array: signal and noise factors | | | | | |
|---|---|---|---|---|---|---|---|---|---|---|---|---|---|
| | | | | | | | | − | + | − | + | − | + (N) |
| Build | *A* | *B* | *C* | *D* | *E* | *F* | *G* | − | − | 0 | 0 | + | + (S) |
| 10 | 4 | − | + | + | 0 | 0 | − | 111.4 | 24.5 | 57.1 | 15.6 | 40.9 | 12.9 |
| | | | | | | | | 104.0 | 28.7 | 56.8 | 22.0 | 38.4 | 13.2 |
| 11 | 4 | 0 | − | − | + | + | 0 | 57.6 | 50.1 | 41.7 | 26.2 | 33.8 | 19.6 |
| | | | | | | | | 68.4 | 49.7 | 42.5 | 27.3 | 37.3 | 21.6 |
| 12 | 4 | + | 0 | 0 | − | − | + | 77.3 | 45.9 | 46.6 | 30.0 | 40.5 | 21.5 |
| | | | | | | | | 69.8 | 52.2 | 44.3 | 30.0 | 34.8 | 21.3 |
| 13 | 5 | − | 0 | + | − | + | 0 | 59.7 | 30.8 | 45.1 | 16.5 | 37.8 | 12.3 |
| | | | | | | | | 66.6 | 28.2 | 46.9 | 19.7 | 34.1 | 13.0 |
| 14 | 5 | 0 | + | − | 0 | − | + | 34.0 | 21.6 | 20.7 | 14.1 | 16.3 | 10.5 |
| | | | | | | | | 39.9 | 23.2 | 22.4 | 13.2 | 15.3 | 11.5 |
| 15 | 5 | + | − | 0 | + | 0 | − | 160.2 | 88.7 | 75.2 | 44.2 | 57.5 | 33.1 |
| | | | | | | | | 115.8 | 73.4 | 65.5 | 48.4 | 54.6 | 36.2 |
| 16 | 6 | − | + | 0 | + | − | 0 | 46.7 | 23.2 | 30.9 | 18.6 | 23.8 | 12.8 |
| | | | | | | | | 49.8 | 23.0 | 31.1 | 17.3 | 23.0 | 11.6 |
| 17 | 6 | 0 | − | + | − | 0 | + | 64.3 | 29.7 | 48.0 | 26.5 | 26.9 | 21.4 |
| | | | | | | | | 71.2 | 36.7 | 52.2 | 28.6 | 28.3 | 18.4 |
| 18 | 6 | + | 0 | − | 0 | + | − | 139.0 | 99.3 | 84.7 | 69.5 | 55.9 | 40.8 |
| | | | | | | | | 121.7 | 87.7 | 75.4 | 69.6 | 78.1 | 38.9 |

## Initial analysis using Taguchi's S/N ratio — analysis (i)

For the initial analysis of this data set we use Taguchi's S/N ratio as given by [12.4]. Table 12.8 is a summary of $\hat{\beta}$, $s_r$, and *SN* for each of the 18 builds from the inner array of Table 12.7. Note that the actual levels of *S* (30, 45 and 60) were used to calculate the $\hat{\beta}$ values.

*Table 12.8* $\hat{\beta}$, $s_r$ and *SN* for each of the 18 runs in Table 12.7

| Build | $\hat{\beta}$ ($\times 10^4$) | $s_r$ ($\times 10^3$) | *SN* |
|---|---|---|---|
| 1 | 3.1 | 7.08 | −27.07 |
| 2 | 5.8 | 11.08 | −25.63 |
| 3 | 6.1 | 12.36 | −26.09 |
| 4 | 5.2 | 9.13 | −24.94 |
| 5 | 4.1 | 6.42 | −23.96 |
| 6 | 4.0 | 6.63 | −24.44 |
| 7 | 4.5 | 6.46 | −23.14 |
| 8 | 3.4 | 5.69 | −24.38 |
| 9 | 4.5 | 11.39 | −28.05 |
| 10 | 8.3 | 21.43 | −28.28 |
| 11 | 6.5 | 7.74 | −21.55 |
| 12 | 6.1 | 7.36 | −21.67 |
| 13 | 8.7 | 19.50 | −26.98 |
| 14 | 12.9 | 13.20 | −20.21 |
| 15 | 3.8 | 4.55 | −21.45 |
| 16 | 10.3 | 15.63 | −23.66 |
| 17 | 7.0 | 8.72 | −21.94 |
| 18 | 3.2 | 3.47 | −20.67 |

Figure 12.6 is a log–log plot of $\hat{\beta}$ against $s_r$ based on the calculations presented in Table 12.8. There is clearly a dependence between $s_r$ and $\hat{\beta}$ in this plot and the gradient is about 1. There is some justification therefore in using the S/N ratio [12.4] as the metric for the analysis.

Taguchi recommends using the signal-to-noise ratio [12.4] *regardless* of whether the gradient is 1 or not. He does *not* recommend plots like Fig. 12.6 as a check on this, and simply calculates a S/N ratio from the data for each run in the orthogonal array. Table 12.9 is the response table for the S/N ratios, while Fig. 12.7 is an effects plot.

Table 12.10 shows a set of 17 (18 − 1) orthogonal contrasts for the 18 builds in Table 12.7. The first five contrasts (labelled $a_1, a_2, \ldots, a_5$) measure various aspects of the effect of the six-level factor (injector type). For example contrast $a_1$ measures the difference between injector types 1, 2 and 3 and types 4, 5 and 6, while contrast $a_2$ measures the difference between types 1 and 4 and types 3 and 6. In fact all of these contrasts have the same coefficients as the contrasts normally applied to $L_{18}$ when there is a two-level

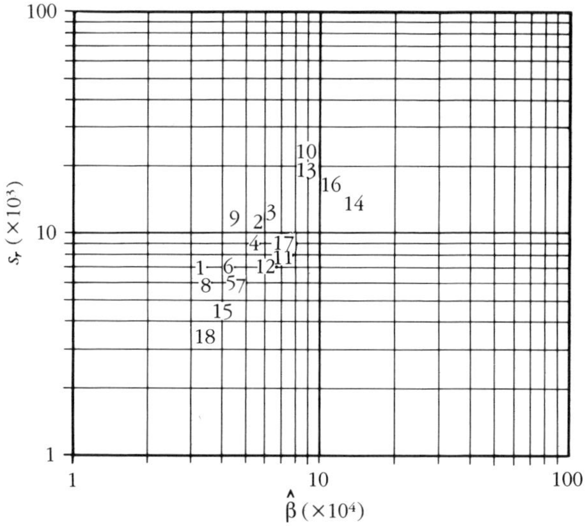


*Fig. 12.6* Starting experiment. Log–log plot of $s_r$ against $\hat{\beta}$

*Table 12.9* Response table for the dynamic S/N ratio

| Level | *A* | *B* | *C* | *D* | *E* | *F* | *G* |
|---|---|---|---|---|---|---|---|
| 1 | −26.27 | −25.68 | −24.19 | −22.85 | −24.41 | −24.10 | −24.30 |
| 2 | −24.45 | −22.95 | −23.66 | −23.62 | −24.63 | −24.15 | −25.05 |
| 3 | −25.19 | −23.73 | −24.51 | −25.88 | −23.31 | −24.10 | −23.00 |
| 4 | −23.83 | | | | | | |
| 5 | −22.88 | | | | | | |
| 6 | −22.09 | | | | | | |

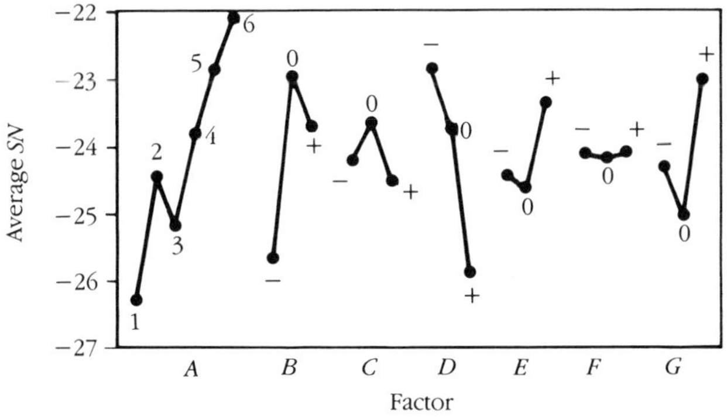


*Fig. 12.7* Starting experiment. Effects plot for the dynamic S/N ratio

*Table 12.10* A set of 17 orthogonal contrasts

| Build | $a_1$ | $a_2$ | $a_3$ | $a_4$ | $a_5$ | $B_\ell$ | $B_q$ | $C_\ell$ | $C_q$ | $D_\ell$ | $D_q$ | $E_\ell$ | $E_q$ | $F_\ell$ | $F_q$ | $G_\ell$ | $G_q$ |
|---|---|---|---|---|---|---|---|---|---|---|---|---|---|---|---|---|---|
| 1 | −1 | −1 | −1 | +1 | −1 | −1 | +1 | −1 | +1 | −1 | +1 | −1 | +1 | −1 | +1 | −1 | +1 |
| 2 | −1 | −1 | −1 | +1 | −1 | 0 | −2 | 0 | −2 | 0 | −2 | 0 | −2 | 0 | −2 | 0 | −2 |
| 3 | −1 | −1 | −1 | +1 | −1 | +1 | +1 | +1 | +1 | +1 | +1 | +1 | +1 | +1 | +1 | +1 | +1 |
| 4 | −1 | 0 | −2 | 0 | +2 | −1 | +1 | −1 | +1 | 0 | −2 | 0 | −2 | +1 | +1 | +1 | +1 |
| 5 | −1 | 0 | −2 | 0 | +2 | 0 | −2 | 0 | −2 | +1 | +1 | +1 | +1 | −1 | +1 | −1 | +1 |
| 6 | −1 | 0 | −2 | 0 | +2 | +1 | +1 | +1 | +1 | −1 | +1 | −1 | +1 | 0 | −2 | 0 | −2 |
| 7 | −1 | +1 | +1 | −1 | −1 | −1 | +1 | 0 | −2 | −1 | +1 | +1 | +1 | 0 | −2 | +1 | +1 |
| 8 | −1 | +1 | +1 | −1 | −1 | 0 | −2 | +1 | +1 | 0 | −2 | −1 | +1 | +1 | +1 | −1 | +1 |
| 9 | −1 | +1 | +1 | −1 | −1 | +1 | +1 | −1 | +1 | +1 | +1 | 0 | −2 | −1 | +1 | 0 | −2 |
| 10 | +1 | −1 | +1 | −1 | +1 | −1 | +1 | +1 | +1 | +1 | +1 | 0 | −2 | 0 | −2 | −1 | +1 |
| 11 | +1 | −1 | +1 | −1 | +1 | 0 | −2 | −1 | +1 | −1 | +1 | +1 | +1 | +1 | +1 | 0 | −2 |
| 12 | +1 | −1 | +1 | −1 | +1 | +1 | +1 | 0 | −2 | 0 | −2 | −1 | +1 | −1 | +1 | +1 | +1 |
| 13 | +1 | 0 | −2 | 0 | −2 | −1 | +1 | 0 | −2 | +1 | +1 | −1 | +1 | +1 | +1 | 0 | −2 |
| 14 | +1 | 0 | −2 | 0 | −2 | 0 | −2 | +1 | +1 | −1 | +1 | 0 | −2 | −1 | +1 | +1 | +1 |
| 15 | +1 | 0 | −2 | 0 | −2 | +1 | +1 | −1 | +1 | 0 | −2 | +1 | +1 | 0 | −2 | −1 | +1 |
| 16 | +1 | +1 | +1 | +1 | +1 | −1 | +1 | +1 | +1 | 0 | −2 | +1 | +1 | −1 | +1 | 0 | −2 |
| 17 | +1 | +1 | +1 | +1 | +1 | 0 | −2 | −1 | +1 | +1 | +1 | −1 | +1 | 0 | −2 | +1 | +1 |
| 18 | +1 | +1 | +1 | +1 | +1 | +1 | +1 | 0 | −2 | −1 | +1 | 0 | −2 | +1 | +1 | −1 | +1 |
| Divisor | 18 | 12 | 12 | 12 | 12 | 12 | 12 | 12 | 12 | 12 | 12 | 12 | 12 | 12 | 12 | 12 | 12 |

factor allocated to the first column (see Table 7.2). The other columns in Table 12.10 define standard linear and quadratic contrasts, which is appropriate because the levels of the three-level factors are (either exactly or approximately) equally spaced.

Figure 12.8 is the Daniel plot for the 17 contrasts (standardized as usual) in Table 12.10 using the S/N ratios in Table 12.9. There is a mild hint in this plot that contrasts $a_1$ and $D_\ell$ (the linear effect of factor $D$) are off the line, but the indication is not at all strong.

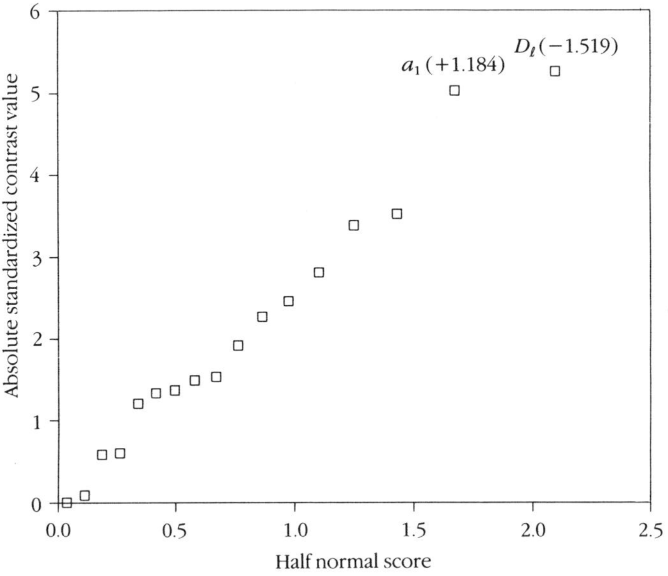


*Fig. 12.8* Starting experiment. Daniel plot of the standardized contrasts for the dynamic S/N ratio. Numbers in brackets are actual effects

As usual we need to maximize the S/N ratio. The value of contrast $a_1$ is $+1.184$, suggesting that injectors 4, 5 and 6 give a larger S/N ratio than 1, 2 and 3 (see the effects plot, Fig. 12.7). Since no other contrast involving injectors appears off the line in Fig. 12.8, we are free to choose any one of types 4, 5 and 6. Injector type 4 is much cheaper than the other two, so the experimenters chose type 4 (injector types 5 and 6 incorporated a heater designed specifically to remove the effect of the ambient temperature). The value of the $D_\ell$ contrast is $-1.519$, and since this is negative we require factor $D_\ell$ at the $(-)$ level in order to maximize the S/N ratio.

As well as the S/N ratios, the slope $\beta$ is also important. A particular value of $\beta$ may well be required to make the engine actually start. We should therefore look for factors that affect the slope. Table 12.11 is a response table based on the $\hat{\beta}$ values in Table 12.8. The corresponding effects plot is shown in Fig. 12.9.

*Table 12.11* Response table for slope $\hat{\beta}$ ($\times 10^4$)

| Level | | *A* | *B* | *C* | *D* | *E* | *F* | *G* |
|---|---|---|---|---|---|---|---|---|
| 1 | − | 5.02 | 6.68 | 5.02 | 5.70 | 5.39 | 6.82 | 4.33 |
| 2 | 0 | 4.40 | 6.60 | 5.39 | 5.76 | 6.64 | 5.56 | 6.62 |
| 3 | + | 4.15 | 4.62 | 7.49 | 6.44 | 5.88 | 5.53 | 6.95 |
| 4 | | 6.93 | | | | | | |
| 5 | | 8.49 | | | | | | |
| 6 | | 6.81 | | | | | | |

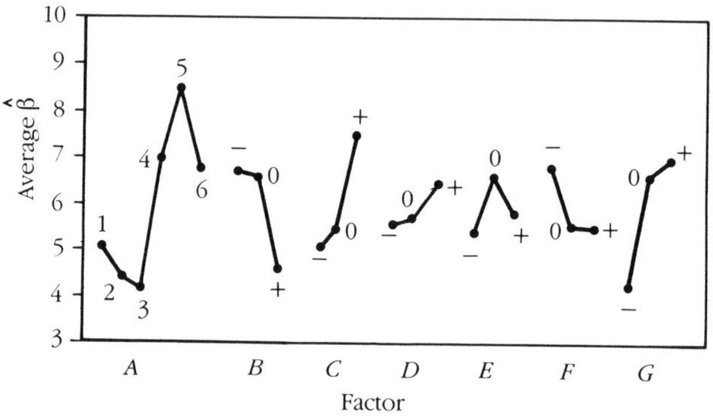


*Fig. 12.9* Starting experiment. Effects plot for the slope based on the $\hat{\beta}$ values in Table 12.8

Figure 12.10 is the full normal plot for the $\hat{\beta}$ effects, again using the contrasts defined in Table 12.10. The reason for showing the full normal plot is that the Daniel plot does not point to the origin. Clearly there is a break in the normal plot around the origin, suggesting that one of the $\hat{\beta}$ values in Table 12.8 is unusual. An obvious candidate is $\hat{\beta}$ for build 14. The numbers in brackets in Fig. 12.10 are the contrast coefficients from Table 12.10 corresponding to build 14. Note that for the line through the negative contrasts in Fig. 12.10 these coefficients are mostly negative, while for the line through the positive contrasts the coefficients are mostly zero or positive. This consistency is a strong indication that $\hat{\beta}$ for build 14 is a little high.

However, in spite of this, four contrasts appear to be well off the line, these being $a_1$, $G_\ell$, $C_\ell$ and $B_\ell$. Since $a_1$ is needed to achieve robustness, factors *G*, *C* and *B* could potentially be used to adjust the slope of the fuel in–fuel out relationship, and this adjustment would be linear with respect to the factor levels.

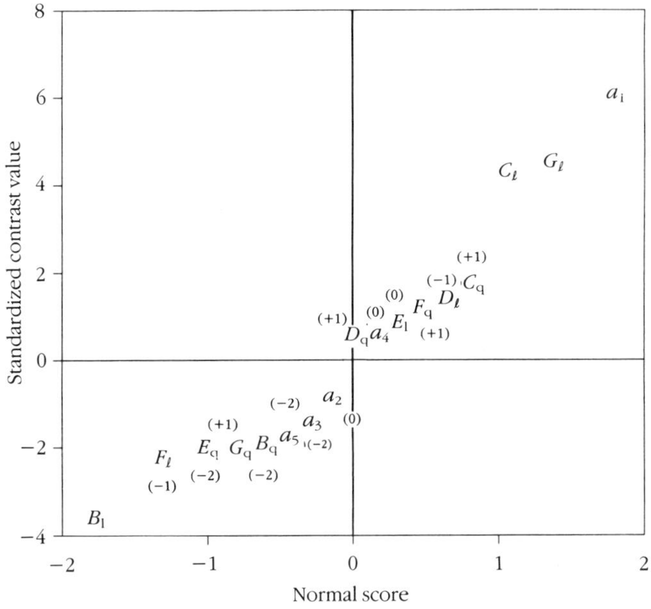


*Fig. 12.10* Starting experiment. Full normal plot for the slope $\hat{\beta}$, based on Table 12.8. The break in the plot suggests that one of the $\hat{\beta}$ values is unusual. The numbers in brackets are the coefficients of build 14 in each contrast

## Further analysis measuring the effect of the signal directly — analysis (ii)

It is worth exploring other ways to analyse this data set, along the lines that were discussed in Section 12.4. In this analysis the signal factor is considered part of the inner array, and the noise factor is left in the outer array. The style of layout is illustrated in Table 12.4, but here the inner array will consist of $3 \times 18 = 54$ 'runs'. Each 'run' now includes four results — two repetitions at each of two noise levels.

Table 12.12 gives details of $\bar{y}$ and $s$ for these 54 runs. As usual $\bar{y}$ is the average of the data for each run, but $s$ represents the ordinary standard deviation estimate, and not the estimate given by equation [12.3], because with this layout we are measuring the effects of the signal factor directly through orthogonal contrasts — so we are no longer concerned with measuring deviations from a fitted line.

Figure 12.11 is a log–log plot of $\bar{y}$ against $s$. Like the plots involving $\hat{\beta}$ and $s_r$, this plot has a slope very close to 1. In Chapter 11 we argued that Taguchi's nominal-the-best (static) S/N ratio is then appropriate to detect dispersion effects (and is almost equivalent to working directly with a

*Table 12.12* $\bar{y}$, $s$ and static S/N ratio for the starting experiment

| | $S = 30$ ms | | | $S = 45$ ms | | | $S = 60$ ms | | |
|---|---|---|---|---|---|---|---|---|---|
| Build | $\bar{y}$ ($\times 10^3$) | $s$ ($\times 10^3$) | Static *SN* | $\bar{y}$ ($\times 10^3$) | $s$ ($\times 10^3$) | Static *SN* | $\bar{y}$ ($\times 10^3$) | $s$ ($\times 10^3$) | Static *SN* |
| 1 | 8.99 | 5.50 | 4.27 | 12.64 | 8.25 | 3.71 | 20.56 | 9.70 | 6.53 |
| 2 | 13.23 | 5.99 | 6.88 | 28.85 | 10.17 | 9.05 | 34.75 | 16.66 | 6.38 |
| 3 | 14.71 | 6.14 | 7.59 | 28.04 | 12.86 | 6.77 | 38.26 | 18.33 | 6.39 |
| 4 | 13.58 | 4.95 | 8.77 | 23.52 | 10.25 | 7.22 | 31.79 | 13.04 | 7.74 |
| 5 | 13.99 | 6.49 | 6.66 | 17.49 | 6.63 | 8.42 | 24.06 | 7.69 | 9.91 |
| 6 | 8.36 | 2.45 | 10.65 | 19.24 | 5.68 | 10.59 | 24.60 | 10.12 | 7.71 |
| 7 | 12.22 | 5.30 | 7.26 | 21.20 | 5.91 | 11.09 | 26.89 | 9.30 | 9.22 |
| 8 | 8.67 | 1.91 | 13.14 | 16.05 | 5.44 | 9.39 | 21.00 | 9.02 | 7.34 |
| 9 | 11.56 | 6.90 | 4.48 | 21.91 | 12.19 | 5.09 | 26.59 | 15.64 | 4.61 |
| 10 | 23.56 | 16.66 | 3.01 | 36.17 | 22.80 | 4.01 | 50.94 | 29.69 | 4.69 |
| 11 | 18.02 | 2.59 | 16.84 | 30.58 | 7.90 | 11.75 | 38.43 | 12.02 | 10.09 |
| 12 | 17.05 | 4.13 | 12.31 | 27.67 | 6.55 | 12.52 | 36.72 | 11.68 | 9.95 |
| 13 | 24.92 | 10.53 | 7.48 | 38.72 | 20.00 | 5.74 | 53.50 | 29.65 | 5.13 |
| 14 | 35.97 | 10.32 | 10.84 | 59.91 | 15.71 | 11.63 | 77.23 | 16.45 | 13.43 |
| 15 | 9.94 | 3.20 | 9.85 | 17.96 | 4.40 | 12.22 | 23.39 | 6.49 | 11.14 |
| 16 | 32.02 | 13.03 | 7.81 | 44.02 | 13.68 | 10.15 | 62.46 | 23.00 | 8.68 |
| 17 | 22.63 | 9.43 | 7.60 | 28.17 | 9.53 | 9.41 | 43.40 | 8.85 | 13.81 |
| 18 | 9.22 | 1.88 | 13.82 | 13.46 | 1.22 | 20.86 | 20.23 | 6.03 | 10.52 |

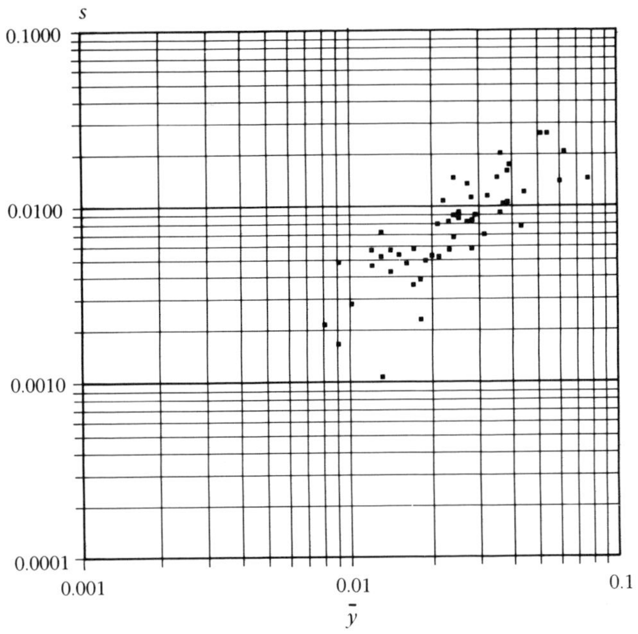


*Fig. 12.11* Starting experiment. Log–log plot of $s$ against $\bar{y}$. There are 54 points, corresponding to 18 builds × 3 levels of $S$

standard deviation after a log transformation of the data). The theoretical justification for the log transformation, as given in Chapter 11, does not really apply here, because the variation captured by $s$ is mostly due to the noise factor, i.e. is not random. Nevertheless we expect the S/N ratio, or the log transformation, to do a good job of decoupling location and dispersion.

To recap, the formula for the static S/N ratio is

$$SN = 20 \log_{10}(\bar{y}/s) \qquad [12.7]$$

The S/N ratios given by [12.7] are in Table 12.12.

Figure 12.12 is a Daniel plot of S/N ratio contrasts developed as an extension of Table 12.10 by measuring the linear and quadratic effects of the signal factor, and all interactions between control factors and the signal factor, 53 (54 − 1) contrasts in all. Three contrasts clearly stand out on this plot: $D_\ell$, $a_1$, and $B_\ell$. Note that a linear effect for $D$ and the $a_1$ contrast were (just about) detected by the Daniel plot given in Fig. 12.8 using Taguchi's dynamic S/N ratio [12.4], but a $B$ effect was not detected by that plot. However $B_\ell$ was the next largest contrast in Fig. 12.8 although it was not labelled there. $B_\ell$ is definitely off the line in Fig. 12.12, and probably $B_q$ too. There is a hint that factor $F$ interacts with the signal factor itself, and contrast $a_2$ is also just off the line. Reading Table 12.10 in conjunction with Table 12.7 shows that contrast $a_2$ measures the difference between injector types 1 and 4

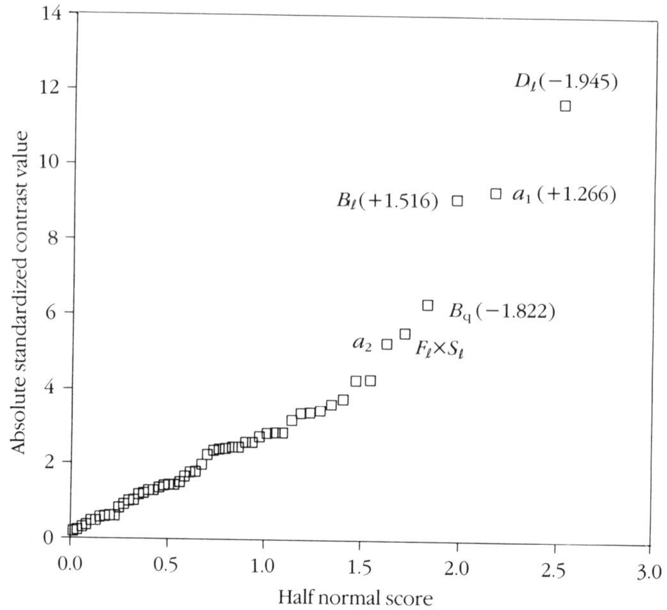


*Fig. 12.12* Starting experiment. Daniel plot of standardized contrasts for the static *SN* values in Table 12.12. Numbers in brackets are actual effects

and types 3 and 6. This contrast is actually positive (+0.876) which suggests that injector types 3 and 6 are on average better than types 1 and 4. Taking this together with contrast $a_1$ suggests that injector type 6 is the most robust. Contrast $B_\ell$ is positive (+1.516) and $B_q$ is negative (−1.822), which points to level (0) as the preferred level for factor *B*, although level (+) is almost as good.

Figure 12.13 is a Daniel plot for 53 location effects using the $\bar{y}$ values from Table 12.12. Contrast $S_\ell$ clearly stands out on this plot. Since there is no quadratic effect for the signal factor the *effect of the signal factor on fuel-to-air ratio is linear* in nature. This conclusion gives some justification to the previous analysis, which assumed a relationship consistent with [12.1].

Apart from $S_\ell$, the set of contrasts off the line in Fig. 12.13 are $a_1$, $G_\ell$, $C_\ell$, and $B_\ell$. Removing these effects and re-plotting yields Fig. 12.14. Most of the active contrasts in this plot are associated purely with main effects of control factors. There are, however, three particularly interesting contrasts, which are individually labelled in Fig. 12.14: $a_1 \times S_\ell$, $G_\ell \times S_\ell$, and $C_\ell \times S_\ell$. Interactions between control factors and the signal factor suggest that these control factors can be used to adjust the slope. Note that $a_1$, $G_\ell$ and $C_\ell$ were all detected by the full normal plot of effects on $\hat{\beta}$ (Fig. 12.10) in the same order. In Fig. 12.10 the contrast $B_\ell$ was also detected as having an effect on $\hat{\beta}$, and in fact the next largest interaction between a control factor and $S_\ell$ in Fig. 12.14 *is* $B_\ell \times S_\ell$. This contrast is among a set that look like they *might* be off the line, but this is not clear (another re-plot might help here). Hence the results of

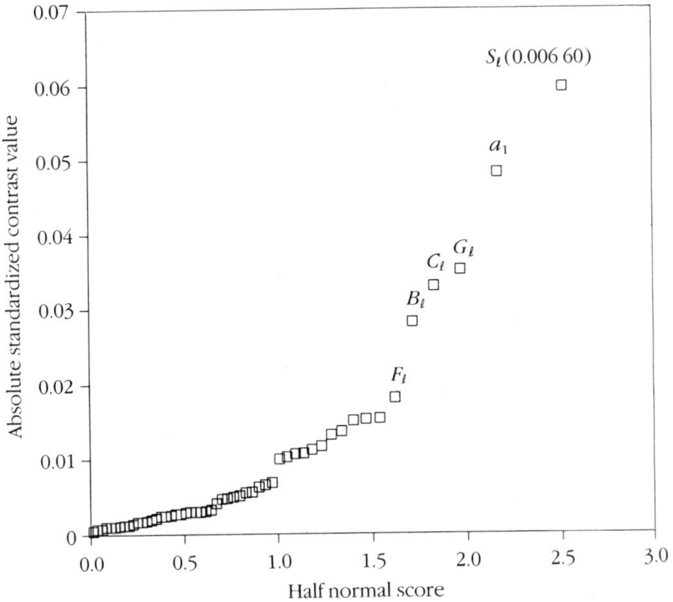


*Fig. 12.13* Starting experiment. Daniel plot of 54 standardized contrasts for $\bar{y}$, where $\bar{y}$ is calculated across the noise factor; main effect of $S$ and all interactions between $S$ and the control factors. Numbers in brackets are actual effects

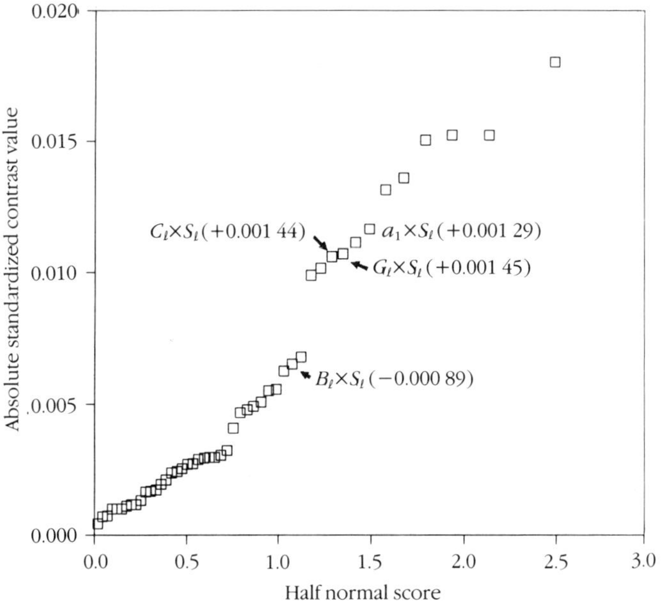


*Fig. 12.14* Starting experiment. Re-plot of Fig. 12.13 removing five contrasts

this analysis, which looks directly at contrasts that measure the effect of the signal factor, are consistent with the analysis of the S/N ratio and $\hat{\beta}$, but the Daniel plot for robustness is now much more clear-cut (compare Fig. 12.12 with Fig. 12.8).

## Measuring the effect of the signal and noise directly — analysis (iii)

Our final approach involves looking at all available contrasts, based on a layout analogous to Table 12.5. As we recommended in Section 12.5, we take logs of the response and the signal factor (taking logs of the reciprocal of the data is equivalent to taking logs of the original data except for a change in sign). Because the levels of the signal factor are not linearly spaced on the log scale, we choose to ignore level (0) here. Since we know from analysis (ii) that the effect of $S$ is essentially linear, dropping level (0) will not make much difference.

Since we now regard $S$ as a two-level factor, the plan has $18 \times 2 \times 2 = 72$ 'runs', so there are 71 contrasts available altogether. These contrasts can be developed from Table 12.10 by considering a main effect for noise $N$ and a single (linear) contrast for the signal $S_\ell$, and all possible interactions between these two effects and the control factors. We work only with a measure of location here (the average of the two repeat tests per run), since any measure

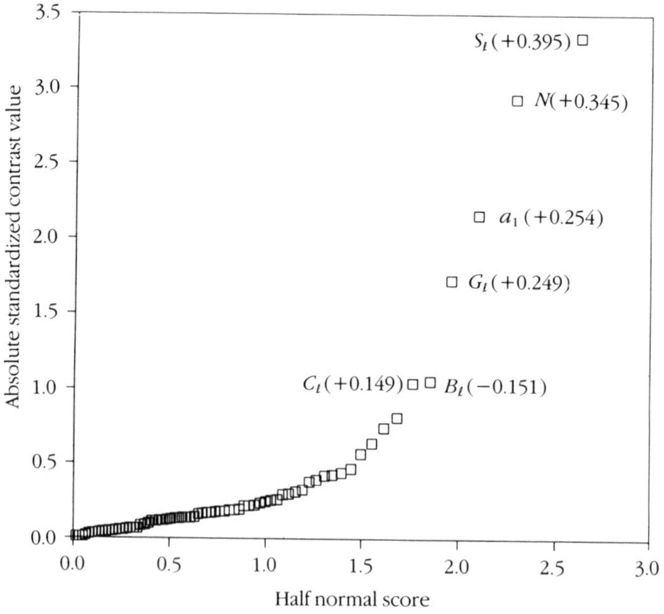


*Fig. 12.15* Starting experiment. Daniel plot of 71 standardized location contrasts, after taking logs of the data and ignoring level (0) of $S$; main effects of $S$, $N$ and the control factors, together with interactions. Numbers in brackets are actual effects

of dispersion will only reflect the repeat test variability. Such an analysis may be of interest to investigate the integrity of the experimental procedure (ideally we should see no dispersion effects), but we will not pursue that here.

Figure 12.15 is a Daniel plot of the 71 contrasts. Clearly there are a number of contrasts that appear off the line. The two largest are $S_\ell$, the (linear) effect of the signal, and $N$, the effect of the noise factor. We should not be surprised that these contrasts are the largest. Other contrasts appearing off the line are $a_1$, $G_\ell$, $B_\ell$, and $C_\ell$. All of these effects can be used to adjust the slope.

Figure 12.16 is a re-plot of Fig. 12.15 with the contrasts mentioned so far removed. Four other contrasts are slightly off the line: $D_\ell$, $B_q$, $G_q$ and $F_\ell$. Hence $B$ and $G$ have a mild quadratic effect on the slope. No interactions between control factors and the noise factor are strongly evident, but we have labelled a set of four interactions with noise that lie just off the line in Fig. 12.16. These contrasts involve the same set of control factors that were highlighted in the previous two analyses.

## Predictions and confirmation runs

Largely based on the evidence of the effects plots for $SN$ and $\hat{\beta}$ illustrated in Figs 12.7 and 12.9, and the Daniel plot of Fig. 12.12, the experimenters decided to predict and try to confirm engine builds that gave a high S/N ratio and a low S/N ratio. These new engine builds are detailed in Table 12.13.

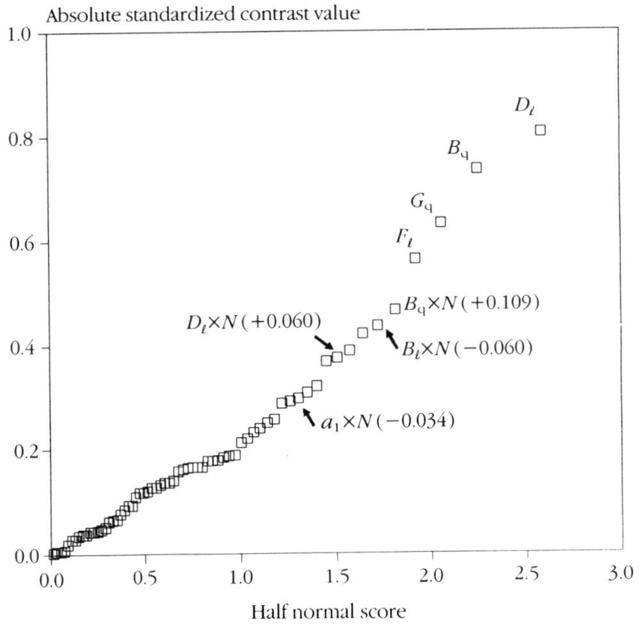


*Fig. 12.16* Starting experiment. Re-plot of Fig. 12.15 removing six contrasts

*Table 12.13* Combinations of control factors predicted to give high and low S/N ratios

(a) High S/N ratio

| Build | *A* | *B* | *C* | *D* | *E* | *F* | *G* |
|---|---|---|---|---|---|---|---|
| 19 | 4 | + | − | − | 0 | − | + |
| 20 | 4 | + | − | − | 0 | + | + |
| 21 | 4 | + | + | − | 0 | − | + |
| 22 | 4 | + | + | − | 0 | + | + |

(b) Low S/N ratio

| Build | *A* | *B* | *C* | *D* | *E* | *F* | *G* |
|---|---|---|---|---|---|---|---|
| 23 | 1 | − | − | + | 0 | − | 0 |
| 24 | 1 | − | − | + | 0 | + | 0 |
| 25 | 1 | − | + | + | 0 | − | 0 |
| 26 | 1 | − | + | + | 0 | + | 0 |

The choice of factor levels centres around the need to achieve a robust system where the effect of temperature on fuel-to-air ratio is minimized. Injector type 4 was chosen because this was roughly comparable with type 6 but much cheaper (the analysis of contrasts in analyses (ii) and (iii) consistently suggested that injector types 4, 5 and 6 were better than types 1, 2 and 3, with not much difference between 4, 5 and 6 themselves). Factor *B* was set at level (+) to yield a high S/N ratio and level (−) for a low S/N ratio to confirm the (positive) linear component of its effect. Conversely, *D* was set at level (−) for the high S/N ratio and (+) for the low because this factor had a (linear) negative effect. Factor *E* was not considered to affect the S/N ratio and was set at level (0), which is the standard setting. Factor *G* was set at level (+) for the high S/N ratio and (0) for the low S/N ratio based purely on the effects plot for the S/N ratio (Fig. 12.7). Factors *C* and *F* were varied between their extremes as a complete $2^2$ experiment since the effects plots indicated that these factors could be used to adjust the slope without much effect on the S/N ratio. However, only factor *C* was consistently evident from the Daniel plots as having a measurable effect on the slope, although factor *F* showed up in Fig. 12.16.

Table 12.14 shows predictions based on the control factor combinations of Table 12.13. For the dynamic S/N ratio and β, the predictions are based on effects detected from the Daniel plots of Figs 12.8 and 12.10. That is, contrasts $D_\ell$ and $a_1$ are assumed to affect the S/N ratio, and contrasts $a_1$, $G_\ell$, $C_\ell$ and $B_\ell$ are assumed to affect β. For the static S/N ratio predictions, it is assumed that the largest effects detected by the Daniel plot in Fig. 12.12 will reproduce, that is $D_\ell$, $a_1$ and $B_\ell$. We do not explore predictions for $\bar{y}$ based on analysis (ii) or analysis (iii) because the prediction equations will involve a lot of terms, although this could be done if required. Refer to Chapter 2 for constructing prediction equations.

*Table 12.14* Predictions for the new builds in Table 12.13

| High S/N ratio predictions | | | | Low S/N ratio predictions | | | |
|---|---|---|---|---|---|---|---|
| | Dynamic | | Static | | Dynamic | | Static |
| Build | *SN* | $\beta$ ($\times 10^4$) | *SN* | Build | *SN* | $\beta$ ($\times 10^4$) | *SN* |
| 19 | −21.42* | 6.46 | 13.00† | 23 | −26.82* | 4.31 | 4.85† |
| 20 | −21.42 | 6.46 | 13.00 | 24 | −26.82 | 4.31 | 4.85 |
| 21 | −21.42 | 8.94 | 13.00 | 25 | −26.82 | 6.79 | 4.85 |
| 22 | −21.42 | 8.94 | 13.00 | 26 | −26.82 | 6.79 | 4.85 |

*If $B_\ell$ and $B_q$ are also assumed active, these predictions become −21.02 for the high S/N ratio and −28.38 for the low S/N ratio
†These predictions should confirm irrespective of the level of the signal factor

The data collected from the confirmation runs is shown in Table 12.15. An initial observation on the data in Table 12.15 is that the variation between the repeat tests is less than for the original experiment (Table 12.7). Again working with the reciprocals of these data, Fig. 12.17 shows plots for the high and low S/N ratio builds.

The effect of noise for the high S/N ratio builds is slightly less than for the low ones, even though the slope is higher. This is just as required. We can calculate dynamic S/N ratios and $\hat{\beta}$ using equations [12.2] and [12.4], and also static S/N ratios using [12.7] for comparisons with the predictions. These numbers are given in Table 12.16. Note that the confirmations for the dynamic S/N ratio, and also the static S/N ratios, match the predictions in Table 12.14 quite well. The confirmations for $\beta$ are not as good. One possible reason is that some of the control factors may exhibit interaction in their effects on $\hat{\beta}$. Because the array chosen to conduct the original experiment was an $L_{18}$ we cannot measure those interactions in the original experiment and use them to predict.

We could use the eight confirmation runs to try to investigate further why the predictions for $\beta$ did not confirm. However, it is much more important to have discovered some confirmed robustness effects, and so we use the eight confirmation runs to assess the robustness effects in the confirmation experiment.

If we define a new two-level factor, *X* say, which is an amalgamation of factors *A*, *B*, *D* and *G* from the original experiment, with levels dictated by the high S/N ratio and low S/N ratio grouping, then we can write the confirmation runs as a new plan matrix for the control factors, given in Table 12.17. Note that the plan is a full factorial in factors *X*, *C* and *F*. Hence we can use this plan to measure interactions $X \times C$, $X \times F$, $C \times F$ and $X \times C \times F$, and to generate contrasts to mimic the analysis of the data from the original $L_{18}$.

When the seven contrasts available from Table 12.17 are applied to the dynamic S/N ratios of Table 12.16, the results are as given in Table 12.18.

*Table 12.15* Data from the confirmation runs

| | Inner array: control factors | | | | | | | Outer array: signal and noise factors | | | | | | |
|---|---|---|---|---|---|---|---|---|---|---|---|---|---|---|
| | | | | | | | | − | + | − | + | − | + | *N* |
| Build | *A* | *B* | *C* | *D* | *E* | *F* | *G* | − | − | 0 | 0 | + | + | *S* |
| 19 | 4 | + | − | − | 0 | − | + | 36.75 | 25.92 | 26.27 | 16.22 | 20.98 | 12.20 | |
| | | | | | | | | 40.11 | 26.28 | 26.53 | 16.97 | 21.91 | 11.79 | |
| 20 | 4 | + | − | − | 0 | + | + | 38.21 | 24.76 | 26.95 | 15.02 | 21.38 | 12.20 | |
| | | | | | | | | 39.92 | 25.72 | 27.08 | 16.23 | 21.16 | 12.47 | |
| 21 | 4 | + | + | − | 0 | − | + | 38.51 | 30.69 | 29.21 | 17.18 | 22.64 | 13.53 | |
| | | | | | | | | 40.69 | 29.87 | 28.81 | 17.73 | 22.71 | 13.54 | |
| 22 | 4 | + | + | − | 0 | + | + | 41.22 | 19.63 | 25.20 | 14.29 | 19.78 | 11.48 | |
| | | | | | | | | 39.85 | 20.76 | 24.82 | 14.68 | 17.23 | 11.10 | |
| 23 | 1 | − | − | + | 0 | − | 0 | 68.39 | 27.49 | 62.58 | 19.66 | 57.22 | 16.98 | |
| | | | | | | | | 119.13 | 29.88 | 59.80 | 19.61 | 57.53 | 16.91 | |
| 24 | 1 | − | − | + | 0 | + | 0 | 81.39 | 47.80 | 56.85 | 23.89 | 53.89 | 21.82 | |
| | | | | | | | | 84.27 | 41.94 | 56.35 | 26.51 | 57.90 | 19.33 | |
| 25 | 1 | − | + | + | 0 | − | 0 | 58.01 | 37.08 | 53.49 | 21.29 | 53.28 | 20.31 | |
| | | | | | | | | 58.18 | 36.83 | 54.20 | 22.25 | 49.89 | 18.73 | |
| 26 | 1 | − | + | + | 0 | + | 0 | 60.39 | 33.16 | 50.96 | 22.63 | 44.14 | 18.53 | |
| | | | | | | | | 63.15 | 25.55 | 49.21 | 23.03 | 48.83 | 16.85 | |

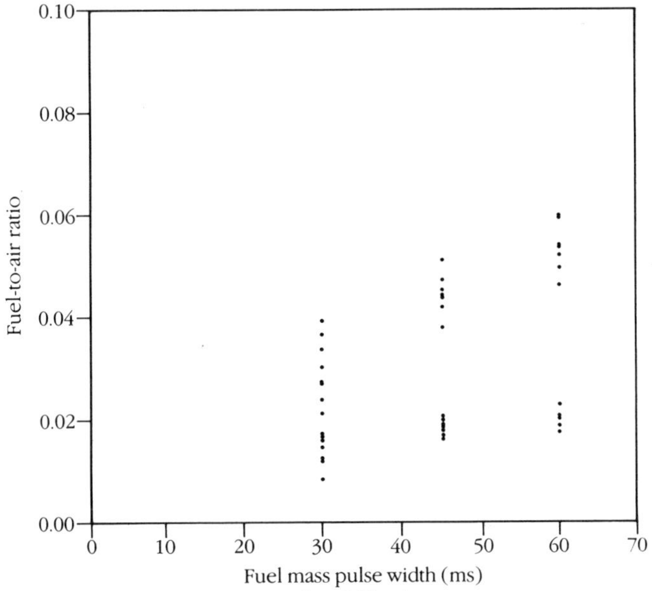


Low S/N ratio

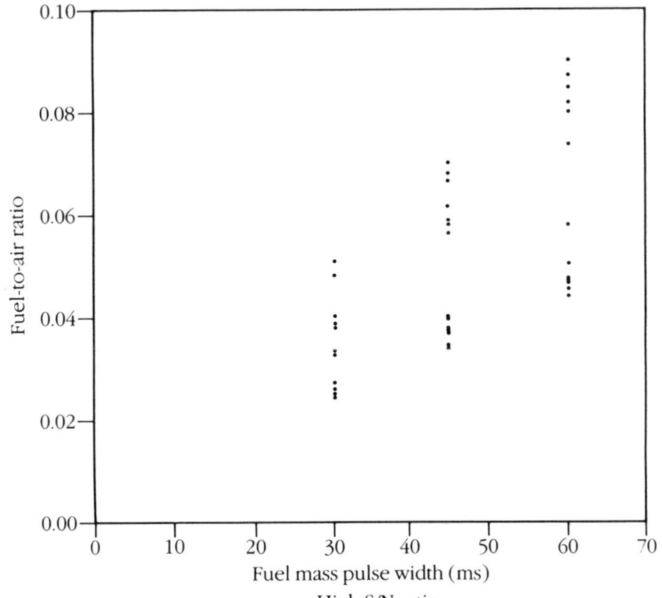


High S/N ratio

*Fig. 12.17* Data from the starting confirmation experiment

*Table 12.16* Confirmation S/N ratios and $\hat{\beta}$ values from the data in Table 12.15

| | Dynamic | | Static *SN* | | |
|---|---|---|---|---|---|
| Build | *SN* | $\hat{\beta}$ | *S*(−) | *S*(0) | *S*(+) |
| 19 | −21.93 | 10.8 | 13.09 | 11.55 | 9.71 |
| 20 | −22.12 | 10.9 | 12.07 | 10.12 | 10.25 |
| 21 | −21.35 | 9.9 | 16.17 | 10.82 | 10.71 |
| 22 | −22.27 | 12.0 | 8.22 | 10.23 | 11.03 |
| 23 | −28.36 | 6.9 | 4.51 | 4.53 | 4.04 |
| 24 | −26.34 | 5.8 | 9.06 | 6.97 | 5.36 |
| 25 | −26.33 | 6.5 | 11.81 | 6.18 | 5.62 |
| 26 | −26.36 | 7.0 | 7.07 | 7.30 | 5.65 |

*Table 12.17* Confirmation runs written out as a new plan

| | Inner array: control factors | | | Outer array: signal and noise factors | | | | | | |
|---|---|---|---|---|---|---|---|---|---|---|
| | | | | − | + | − | + | − | + | *N* |
| Build | *X* | *C* | *F* | − | − | 0 | 0 | + | + | *S* |
| 19 | + | − | − | | | | | | | |
| 20 | + | − | + | | | | | | | |
| 21 | + | + | − | | | | | | | |
| 22 | + | + | + | | | | | | | |
| 23 | − | − | − | | | | | | | |
| 24 | − | − | + | | | | | | | |
| 25 | − | + | − | | | | | | | |
| 26 | − | + | + | | | | | | | |

Note that the only large effect is due to 'factor' *X*, so this just confirms that changing factors *A*, *B*, *D* and *G* in the manner dictated in Table 12.15 had a positive effect on the S/N ratio as intended. A Daniel plot of the seven contrasts in Table 12.18 shows that only contrast *X* falls off the line.

*Table 12.18* Effects on the dynamic S/N ratio based on the plan matrix in Table 12.17

| Effect | Contrast value |
|---|---|
| $X$ | +4.93 |
| $C$ | +0.61 |
| $F$ | +0.22 |
| $X \times C$ | +0.39 |
| $X \times F$ | −0.77 |
| $C \times F$ | −0.69 |
| $X \times C \times F$ | +0.33 |

Figure 12.18 is a Daniel plot of contrasts constructed using the static S/N ratios in Table 12.16. There are 23 contrasts, developed by taking the seven that are available from Table 12.18 together with the main effects $S_\ell$ and $S_q$, and all possible interactions between these effects. This picture should be compared directly with Fig. 12.12. In Fig. 12.18, factor $X$ again stands out as well apart from the others. A re-plot just removing this contrast gives a good straight line (not shown here). Figure 12.18 confirms the evidence from Table 12.18.

Finally, Fig. 12.19 is a plot of 31 location contrasts based on Table 12.17, which can be compared directly to Figs 12.15 and 12.16. As in analysis (iii) above, Table 12.17 is re-written to resemble Table 12.5, but with two repeat results on each line, and level (0) of $S$ is ignored. Effects due to $N$ and $S_\ell$ stand out again. The values of the raw contrasts are +0.345 for $N$, which is in

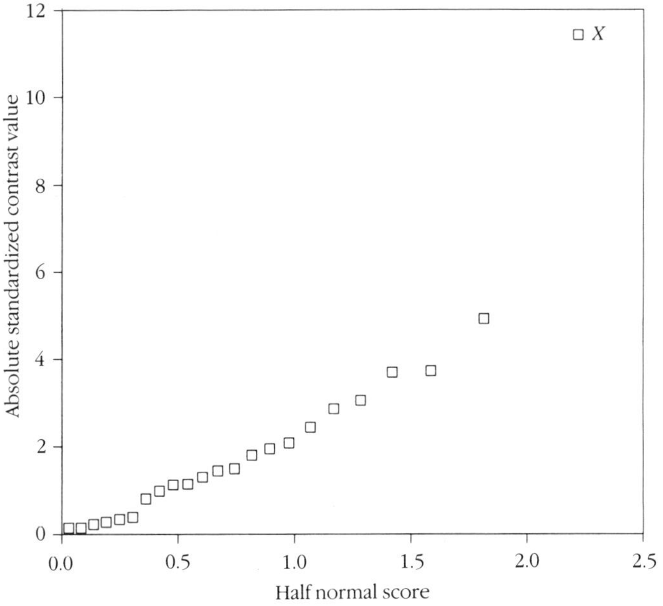


*Fig. 12.18* Starting confirmation experiment. Daniel plot for static *SN*, treating the confirmation builds as a full factorial in *S*, *C*, *F* and *X*, where *X* is an amalgamation of *A*, *B*, *D*, and *G*. Compare this plot with Fig. 12.12

strong agreement with the effect in Fig. 12.15, and +0.285 for $S_\ell$. The average strength of the signal is less here than in the original experiment (+0.395 in Fig. 12.15) because the combinations of control factor levels are more restricted. Note that contrast $X$ stands out in Fig. 12.19 because some of the factors that make up $X$ have effects on the slope. The presence of the $X \times N$ interaction confirms that factors that make up $X$ have robustness effects. The $X \times N$ interaction is negative (i.e. the effect of noise decreases as $X$ changes from (−) to (+)) as required.

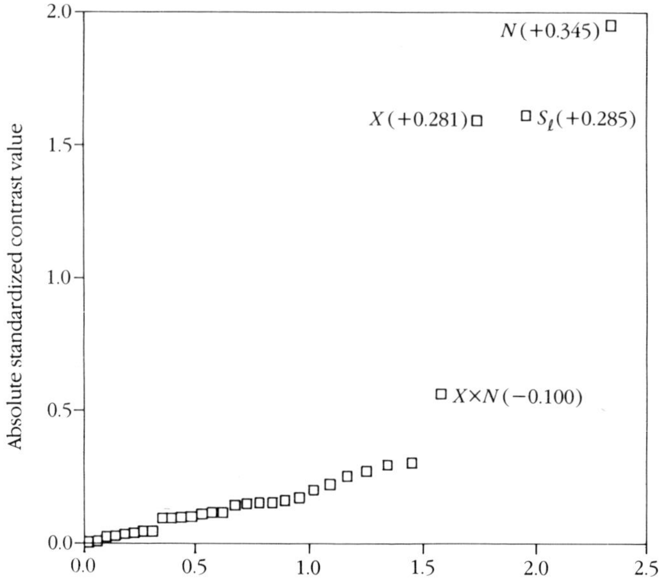


*Fig. 12.19* Starting confirmation experiment. Daniel plot of 31 contrasts, ignoring level (0) of $S$: main effects for $S$, $N$, $C$, $F$ and $X$ and all interactions. Compare this plot with Figs 12.15 and 12.16. Numbers in brackets are actual effects

## Final comments on the starting experiment

After each engine build had been tested, the experimenters attempted to start the engine to clear out the cylinders prior to the next build. They found that builds 19 to 22 started very quickly irrespective of the temperature, whereas engines from builds 23 to 26 took considerably longer. If the engines had not started, the effects on $\hat{\beta}$ would have been investigated more thoroughly to establish which factors could be used for tuning.

Further improvements to robustness might also be possible by exploring factor $B$ (distance from injector tip to valve head) between level (0) and level (+) because of the quadratic nature of the effects of this factor on robustness measures. Fig. 12.20 illustrates this point. Fig. 12.20(a) shows the estimated quadratic effect on factor $B$ on the static S/N ratio. The effects $B_\ell = +1.516$ and $B_q = -1.822$ have been taken from the Daniel plot in Fig. 12.12. Since we are required to *maximize* the S/N ratio, a level for factor $B$ somewhere between (0) and (+) would be worth trying. The same point is illustrated in Fig. 12.20(b). This plot shows the quadratic nature of the effect of factor $B$ on *the effect of the noise* $N$ on the (logged) fuel-to-air ratio. The effects $B_\ell = -0.060$ and $B_q = +0.109$ have been taken from the interaction contrasts $B_\ell \times N$ and $B_q \times N$ in Fig. 12.16. Since we are required to

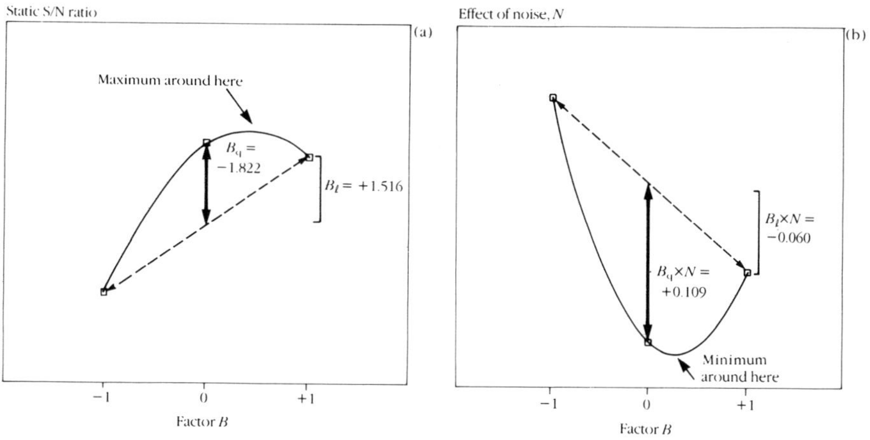


*Fig. 12.20* Effects plots for factor *B* on robustness measures. (a) effect of *B* on the static *SN* ratio. (b) interaction between factor *B* and noise *N* on the (logged) fuel-to-air ratio

*minimize* the effect of the noise, it is clear from Fig. 12.20(b) that a level of factor *B* somewhere between (0) and (+) would be worth trying, which is exactly the same conclusion as from Fig. 12.20(a).

Also of interest is the amount of exhaust emissions during the ignition cycle, and for the first 30 seconds of idle. Engine builds 23 to 26 produced levels of emissions (hydro carbons and carbon monoxide) at −15 °C roughly similar to the standard engine (i.e. the engine configuration prior to the experiment). However, builds 19 to 22, the robust configuration, dramatically reduced these emissions by about one half.

Emissions might well be described as error states in terms of the ideal function of engine starting (as defined by the fuel in — fuel out model), and so by *maximizing ideal function* the experimenters have *minimized the extent of the error*, without this being the primary focus of the experiment. Hence this case study provides some empirical evidence to support Taguchi's approach to engineering — engineer in the function, do not engineer out problems.

## SUMMARY OF CHAPTER 12

The function of a dynamic system is to produce a particular output in response to a particular input, where the input varies according to the intention of the user. When the input and output are quantities of energy,

Taguchi's concept of ideal function can be expressed by a linear input–output (signal–response) relationship that passes through the origin.

One of the ways in which noise can affect such a system is to alter the slope of the input–output relationship. The effect of noise then increases with the strength of the signal, which implies an interaction between signal and noise — a smaller interaction means a more robust system.

A typical experimental plan for investigating a dynamic system would have three levels of the signal factor *S* and two levels of a (possibly compounded) noise factor *N*. The data can be summarized by an average slope $\hat{\beta}$ (chosen by least squares) and a standard deviation $s_r$ calculated from the residual sum of squares. Taguchi combines $\hat{\beta}$ and $s_r$ into a single formula, which we call the dynamic signal-to-noise ratio. A dynamic system can be seen as a generalization of the nominal-is-best situation introduced in Section 8.4, and there is a strong similarity between the dynamic *SN* formula and Taguchi's nominal-is-best *SN* formula [8.1]. We refer to [8.1] as the static S/N ratio. The dynamic S/N ratio is likely to do a reasonable job when there is a link between the average slope and the noise effect, arising from factors that have a proportional effect on both. The situation is captured in Fig. 12.3.

Experiments can be run to try to discover robust dynamic systems by changing the levels of a set of control factors. The control factor configurations make up the inner array, and the outer array holds the levels of the signal and noise factors. The dynamic S/N ratio can be applied to each row of the inner array, and the effects of the control factors established in the usual way. As before, the aim is to maximize the S/N ratio. Factors that affect the slope but not the S/N ratio can be used to tune the gradient of the signal–response relationship. We recommend this approach only if a log–log plot of $s_r$ against $\hat{\beta}$ has a discernible linear pattern with a slope of about 1.

An alternative method is based on laying the experiment out in a different way, with the signal factor incorporated into the inner array. This layout resembles those seen in Chapters 8 and 9, and can be analysed for location and dispersion effects using orthogonal contrasts, bearing in mind that any measure of dispersion is also a measure of robustness. If the ordinary standard deviation $s$ is used to measure dispersion, it is possible to apply Taguchi's analysis based on the static S/N ratio, but we recommend making a log–log plot of $s$ against $\bar{y}$ to check whether this S/N analysis would be sensible.

Another way to make use of orthogonal contrasts is to write out the whole experiment as a single array, from which the effects of the signal, noise and control factors, and their interactions, can be measured. A three-way interaction involving the linear effect of *S*, *N* and a control factor would indicate a robustness effect, but the corresponding two-way interactions and main effects would also be active, so the interpretation of contrasts for robustness effects is more complicated in the dynamic framework.

If the system can be represented as in Fig. 12.3, a log transformation of both the signal and the response will have two advantages: it reduces the levels of the interactions that need to be interpreted (robustness effects show up as interactions between $N$ and the control factors, and factors that can be used to adjust $\beta$ will have main effects), and it decouples the noise effect from the average slope. After transformation, a set of lines that diverge from the origin become a set of parallel lines, and our aim is to find control factor settings that change the intercept and bring the lines closer together.

# References

Bisgaard S 1988 *A Practical Aid for Experimenters* Starlight Press, Madison, Wisconsin

Box G E P 1988 Signal-to-noise ratios, performance criteria and transformations. *Technometrics* **30**: 1–40

Box G E P, Bisgaard S, Fung C 1990 *Designing Industrial Experiments* BBBF Books, Illinois

Box G E P, Draper N R 1987 *Empirical Model-Building and Response Surfaces* Wiley, New York

Box G E P, Fung C A 1986 Studies in quality improvement: minimizing transmitted variation by parameter design. *Report 8* University of Wisconsin-Madison, Center for Quality and Productivity Improvement

Box G E P, Hunter W G, Hunter J S 1978 *Statistics for Experimenters* Wiley, New York

Burn G R 1990 Quality function deployment. In Dale B G, Plunkett J J (eds) *Managing Quality* Philip Allan, Hemel Hempstead

Daniel C 1959 Use of half-normal plots in interpreting factorial two-level experiments. *Technometrics* **1**: 311–41

Daniel C 1976 *Applications of Statistics to Industrial Experimentation* Wiley, New York

Deming W E 1986 *Out of the Crisis* Cambridge University Press, Cambridge

Dey A 1985 *Orthogonal Fractional Factorial Designs* Wiley Eastern, New Delhi

Draper N R 1985 Small composite designs. *Technometrics* **27**: 173–80

Fewkes J H, Yarwood J 1959 *Electricity and Magnetism* London: University Tutorial Press — Electricity, magnetism and atomic physics series; Vol 1

Grove D M, Davis T P 1991 On Taguchi's idle column method. *Technometrics* **33**: 349–53

Hamada M, Wu C F J 1991 Analysis of censored data from highly fractionated experiments. *Technometrics* **33**: 25–38

Hunter J S 1985 Statistical design applied to product design. *Journal of Quality Technology* **17**: 210–21

Ishikawa K 1982 *Guide to Quality Control* Asian Productivity Organisation, Tokyo

John P W M 1990 Time trends and factorial experiments. *Technometrics* **32**: 275–82

Logothetis N, Wynn H P 1989 *Quality Through Design* Oxford University Press, Oxford

Margolin B H 1969 Orthogonal main effect plans permitting estimation of all two-factor interactions for the $2^n 3^m$ factorial series of designs. *Technometrics* **11**: 747–62

Owen M 1989 *SPC and Continuous Improvement* IFS Publications, Bedford

Phadke M S 1989 *Quality Engineering Using Robust Design* Prentice-Hall, Englewood Cliffs, NJ

Plackett R L, Burman J P 1946 The design of optimum multifactorial experiments. *Biometrika* **33**: 305–25

Roquemore K G 1976 Hybrid designs for quadratic response surfaces. *Technometrics* **18**: 419–23 (see also *Technometrics* **19**: 106)

Ryan B F, Joiner B L, Ryan T A 1985 *MINITAB Handbook* PWS-Kent, Boston

Starks T H 1964 A note on small orthogonal main effect plans for factorial experiments. *Technometrics* **6**: 220–2

Taguchi G 1986 *Introduction to Quality Engineering* Quality Resources, White Plains, New York

Taguchi G 1987 *System of Experimental Design* vol 1, Kraus, White Plains, New York

Taguchi G, Wu Y 1979 *Introduction to Off-Line Quality Control* Central Japan Quality Control Association, Nagoya

Wheeler D 1988 *Understanding Industrial Experimentation* SPC Press, Knoxville, Tennessee

Wheeler D 1989 *Tables of Screening Designs* 2nd edn, SPC Press, Knoxville, Tennessee

Wheeler D, Chambers D S 1986 *Understanding Statistical Process Control* SPC Press, Knoxville, Tennessee

# Index


Additive, additivity, 38, 82–3, 304
Aliasing, 41
Analysis of variance (anova), 51, 120, 142, 148
Augmentation, 85

Background variation, 91–6
  Linear and quadratic trends, 95
Balance, 7, 100, 137, 175
Blocking, 77, 80, 91–4, 168–9
Box–Behnken designs, 144, 153, 170–1

Canonical analysis, 169
Case studies
  Air bags (sled tests), 24, 29
  Carburettor assembly, 4
  Desk-top fan, 282
  Engine mapping, 103, 115, 128, 137, 280
  Engine starting, 329
  Fuel tanks, 247
  Glove box lids, 56
  Piston ring spacers, 267
  Rear seat belts, 224
  Tee clamps, 198, 210
  Tyre testing, 153
  Wheatstone bridge, 237, 305
Central composite designs, 136–41, 164–7
Centre point, 126, 137, 155
Change-one-thing-at-a-time, 3, 10–11, 35
Code, coding, 4, 25, 31, 98, 105, 185
Closed set of columns, 181
Column collapsing, 177
Column combining, 181
Confirmation, 9
  Confirmation experiment, 83
  Confirmation run, 9, 83
Confounding, 41
  Confounding in mixed-level plans, 176, 180–1, 186
  Confounding in three-level plans, 124
  Confounding in two-level plans, 41–4, 76–7, 79–85
  Confounding of robustness and location effects, 229
  Pattern of confounding, 44, 192
Contrast, 7, 28–9
  Checking contrasts, 117, 140–1, 149
  Contrast matrix, 30, 57
  Contrasts for experiments on dynamic systems, 321
  Contrasts in mixed-level experiments, 180–2, 185–6, 189
  Contrasts in three-level experiments, 106–12
  Contrasts in two-level experiments, 28–9
  Curvature contrast, 127
  Generating contrasts in a spreadsheet, 29
  Linear and quadratic contrasts in a spreadsheet, 107
  Linear contrast, 107, 182
  Orthogonal contrasts, 29
  Quadratic contrast, 107, 175

Replication contrast, 155
Standardized contrast, 117, 121, 144, 155–6, 172–3
Standardized contrasts in a spreadsheet, 121
Control charts, 18

Daniel plot, *see* Normal plot
Degrees of freedom
$f_\sigma$, the degrees of freedom for estimating $\sigma$, 53
Residual degrees of freedom, 148–9
Deming, 1, 16, 18
Dispersion, 17, 196

Effect, 7, 28
Active effect, 20
Apparent effect, 20
Dispersion effect, 17, 196–7, 200, 203, 207, 212, 300–2
Effects plot, 8, 101
Linear effect, 106
Location effect, 17, 212
Main effect, 26, 99–100, 108–9
Quadratic effect, 106
Real effect, 18, 20–1
Robustness effect, 228
Efficiency, 2, 35
Energy, transfer of, 298
and the SN ratio, 302
in the dynamic setting, 317
Experimental design, 6
Experimental error, 21
Experimental plan, 6, 57
Extended equation, 155

*F* test, 54, 150
Critical values, 55, 73
Factor, 3
Adjustment or tuning factor, 212
Control factor, 222, 232
Noise factor, 222, 236
Signal factor, 317
Factorial experiment, 3
Complete factorial experiment, 38
Fractional factorial experiment, 39
Full factorial experiment, 38
Five-level plans, 167–9
Fold-over, *see* Reflection
Follow-up experiment, 6, 12, 85, 207, 348

Guidelines for running an experiment, 12

Half replicate, 39

Ideal function, 298
Idle column method, 187–9
Inner array, 223
Inner product, 28
Interaction, 10
Higher-order interactions, 43
Interaction between control and noise factors, 223, 273
Interaction graph, 32
Interaction in mixed-level experiments, 176, 180–1, 185–6
Interaction in three-level experiments, 109–10, 116–17
Interaction in two-level experiments, 25, 27–8, 82–4, 192
Three-way interaction, 33
Ishikawa, 19
Iteration, 255–7
Iteration in a spreadsheet, 259

$L_4(2^3)$ orthogonal array, 39
$L_8(2^7)$ orthogonal array, 31
Generating $L_8(2^7)$, 77
Multiplication table for $L_8(2^7)$, 43
Plans based on $L_8(2^7)$, 42–4, 77
$L_9(2^4)$ orthogonal array, 99
$L_{12}(2^{11})$ orthogonal array, 78, 83, 200
$L_{16}(2^{15})$ orthogonal array, 47
Generating $L_{16}(2^{15})$, 82
Multiplication table for $L_{16}(2^{15})$, 79
Plans based on $L_{16}(2^{15})$, 81
$L_{16}(3^7)$ orthogonal array, 175
$L_{18}(2^1.3^7)$ orthogonal array, 176
$L_{27}(3^{13})$ orthogonal array, 125, 165
$L_{36}(2^{11}.3^{12})$ orthogonal array, 178–9
Least squares, 36, 140, 145, 319
Level, 3
Linear graphs, 82, 190–2
Loss function, *see* Quality loss function

Management, 3, 10–13
Margolin's designs, 186–7
Maxwell distribution, 302
Missing response value, 160, 255
Multi-factor experiment, 3
Multi-stage process, 94
Multiple regression, 145, 151, 155, 160, 163, 173
Regression in a spreadsheet, 147
Multiplication table for an orthogonal array, 43

Nested factors, 189
Noise, 18, 20–1, 198, 234
Compounded noise, 223, 309–12

  Inner noise, 309
  Outer noise, 309
Nominal value, 232, 235, 313
Normal plot, 48, 62–8
  Daniel (half normal) plot, 48, 67–8, 117, 119
  Full normal plot, 48, 64–6
  Normal plots for computer experiments, 226
  Normal plots in a spreadsheet, 68
  Normal scores, 65, 69–72
  Re-plotting, 68

Orthogonal, orthogonality, 28, 31, 112, 140–1, 161, 174–5, 189
  Checking orthogonality in a spreadsheet, 29, 112, 141
  Orthogonal array, 31, 98, 174
  Orthogonal contrasts, 29, 66, 106
  Orthogonal main effect plan, 185
Outer array, 223

Parameter design, 222, 234
Partial reflection, 86
PDCA cycle, 1, 90
PDSA cycle, 2
Poisson distribution, 61
Prediction, 9, 21, 36–8, 101–2, 104, 114–15, 152, 207
  Predicted effect, 38
  Predicted response value, 115, 152, 169
  Second-order prediction equation, 115, 117, 243
Proportional frequencies, 175

Quadratic curve, 106
Qualitative factor, 4, 101, 185
Quality characteristic, 4, 295
  Larger-the-better quality characteristic, 215, 217–19
  Nominal-is-best quality characteristic, 215–17
  Smaller-the-better quality characteristic, 215, 224, 226
Quality engineering, 298
Quality loss function, 13–16
Quantitative factor, 4, 101
  Equally spaced levels, 104

Randomization, 87–91
  Randomization of the run order in a spreadsheet, 90
Re-coding, 28, 31, 108–9, 177, 180, 182
Re-fitting, 151, 161
Reflection, 85–7, 273
  Reflection in a spreadsheet, 87
Repetition, 198
Replication, 155, 287
Residual, 122, 148, 159, 206
  Standardized residual, 123
Response, 4
  Choosing the response variable, 295–8
  Response surface, 113
  Response table 7, 100
Resolution number, 74
Ridge analysis, 169
Robustness, 18, 222, 228
  Robustness in the dynamic setting, 323
Rotatable designs, 168
Run, 5
  Run order, 87–91, 153

Saturated design, 75, 100
Screening, 83, 124
Second-order equation, 115
Separability, 212
Sequential experimentation, 83, 128, 168
Shewhart, 1, 18
Signal-to-noise (SN) ratio, 215–16, 240, 299
  Dynamic SN ratio in a spreadsheet, 320
  SN ratio for dynamic systems, 320
  Static SN ratio, 321
Split plot design, 92–4
Spreadsheet, 19
Standard deviation
  Constant $\sigma$ model, 52
  $s$, 197
  $s_r$, 320
  $\sigma$, 53
Star points, 137
Statistical control, 16, 21, 196
Statistical process control (SPC), 159, 279
Statistical significance, 55
Strategy
  Engineering strategy, 313
  Experimentation strategy, 80, 82–5, 124, 128, 132
  Two-stage strategy for optimization, 216, 235
Sum of squares, 51
  Contribution to $SS_T$, 51
  Residual sum of squares, 148–9, 320
  $SS_T$, the total sum of squares, 51
  $SS_\sigma$, the sum of squares for estimating $\sigma$, 52, 142, 162–3
  Sums of squares in a spreadsheet, 52
System design, 313

*t* test, 150
  Critical values, 172
Taguchi, ix, 13–16, 18, 37, 75–6, 82–4, 177, 190, 215–16, 223, 237, 243, 245, 298–305, 309, 312–14, 320, 323–4
Teamwork, 10–11
$3^3$ plan, 116, 136–7
$3^k$ plan, 124
Tolerance design, 245, 314
Transformation
  Factor transformation, 120, 280, 305
  Response transformation, 120, 212, 300–2, 327
  Response transformation in a spreadsheet, 219
  Response transformations and SN ratios, 299
Two-level plus centre point design, 126, 168
$2^2$ plan, 37
$2^3$ plan, 38

Variance function, 144, 168
Variation, 13–18
  Between-block variation, 94
  Common causes of variation, 16, 18
  Piece-to-piece variation, 14, 234, 309
  Random variation, 16, 21, 234
  Special causes of variation, 16, 18, 21, 87
  Stable variation, 16, 21, 196–8
  Transmitted variation, 232–5
  Within-block variation, 94

*X* matrix, 145, 154, 163